THE
NEW HYMNAL
FOR
AMERICAN YOUTH

EDITED BY
H. AUGUSTINE SMITH

A BOOK
PROVIDING HYMNS, UNISON AND RESPONSIVE
READINGS, LITANIES AND PRAYERS, WORSHIP
SERVICES, AND OTHER DEVOTIONAL MATERIAL

FOR
INTERMEDIATES, SENIORS, AND YOUNG PEOPLE

New York
FLEMING H. REVELL COMPANY
London and Edinburgh

COPYRIGHT, 1930, BY
FLEMING H. REVELL COMPANY

ACKNOWLEDGMENT

For the use of all copyrighted hymns, readings and music included in this hymnal, permission has been secured from the author or from his authorized publisher.

Every effort has been made to trace the ownership of all copyright material. Should any infringement have been unconsciously made, the Editor desires hereby to express his regrets. He will be glad on notification to make proper acknowledgment in future editions of this book.

Introduction

"We are the music makers,
And we are the dreamers of dreams,
Wandering by lone sea-breakers,
And sitting by desolate streams;
World-losers and world-forsakers,
On whom the pale moon gleams:
Yet we are the movers and shakers
Of the world forever, it seems."

There will probably never be a time when music will not be a vital part of the acts of worship. The functioning of worship includes the working of those mysterious elements of human feeling which may not be accurately measured or controlled, but which must nevertheless be recognized, and used if possible, in the development of the finest and best that worship can give. The emotional element in worship, properly aroused, leads to that higher and finer form of religious experience which may be called fruition. Worship merely as contemplation would never lead out of itself. Music affords a universal means of expression, either actually, or vicariously, and its use guarantees to religion one of her greatest ministries, leading out of self to the great world where love and service unite for the building of the Kingdom of God.

This is not just another hymnal, — it is a hymnal which has been prepared with painstaking labor, to meet the need of youth for expression through music, in an age when method must keep pace with content; and when training in the art of worship has become a recognized part of the program for the religious education of youth.

This hymnal emerges from a background of practical idealism. The recognition of the great motivating ideal of Christianity is to be noted in classification and arrangement, as well as in the content of the hymns themselves. Special effort has been made to select those hymns and hymn tunes which will meet the needs of the younger adolescent group, and to relate worship to everyday life.

We, the Music Makers, present this hymnal to the youth of America, with the hope that through its use they may give expression to an ever higher and more vital feeling of desire to find God, and to make his purposes known in a world of persons and things.

Introduction

EDITOR'S NOTE

The Editor desires to express his obligation to many interested co-workers who have aided in the preparation of this book.

MISS LAURA ARMSTRONG

REV. AND MRS. EDWARD H. BONSALL

DR. LEROY B. CAMPBELL

MR. CHARLES I. DAVIS

PROF. EARL MARLATT

MRS. LUCIA MAY SMITH

PROF. EDITH LOVELL THOMAS

PROF. OSBERT W. WARMINGHAM

Table of Contents

	PAGE
INTRODUCTION	iii
INDEX OF FIRST LINES	vii
ALPHABETICAL INDEX OF TUNES	xi
METRICAL INDEX OF TUNES	xiii
INDEX OF AUTHORS, TRANSLA-TORS, SOURCES	xvi
INDEX OF COMPOSERS, ARRANGERS, SOURCES	xix
THE HYMNS	1–282
INTRODUCTION TO WORSHIP SECTION	284

	PAGE
INDEX TO WORSHIP SECTION	285–287
SUMMARY OF SERVICES OF WORSHIP	288
AIDS TO WORSHIP	289–293
UNISON READINGS	294–295
RESPONSIVE READINGS	296–304
SCRIPTURE SELECTIONS	305–306
PRAYERS AND HIGH RESOLVES	307–315
DEVOTIONAL POETRY AND PROSE	316–340
SERVICES OF WORSHIP	341–368

The Hymns

	NUMBER
THE FATHER GOD	
Morning Worship	1–15
Evening Worship	16–25
The Mighty God	26–38
Maker of Heaven and Earth	39–47
Shepherd of Souls	48–59
THE ETERNAL SPIRIT	60–67
THE LIVING WORD	68–74
CHRIST, THE SON	
Emmanuel — God with us	75–96
The Growing Christ	97–103
Master and Friend	104–113
The Day of Hosannas	114–118
The Way of the Cross	119–124
The Risen Christ	125–135
The Living Christ	136–143
THE CHRISTIAN WAY OF LIFE	
Following the Christ	144–151
Fellowship with Christ	152–160
The Temple of the Body	161–170
The Rule of the Spirit	171–179

	NUMBER
Trustworthiness	180–189
Good Workmanship	190–195
Loyalty	196–204
Courage	205–212
The Quest of Truth	213–221
The Quest of Beauty	222–229
The Quest of Goodness	230–236
Friendship	237–246
THY KINGDOM COME	
The Challenge of Service	247–255
Torchbearers	256–263
Community Love	264–270
Fatherland	271–283
World Friendship	284–297
World Fellowship in Christ	298–306
The Living Church	307–312
Home Shrines	313–318
SEASONS AND HOLY DAYS	319–328
LIFE EVERLASTING	329–333
DOXOLOGIES, OFFERTORIES, RESPONSES	334–344

Index of First Lines

	HYMN
A mighty fortress is our God	210
Abide with me, fast falls the eventide	20
All beautiful the march of days	326
All creatures of our God and King	45
All glory, laud and honor	116
All hail the power of Jesus' name	135
All my heart this night rejoices	85
All the past we leave behind	211
All things are thine	310
All things come of thee, O Lord	341
Ancient of days	34
And did those feet in ancient time	269
Angel voices ever singing	228
Angels, from the realms of glory	88
Another year of setting suns	328
Are ye able, said the Master	205
Art thou weary, art thou languid	151
As comes the breath of spring	65
As with gladness men of old	95
At length there dawns the glorious day	286
Awake, my soul, stretch every nerve	195
Backward we look, O God of all our ways	233
Be of good cheer	193
Be strong! we are not here to play	182
Be thou my vision, O Lord of my heart	236
Believe not those who say	183
Beneath the cross of Jesus	120
Bless thou the gifts	340
Blest be the tie that binds	312
Blest land of Judea	105
Blow, golden trumpets	134
Book of books, our people's strength	69
Break thou the bread of life	71
Breathe on me, breath of God	61
Brightly beams our Father's mercy	253
Brightly gleams our banner	208
Bring, O morn, thy music	5

	HYMN
Christ of the upward way	235
Christ, the Lord, is risen today	129
Christian, dost thou see them	179
Christians, lo, the star appeareth	90
City of God, how broad and far	267
Come, let us join with faithful souls	241
Come, O Lord, like morning sunlight	14
Come, thou almighty King	38
Come, ye thankful people, come	322
Comrades, known in marches many	238
Crown him with many crowns	136
Day is done, gone the sun	344
Day is dying in the west	17
Dear God, our Father, at thy knee confessing	153
Dear Lord and Father of mankind	152
Dear Lord, who sought at dawn of day	112
Down the dark future	292
Draw nigh to thy Jerusalem	118
Draw thou my soul, O Christ	149
Easter flowers are blooming bright	126
Fairest Lord Jesus	137
Faith of our fathers	256
Far round the world thy children	8
Father eternal, ruler of creation	287
Father in heaven, hear us today	161
Father in heaven, who lovest all	175
Father of lights	1
Father, we praise thee, now the night	26
Father, who on man doth shower	171
Father, whose will is life and good	169
Fight the good fight with all thy might	207
Fling out the banner	304
For all the saints	330
For mercy, courage, kindness, mirth	165
For the beauty of the earth	46
Forget them not, O Christ, who stand	260
Forward through the ages	263

vii

Index of First Lines

	HYMN		HYMN
From homes of quiet peace	315	I bind my heart this tide	121
From the eastern mountains	94	I cannot put the presence by	139
		I cannot think or reason	122
Galilee, bright Galilee	106	I heard the voice of Jesus say	147
Gather us in, thou love that fillest all	300	I know not how that Bethlehem's Babe	143
Gird us, O God, with humble might	246	I know not what the future hath	332
Glad that I live, am I	172	I love thy kingdom, Lord	311
Glory be to the Father	335	I need thee every hour	150
Glory to the King of Angels	337	I sought his love in sun and stars	142
God, bless our native land	283	I thank thee, Lord, for life	166
God of our fathers, known of old	282	I vow to thee, my country	331
God of our fathers, whose almighty hand	273	I would be true	177
God of our youth, to whom we yield	162	If I can stop one heart from breaking	242
God of the earth, the sky, the sea	49	Immortal love, forever full	140
God of the glorious sunshine	42	In Christ there is no East or West	299
God of the nations, near and far	296	In heavenly love abiding	48
God of the nations, who from dawn	274	In life's earnest morning	213
God of the shining hosts	289	In the cross of Christ I glory	124
God of the strong, God of the weak	212	In the hour of trial	178
God send us men	255	In the lonely midnight	89
God that madest earth and heaven	18	Into the woods my Master went	119
God the Omnipotent	284	It came upon the midnight clear	78
God who created me	170		
God who made the earth	58	Jesus calls us o'er the tumult	144
God who touchest earth with beauty	223	Jesus, lover of my soul	157
God's trumpet wakes the slumbering world	203	Jesus, Saviour, pilot me	160
Great Master, touch us with thy skilful hand	222	Jesus shall reign where'er the sun	305
		Jesus, the very thought of thee	158
Hail, the glorious golden city	264	Jesus, thou divine Companion	191
Hail the hero workers	190	Joy to the world, the Lord is come	76
Hail to the brightness	303	Joyful, joyful, we adore thee	43
Hail to the Lord's anointed	301	Judge eternal, throned in splendor	277
Hark, hark, my soul	329	Just as I am, thine own to be	145
Hark! the herald angels sing	77		
Hark! the vesper hymn is stealing	16	Lamp of our feet, whereby we trace	72
He who would valiant be	204	Lead, kindly light	333
Hear our prayer, O Lord	342	Lead on, O King eternal	199
Heaven is here, where hymns of gladness	240	Let the whole creation cry	44
Heralds of Christ	258	Let the words of my mouth	338
Holy Father, thou hast given	73	Let there be light, Lord God of hosts	291
Holy, holy, holy, Lord God almighty	4	Let us with a gladsome mind	32
Holy, holy, holy, Lord of Hosts	336	Life has loveliness to sell	227
Holy, holy, holy, Lord, thy disciples	107	Life of ages, richly poured	214
Holy Spirit, truth divine	60	Lift up our hearts, O King of Kings	295
Hosanna, loud Hosanna	117	Lift up your hearts	3
How firm a foundation	74	Light of the world, we hail thee	9
How strong and sweet my Father's care	53	Little things that run and quail	243
		Lord, as we thy name profess	176

	HYMN
Lord, for tomorrow and its needs	317
Lord God of hosts, whose purpose	247
Lord, guard and guide the men who fly	290
Lord Jesus, Son of Mary	86
Lord of all being, throned afar	33
Lord of health, thou life within us	167
Lord, speak to me, that I may speak	251
Lord, we come with hearts aflame	250
Love divine, all love excelling	67
Love thyself last	239
March on, O soul, with strength	184
Marching with the heroes	259
Master, no offering	252
'Mid all the traffic of the ways	159
Mine eyes have seen the glory	280
My country is the world	294
My country, 'tis of thee	279
My faith it is an oaken staff	185
My faith looks up to thee	155
My God, I thank thee who hast made	51
My Master was so very poor	110
Nearer, my God, to thee	156
No longer, Lord, thy sons shall sow	132
Not in vain the distance beacons	297
Now in the days of youth	146
Now thank we all our God	325
Now the day is over	23
Now with creation's morning song	10
O beautiful for spacious skies	271
O beautiful, my country	275
O blessed day of Motherhood	318
O brother man, fold to thy heart thy brother	244
O Christ, the Way, the Truth, the Life	216
O Christ, who holds the open Gate	234
O come, all ye faithful	83
O come, let us worship	343
O come, O come, Emmanuel	75
O day of rest and gladness	15
O Father, thou who givest all	316
O God, beneath thy guiding hand	270
O God of truth, whose living word	181
O God, I cried, no dark disguise	40
O God, who workest hitherto	189
O gracious Father of mankind	66
	HYMN
O happy home, where thou art loved	313
O Jesus, I have promised	196
O Jesus, once a Nazareth boy	174
O Jesus, thou art standing	148
O Jesus, youth of Nazareth	103
O joyous Easter morning	125
O life that maketh all things new	219
O little town of Bethlehem	82
O Lord, all glorious, life of life	31
O Lord of heaven and earth and sea	56
O Lord of life, thy quickening voice	13
O Lord, our God, thy mighty Hand	272
O Lord, thy benediction give	218
O love that wilt not let me go	154
O Maker of the sea and sky	37
O Master, let me walk with thee	197
O Master Workman of the race	98
O native land, how fair you seem	281
O Son of man, our hero strong and tender	109
O Son of man, thou madest known	188
O Splendor of God's glory bright	11
O star of truth down-shining	200
O thou great Friend	141
O thou whose glory shone like fire	309
O thou whose gracious presence	314
O word of God incarnate	68
O worship the King	36
O ye who taste that love is sweet	248
O young Mariner	231
O Zion, haste, thy mission	306
On wings of living light	131
Once more the liberal year laughs out	324
Once to every man and nation	220
Onward, Christian soldiers	209
Our God, our help, in ages past	28
Pass on the torch, pass on the flame	229
Peacefully round us the shadows	21
Praise God from whom all blessings flow	334
Praise the Lord, ye heavens, adore him	30
Praise to the Lord, the Almighty	35
Praise we the Lord who made all beauty	224
Rejoice, ye pure in heart	27
Ride on, ride on, in majesty	115
Ring out, wild bells	327
Rise up, O men of God	254

Index of First Lines

	HYMN
Saviour, again to thy dear name.	24
Seek not afar for beauty, lo, it glows.	225
Send down thy truth, O God	268
Shepherd of tender youth.	138
Silent night, holy night.	81
Slowly, by thy hand unfurled	217
Spirit of God, descend upon my heart	62
Spirit of God, for every good	64
Spirit of life in this new dawn.	63
Stand fast for Christ, thy Saviour	180
Stand up, stand up for Jesus	201
Still, still with thee	6
Strong of body, high of spirit	163
Strong Son of God, immortal love	215
Sun of my soul, thou Saviour dear.	22
Take my life and let it be	198
Temper my spirit, O Lord	173
The body, Lord, is ours to keep	164
The church's one foundation	308
The day is past, the shadows round	19
The day of resurrection	127
The earth is hushed in silence.	7
The fathers built this city	266
The first Noel the angel did say.	79
The gray hills taught me patience	186
The heavens declare thy glory.	41
The hidden years at Nazareth.	97
The King of love my Shepherd is	50
The kings of the east are riding	92
The land we love is calling	276
The light along the ages	128
The lone, wild fowl, in lofty flight	59
The Lord bless you and keep you	25
The Lord is my Shepherd.	57
The Maker of the sun and moon	87
The ships glide in at the harbor's mouth	226
The Son of God goes forth to war	262
The spacious firmament on high.	47
The spring again is here	319
The strife is o'er, Alleluia.	133
The summer days are come again	321
The touch of human hands	237
The winter night was dark and still	80
There's a beautiful star.	93
There's a light upon the mountains	285
There's a song in the air	84

	HYMN
There's a wideness in God's mercy.	55
There's not a bird with lonely nest.	52
These things shall be — a loftier race	293
Thine arm, O Lord, in days of old	111
This is my Father's world	39
Thou art my Shepherd.	54
Thou didst leave thy throne	101
Thou Lord of light, across the years	257
Thou who taught the thronging people.	113
Through the dark the dreamers came	91
Thy hand, O God, has guided.	307
Thy palm trees fed with dew and sun	114
Thy Word is like a garden, Lord	70
To every man there openeth	232
To the knights in the days of old	230
Watchman, tell us of the night	298
We bear the strain of earthly care	194
We bless thee, Lord, for all this common life	221
We give thee but thine own	339
We know the paths wherein our feet.	187
We plough the fields and scatter.	323
We praise thee, God, for harvests earned	206
We praise thee, O God, our Redeemer	29
We thank thee, Lord, thy paths.	249
We three kings of Orient are	96
We would see Jesus, lo, his star	100
Welcome, happy morning.	130
Welcome, morning, bright and blue	168
We've a story to tell to the nations	302
When I survey the wondrous cross.	123
When morning gilds the skies	2
When the golden evening gathered.	108
When the Lord of love was here.	104
When through the whirl of wheels	192
When thy heart with joy o'erflowing.	245
When wilt thou save the people	288
Where cross the crowded ways of life.	265
Who goes there, in the night	261
Who is on the Lord's side.	202
Wild roars the blast	278
With happy voices singing	320
Worship the Lord in the beauty.	12
Ye fair green hills of Nazareth	102
Young and radiant he is standing	99

x

Alphabetical Index of Tunes

	HYMN
Abends	218
Aberystwyth	298
Adeste Fideles	83
Aeterna Christi Munera	11
Agni	173
Alford	266
All Hallows	276
All Saints New	262, 286
Almsgiving	56
America	279
Amesbury	98
Ancient of Days	1, 34, 247
Angel Voices	228
Angel's Story	196
Antioch	76
Ar Hyd Y Nos	18
Arizona	59
Armageddon	202
Armonia Biblica	240
Armstrong	104
Arthur's Seat	184
Ase's Death	261
Ashland	105
Aurelia	308
Austrian Hymn	264
Bassett	169
Battle Hymn of Republic	280
Beacon Hill	205
Beautiful Star	93
Beatitudo	216, 246
Beecher	67
Beechwood	58
Belleville	317
Beloit	316
Benediction	25
Berthold	320
Bethany	156
Boylston	312
Bread of Life	71
Brookfield	188
Bullinger	245
Canonbury	251, 309, 340
Carlisle	315
Carol	78
Chalice	230
Charity	242
Chautauqua	17
Chenies	41
Christe Sanctorum	26
Christmas	195
Christmas Song	84

	HYMN
Church Vigilant	224
College	113
Commonwealth	288
Comrade Heart	237
Comrades of the Cross	122
Conisborough	222
Coronation	135
Country Lanes	172
Creation	47
Crusader	241
Crusader's Hymn	137
Curfew	21
Cushman	100
Decision	232
Deed	187
Delhi	248
Deo Gratias	226
Deventer	257
Diademata	136
Dix	46, 95
Dolut	164
Dominus regit me	50
Dort	283
Dreamers	91
Dresden	323
Dublin	243
Duke Street	278, 305
Dunblane Cathedral	8
Eagley	189
Easter Flowers	126
Eaton	103
Ebenezer	220
Ecclesfield	310
Ein Feste Burg	210
Ellacombe	117
Ellah	289
Ellers	24
Ellingham	198, 214
England's Lane	168
Eudora	53
Eventide	20
Faben	30
Faithful	125
Faithfulness	52
Fealty	121
Felix	6, 153
Field	249
Follow the Gleam	230
Fortitude	182
Fortunatus	130
From Strength to Strength	146

	HYMN
Gabriel	70, 174
Galilee	144
Gannett	5
Garden City	268
Geneva	223
Germany	10, 265
Gloria Patria	335
Godfrey	65, 259
God's Love	42
Golden Trumpets	134
Gratitude	233
Hagerup	281
Hamburg	123
Harvard	142
Hesperus	63
Hollingside	157
Holy Cross	328
Hosanna	114
Hursley	22
Hymn to Joy	43
Il Buon Pastor	167
In Corde Meo	338
Industry	192
Innocents	32
Italian Hymn	38
Jerusalem	269
Jubilate	131
Just as I am	145
King Edward	183
Kings of Orient	96
Kirby Bedon	138
Kremser	29
Kucken	227
Lambeth	72
Lancashire	127, 199
Land of Rest	321
Lanier	119
Lasst uns Erfreuen	45
Laudes Domini	2
Leipzig	290
Lest we forget	162, 282
Lobe den Herren	35
Londonderry	109
Lonely Midnight	89
Lord's Day	7
Louvan	31
Love Divine	191
Love's Offering	252
Lower Lights	253

xi

	HYMN
Lucerne	14
Lux Benigna	333
Lynde	54
Lyons	36
Manchester	186
Margaret	101
Marion	27
Martineau	200
Martyn	157
Maryton	197
Mater	318
Materna	271
Melrose	165, 255
Mendelssohn	77
Mendon	293
Mercy	60
Merrial	23
Message	302
Miles Lane	135
Monkland	127
Monsell	12
Morecambe	62, 141
Morley	213
Morning Star	239
Mount Calvary	212
Mozart	327
Mt. Holyoke	285, 297
Munich	68
Muswell Hill	185
My Master	110
National Hymn	273
Nazareth	97
Need	150
Neilson	180
Nicæa	4
Nox Praecessit	267
Nun Danket	325
Oberlin	6
Offertory	341
Old Hundredth	334
Old 124th	287
Oliver	221
Olivet	155
Ombersley	212
Onward	263
Parousia	86
Passion Chorale	48
Pastor Regalis	294
Peek	177
Peel Castle	19
Penitence	178
Penitentia	300

	HYMN
Pentecost	207, 291
Phoenix	111
Picardy	277
Picton	118
Pilgrims	329
Pilot	160
Pioneers	211
Pisani	163
Poland	57
Portuguese Hymn	74
Pro Patria	258
Queenswood	181
Quem Pastores Laudavere	171
Qui Tenet	234
Rathbun	124
Regent Square	88, 337
Renascence	40
Republic	272
Rochester	166
Roland	44
Rosmore	94, 190
Rotterdam	15, 129
Rugby	170
Russian Hymn	284
St. Agnes	159, 193
St. Andrew of Crete	179
St. Anne	28
St. Athanasius	73, 250
St. Bede	139
St. Bees	176
St. Catherine	49, 256
St. Christopher	120
St. Crispin	33, 215
St. Drostane	115
St. Dunstan's	204
St. Edmund	149
St. George's Windsor	322
St. Gertrude	209
St. Hilda	148
St. Leonard	66
St. Louis	82
St. Margaret	154
St. Peter	299
St. Theodulph	116
St. Theresa	208
St. Thomas	254, 311
Saints of God	102
Salve Domine	9, 275
Sanctus	336
Santa Trinita	37
Sardis	90, 238
Sarum	330
Sawley	158, 296
Saxby	175, 206

	HYMN
Schumann	339
Serenity	140, 194
Seymour	217
Shackelford	326
Sherwin	106
Sine Nomine	330
Soho	13
Son of Man	99
Southampton	161
Spes Mea in Deo	235
Springfield	292
Stella	85
Stephanos	151
Stille Nacht	81
Stirewalt	112
Stockwell, New	108
Strength and Stay	244
Summerford	274
Sundown	231
Swansea	69
Taps	344
Terra Beata	39, 319
Thanksgiving	219
The First Noel	79
Thornbury	307
Tidings	306
Ton y Botel (*See* Ebenezer)	220
Torchbearers	229
Town of Bethlehem	80
Trentham	61
Trinity	107
Truro	260, 295
Two Fatherlands	331
Veni Emmanuel	75
Veritas	143
Vesalius	313
Vesper Hymn	16
Victory	64, 132
Village	87
Vision	236
Vox Dilecti	147
Wallace	92
Waltham	304, 324
Warren	332
Warrior	203
Watchman	298
Webb	201, 301
Wellesley	55
Wentworth	51
Wesley	303
Whittier	152, 314
Willingham	225
Woodlands	3
Worgan	129

Metrical Index of Tunes

S. M.

	HYMN
Ase' Death	261
Boylston	312
Carlisle	315
Garden City	268
King Edward	183
St. Thomas	254, 311
Schumann	339
Trentham	61

S. M. D., with Refrain

Marion	27

S. M. D.

Diademata	136
From Strength to Strength	146
Terra Beata	39, 319

C. M.

Antioch	76
Beatitudo	216, 246
Bassett	169
Christmas	195
Coronation	135
Eagley	189
Holy Cross	328
Lambeth	72
Miles Lane	135
Nox Praecessit	267
St. Agnes	159, 193
St. Anne	28
St. Peter	299
Sawley	158, 296
Serenity	140, 194
Soho	13
Veritas	143
Village	87

C. M. D.

All Saints New	262, 286
Amesbury	98
Carol	78
Crusader	241
Gabriel	70, 174
Land of Rest	321
Mater	318
Materna	271
Nazareth	97
Phoenix	111
Queenswood	181
Republic	272
St. Leonard	66
Shackelford	326

	HYMN
Town of Bethlehem	80
Vox Dilecti	147
Warrior	203

L. M.

Abends	218
Aeterna Christi Munera	11
Arizona	59
Beloit	316
Brookfield	188
Canonbury	251, 309, 340
Deventer	257
Duke Street	278, 305
Eaton	103
Ecclesfield	310
Faithfulness	52
Germany	10, 265
Golden Trumpets	134
Hagerup	281
Hamburg	123
Hesperus	63
Hursley	22
Louvan	31
Leipzig	290
Maryton	197
Melrose	165, 255
Mendon	293
Mozart	327
My Master	110
Old Hundredth	334
Ombersley	212
Pentecost	207, 291
Qui Tenet	234
Renascence	40
St. Crispin	33, 215
St. Drostane	115
Santa Trinita	37
Saxby	175, 206
Stirewalt	112
Thanksgiving	219
Torchbearers	229
Truro	260, 295
Waltham	304, 324

L. M. D., with Refrain

St. Catherine	256

L. M. D.

Creation	47
Jerusalem	269

2, 10, 10, 10

Fortitude	182

5, 6, 6, 4

	HYMN
Beechwood	58

5, 6, 6, 4, 6, 6, 6, 4

Lynde	54

6, 4, 6, 4, with Refrain

Need	150

6, 4, 6, 4, D.

Bread of Life	71

6, 4, 6, 4, 6, 6, 4

Love's Offering	252

6, 4, 6, 4, 6, 6, 4

Bethany	156
St. Edmund	149

6, 5, 6, 5

Country Lanes	172
Merrial	23

6, 5, 6, 5, D.

Godfrey	259
Lonely Midnight	89
Morley	213
Penitence	178
St. Andrew of Crete	179

6, 5, 6, 5, D., with Refrain

Armageddon	202
Onward	263
Rosmore	94, 190
St. Gertrude	209
St. Theresa	208

6, 5, 6, 5, 6, 6, 6, 5

St. Dunstan's	204

6, 6, 4, 6, 6, 6, 4

America	279
Dort	283
Italian Hymn	38
Kirby Bedon	138
Olivet	155
Pastor Regalis	294

6, 6, 6, 6, 6, 6

Laudes Domini	2

HYMN

6, 6, 6, 6, D.
Comrade Heart 237
Godfrey 65
Rugby 170

6, 6, 6, 6, 8, 8
Arthur's Seat 184
Jubilate 131

6, 6, 6, 6, 12, 12
Christmas Song 84

6, 7, 6, 7, 6, 6, 6, 6
Nun Danket 325

6, 7, 7, 7, 6, 6, 7, 7, 7
Fealty 121

6, 8, 8, 8, 8
Rochester 166

7, 6, 7, 6
Manchester 186
Parousia 86

7, 6, 7, 6, with Refrain
Lord's Day 7

7, 6, 7, 6, D.
All Hallows 276
Angel's Story 196
Aurelia 308
Berthold 320
Chenies 41
Comrades of the Cross . . . 122
Ellacombe 117
Faithful 125
God's Love 42
Lancashire 127, 199
Martineau 200
Munich 68
Passion Chorale 48
Rotterdam 15, 128
St. Hilda 148
St. Theodulph 116
Salve Domine 9, 275
Thornbury 307
Webb 201, 301

7, 6, 7, 6, D., with Refrain
Dresden 323

7, 6, 7, 6, 8, 8, 8, 5
Commonwealth 288

7, 6, 8, 6, D.
Alford 266
Neilson 180

7, 6, 8, 6, 8, 6, 8, 6
St. Christopher 120

7, 7, 5, 7, 7, 5
Armstrong 104

HYMN

7, 7, 7, 6, with Refrain
Easter Flowers 126

7, 7, 7, 7
Ellingham 198, 214
Innocents 32
Mercy 60
St. Bees 176
Seymour 217

7, 7, 7, 7, with Alleluia
Worgan 129

7, 7, 7, 7, 4
Chautauqua 17

7, 7, 7, 7, 7, 7
Dix 46, 95
England's Lane 168
Kucken 227
Pilot 160
St. Athanasius 73, 250

7, 7, 7, 7, D.
Aberystwyth 298
Hollingside 157
Martyn 157
Roland 44
St. George's, Windsor . . . 322
Sherwin 106
Watchman 298

7, 7, 7, 7, D., with Refrain
Mendelssohn 77

7, 8, 8, 8, 8, 7
Pioneers 211

8, 4, 8, 4
Belleville 317

8, 4, 8, 4, 8, 4
Wentworth 51

8, 4, 8, 4, 8, 8, 8, 4
Ar Hyd Y Nos 18

8, 5, 8, 3
Bullinger 245
Stephanos 151

8, 5, 8, 5
College 113
Geneva 223

8, 5, 8, 5, 8, 4, 3
Angel Voices 228

8, 6, 6, 8, 6, 6
Stella 85

HYMN

8, 6, 8, 6, 6
Warren 332

8, 6, 8, 6, 7, 6, 8, 6
St. Louis 82

8, 6, 8, 6, 8, 6
St. Bede 139

8, 6, 8, 6, 8, 8,
Harvard 142

8, 6, 8, 6, 8, 8, 8, 6
Muswell Hill 185

8, 6, 8, 8, 6
Whittier 152, 314

8, 7, 8, 7
Dominus Regit Me 50
Galilee 144
Lucerne 14
Rathbun 124
Sardis 90
Wellesley 55

8, 7, 8, 7, with Refrain
Lower Lights 253
Regent Square 88

8, 7, 8, 7, 6, 6, 6, 6, 7
Ein Feste Burg 210

8, 7, 8, 7, 7
Il Buon Pastor 167

8, 7, 8, 7, 8, 7
Picardy 277
Regent Square 88, 337

8, 7, 8, 7, D.
Armonia Biblica 240
Austrian Hymn 264
Beecher 67
Ebenezer 220
Faben 30
Hymn to Joy 43
Love Divine 191
Pisani 163
Son of Man 99
Vesper Hymn 16

8, 8, 4, 4, 8, 8, with Alleluia
Lasst uns Erfreuen 45

8, 8, 8
Delhi 248

8, 8, 8, with Alleluia
Victory 64, 132

HYMN

8, 8, 8, 4
Almsgiving 56
Eudora 53

8, 8, 8, 6
Just as I am 145

8, 8, 8, 6, with Refrain
Kings of Orient 96

8, 8, 8, 7
Quem Pastores Laudavere . 171
Sardis 238

8, 8, 8, 8, 6
St. Margaret 154

8, 8, 8, 8, 8, 5
Dolut 164

8, 8, 8, 8, 8, 8
Lest we forget 162, 282
Saints of God 102
St. Catherine 49
Swansea 69
Veni Emmanuel 75

9, 8, 9, 8
Church Vigilant 224

10, 4, 10, 4, 10, 10
Lux Benigna 333

10, 7, 10, 7
Deo Gratias 226

10, 8, 8, 7, 7, with Refrain
Message 302

10, 10, 9, 10
Vision 236

10, 10, 10, 4
Deed 187
Sarum 330
Sine Nomine 330

10, 10, 10, 10
Conisborough 222
Dunblane Cathedral 8
Ellah 289
Ellers 24

HYMN

Eventide 20
Field 249
Gratitude 233
Morecambe 62, 141
National Hymn 273
Oliver 221
Peel Castle 19
Penitentia 300
Picton 118
Pro Patria 258
Spes Mea in Deo 235
Summerford 274
Willingham 225
Woodlands 3

10, 10, 11, 11
Lyons 36

11, 10, 11, 9
Russian Hymn 284

11, 10, 11, 10
Ancient of Days . . . 1, 34, 247
Curfew 21
Cushman 100
Felix 6, 153
Industry 192
Morning Star 239
Oberlin 6
Peek 177
Springfield 292
Strength and Stay 244
Vesalius 313
Wesley 303

11, 10, 11, 10, with Refrain
Pilgrims 329
Tidings 306

11, 10, 11, 10, 10
Old 124th 287

11, 10, 11, 10, D.
Londonderry 109

11, 11, 11, 5
Christe Sanctorum 26

11, 11, 11, 11
Ashland 105
Poland 57
Portuguese Hymn 74

11, 11, 11, 11, with Refrain
Fortunatus 130

HYMN

11, 12, 12, 10
Nicæa 4
Trinity 107

12, 10, 12, 10
Monsell 12

12, 11, 12, 11
Kremser 29

12, 13, 12, 10
Gannett 5

14, 14, 4, 7, 8
Lobe den Herren 35

15, 15, 15, 6, with Refrain
Battle Hymn of the Republic 280

15, 15, 15, 15
Mt. Holyoke, ... 285, 297

Irregular
Adeste Fideles 83
Agni 173
Beacon Hill 205
Beautiful Star 93
Benediction 25
Chalice 230
Charity 242
Crusader's Hymn 137
Decision 232
Dreamers 91
Dublin 243
Follow the Gleam 230
Gloria Patri 335
Hosanna 114
In Corde Meo 338
Lanier 119
Margaret 101
Offertory 341
Sanctus 336
Southampton 161
Stille Nacht 81
Stockwell New 108
Sundown 231
Taps 344
The First Noel 79
Two Fatherlands 331
Wallace 92

Index of Authors, Translators and Sources

Adams, John Coleman (1849–), 206.
Adams, John Greenleaf (1810–1887), 240.
Adams, Sarah Flower (1805–1848), 156.
Addison, Joseph (1672–1719), 47.
Adler, Felix (1851–), 264.
Alexander, Cecil Frances (1823–1895), 144.
Alford, Henry (1810–1871), 322.
Ambrose of Milan (340–397), 11.
Ames, Charles Gordon (1828–1912), 161.
Andrew of Crete (660–732), 179.
Anonymous, 7, 30, 53, 125, 174, 294, 343, 344.
Armstrong, John (1813–1856), 218.

Babcock, Maltbie Davenport (1858–1901), 39, 182.
Bacon, Leonard (1802–1881), 270.
Baker, Henry Williams (1821–1877), 50.
Baring-Gould, Sabine (1834–1924), 23, 209.
Barton, Bernard (1784–1849), 72.
Bates, Katharine Lee (1859–1929), 92, 114, 153, 271.
Beeching, Henry Charles (1859–1919), 170.
Benson, Arthur Christopher (1862–), 319.
Benson, Louis FitzGerald (1855–), 11, 80, 314.
Binyon, Laurence (1869–), 165.
Birks, Thomas Rawson (1810–1883), 41.
Blaisdell, James Arnold (1867–), 90.
Blake, William (1757–1827), 269.
Blanchard, Ferdinand Quincy (1876–), 103.
Blatchford, Ambrose Nichols (1842–1924), 21.
Bliss, Philip Paul (1838–1876), 253.
Bode, John Ernest (1816–1874), 196.
Bonar, Horatius (1808–1889), 147, 222, 337.
Bowie, Walter Russell (1882–), 274.
Bowring, John (1792–1872), 124, 298.
Braley, Berton (1882–), 250.
Bridges, Matthew (1800–1894), 136.
Bronte, Anne (1820–1849), 183.
Brooke, Stopford Augustus (1832–1918), 44, 104.
Brooks, Charles Timothy (1813–1883), 283.
Brooks, Phillips (1835–1893), 82.
Bruce, William (1812–1882), 73.
Bryn Mawr College, 230.
Bunyan, John (1628–1688), 204.
Burton Henry (1840–), 19, 37, 285.
Butcher, John Williams, 166.
Butler, Henry Montagu (1833–1918), 3.
Byrne, Mary, 236.

Cady, Julia Bulkley (1882–), 29.
Campbell, Jane Montgomery (1817–1878), 323.
Caswall, Edward (1814–1878), 2, 10, 158.
Chadwick, John White (1840–1904), 328.
Chandler, John (1806–1876), 11.
Cherryman, Myrtle Koon, 281.
Chorley, Henry Fothergill (1808–1872), 284.
Clark, Thomas Curtis (1877–), 142, 237, 261.
Claudius, Matthias (1740–1815), 323.
Clement of Alexandria (170–220), 138.
Clephane, Elizabeth Cecilia (1830–1869), 120.
Coffin, Henry Sloane (1877–), 75.
Conder, Eustace Rogers (1820–1892), 102.
Copenhaver, Laura, 258.
Coster, George Thomas (1835–1912), 184.
Crane, William M. (1880–), 86.
Croly, George (1780–1860), 62.
Cross, Allen Eastman, 97, 99, 186, 229, 278.

Davis, Ozora Stearns (1866–), 194, 286.
Dawson, William James (1854–1928), 108.
Dearmer, Percy (1867–1936), 26, 69, 167, 171.
Deland, Margaret (1857–), 134.
Dexter, Henry Martyn (1821–1890), 138.
Dickinson, Emily (1830–1886), 242.
Dix, William Chatterton (1837–1898), 95.
Doane, George Washington (1799–1859), 304.
Doane, William Croswell (1832–1913), 34.
Doddridge, Philip (1702–1751), 195.
Draper, William Henry (1855–), 45, 315.
Drinkwater, John (1882–), 187.
Duffield, George (1818–1888), 201.
Dwight, John Sullivan (1813–1893), 283.
Dwight, Timothy (1752–1817), 311.

Edgar, Mary S., 223.
Ellerton, John (1826–1893), 24, 130, 284.
Elliott, Ebenezer (1781–1849), 288.
Elliott, Emily Elizabeth Steele (1836–1897), 101.
English Carol, 79.

Faber, Frederick William (1814–1863), 55, 256, 329.
Farningham, Marianne (1834–1909), 145.
Farrington, Harry Webb (1880–), 112, 143.
Fawcett, John (1740–1817), 312.
Felton, Richard, 163.
Findlater, Sarah Laurie (1823–1907), 313.
Fletcher, Frank (1870–), 109.

Forbush, William Byron (1868–1928), 162.
Fortunatus, Venantius (530–609), 131.
Foulkes, William Hiram (1877–   ), 246.
Francis of Assisi (1182–1226), 45.
Freckleton, Thomas Wesley (1827–1903), 189.
Freeman, Robert (1878–   ), 233.
Furness, William Henry (1802–1896), 217.

Gannett, William Channing (1840–1928), 5.
Gerhardt, Paul (1607–1676), 85.
German, 2, 137.
Gilder, Richard Watson (1844–1909), 212.
Gillman, Frederick John, 255.
Gladden, Washington (1836–1918), 197.
Grant, Robert (1785–1838), 36.
Greek Hymn, 335.
Gregory the Great (540–604), 26.

Halpine, Charles Graham (1829–1868), 238.
Hamilton, Mary C. D., 290.
Harmony in Praise, 31.
Hartshorne, Hugh (1885–   ), 322.
Hastings, Thomas (1784–1872), 303.
Hatch, Edwin (1835–1889), 61.
Havergal, Frances Ridley (1836–1879), 198, 202, 251.
Hawks, Annie Sherwood (1835–1918), 150.
Haycroft, Margaret Scott, 54.
Heber, Reginald (1783–1826), 4, 18, 262.
Hedge, Frederick Henry (1805–1890), 210.
Hodder, Edwin (1837–1904), 70.
Holland, Henry Scott (1847–1918), 277.
Holland, Josiah Gilbert (1819–1881), 84.
Holmes, John Haynes (1879–   ), 296, 316.
Holmes, Oliver Wendell (1809–1894), 33.
Hopkins, John Henry (1820–1891), 96.
Hopper, Edward (1818–1888), 160.
Hosmer, Frederick Lucian (1840–1928), 18, 263, 275.
Housman, Laurence (1865–   ), 87, 287.
How, William Walsham (1823–1897), 68, 131, 148, 330, 339.
Howe, Julia Ward (1819–1910), 280.
Hughes, Thomas (1826–1896), 181.
Hull, Eleanor, 236.

Irish Hymn, 236.

John of Damascus (8th Century), 127.
Johnson, Samuel (1822–1882), 214, 267.

Keble, John (1792–1866), 22.
Kemp, Harry Hibbard, (1883–   ), 139.
Ken, Thomas (1637–1711), 334.
Kipling, Rudyard (1865–   ), 175, 282.
Knapp, Shepherd (1873–   ), 247.

Lanier, Sidney (1842–1881), 119.
Larcom, Lucy (1826–1893), 149.

Lathbury, Mary Artemisia (1841–1913), 17, 71.
Latin Hymns, 75, 83, 133, 158.
Laufer, Calvin Weiss (1874–   ), 249.
Lee, Harry, 110.
Littlefield, Milton S. (1864–   ), 14, 188.
Longfellow, Henry Wadsworth (1807–1882), 292.
Longfellow, Samuel (1819–1892), 49, 60, 203, 219, 321, 340.
Lowell, James Russell (1819–1891), 220.
Luther, Martin (1483–1546), 210.
Lynch, Thomas Toke (1818–1871), 185.
Lyte, Henry Francis (1793–1847), 20.

MacDonald, George (1824–1905), 13.
MacFadyen, H. R., 59.
MacKaye, Percy (1875–   ), 107.
Mahlmann, Siegfried Augustus (1771–1826), 283.
Marlatt, Earl, 63, 91, 132, 193, 205, 242.
Masefield, John (1874–   ), 234.
Masterman, John Howard Bertram (1867–   ), 295.
Mathams, Walter John (1854–   ), 146, 180, 235.
Matheson, George (1842–1906), 154, 300.
Mathews, Basil Joseph (1879–   ), 8.
McGregor, Ernest, 318.
Merrill, William Pierson (1867–   ), 254.
Millay, Edna St. Vincent (1892–   ), 40.
Milman, Henry Hart (1791–1868), 115.
Milton, John (1608–1674), 32.
Mohr, Joseph (1792–1848), 81.
Monsell, John Samuel Bewley (1811–1875), 9, 12, 207.
Montgomery, James (1771–1854), 57, 88, 178, 301.
Moore, Thomas (1779–1852), 16.

Neale, John Mason (1818–1866), 75, 116, 127, 151, 179.
Neander, Joachim (1650–1680), 35.
Newman, John Henry (1801–1890), 333.
Nichol, Henry Ernest (1862–   ), 302 (see "Colin Sterne").
Nicholson, Mary Ann, 126.
Ninde, Henry S., 113.
Noel, Baptist W., 52.
North, Frank Mason (1850–   ), 257, 265.
Numbers, 25.

Oakley, Ebenezer Sherman (1865–   ), 213.
Oakeley, Frederick (1802–1880), 83.
Osler, Edward (1798–1863), 30.
Oxenham, John, 159, 232, 299.

Palmer, Ray (1808–1887), 155.
Park, John Edgar (1879–   ), 100.
Parker, Edwin Pond (1836–1925), 176, 252.
Parker, Theodore (1810–1860), 141.

Partridge, Sybil F., 317.
Paxton, Thomas, 42.
Perronet, Edward (1726–1792), 135.
Pierpont, Folliott Sandford (1835–1917), 46.
Plumptre, Edward Hayes (1821–1891), 27, 111, 307.
Pott, Francis (1839–1909), 133, 228.
Potter, Thomas Joseph (1827–1873), 208.
Procter, Adelaide Ann (1825–1864), 51.
Prudentius, Aurelius Clemens (348–414), 10.

Rawnsley, Hardwicke Drummond (1851–1920), 169.
Raymond, Rossiter Worthington (1840–1918), 93.
Reese, Lizette Woodworth (1856–   ), 172.
Rhodes, Sarah Betts (1870–   ), 58.
Ritchie, David Lake, 65.
Rinkhart, Martin (1586–1649), 325.
Rippon's, John, *Selection* (1751–1836), 74.
Roberts, Daniel C. (1841–1907), 273.
Rossetti, Christina Georgina (1830–1894), 248.
Rowland, May A., 289.

St. Stephen of Mar Saba, 8th Century, 151.
Sangster, Margaret Elizabeth (1838–1912), 226, 260.
Savage, Minot Judson (1841–1918), 200, 225.
Sears, Edmund Hamilton (1810–1876), 78.
Sherwin, William Fiske (1826–1888), 106.
Shurtleff, Ernest Warburton (1862–1917), 199.
Sill, Edward Rowland (1841–1887), 268.
Smith, Samuel Francis (1808–1895), 279.
Squier, George L., 216.
Spencer, Anna Garlin (1851–   ), 190.
Spitta, Carl Johann Philip (1801–1859), 313.
Spring-Rice, Cecil (1859–1918), 331.
Stephens, James (1882–   ), 243.
Sterne, Colin (Henry Ernest Nichol), 1862–   ), 302.
Stock, Eleanor B., 164.
Stocking, Jay Thomas (1870–   ), 98.
Stone, Samuel John (1839–1900), 308.
Stowe, Harriet Beecher (1812–1896), 6.

Studdert-Kennedy, Geoffrey Anketell (1883–1929), 192.
Symonds, John Addington (1840–1893), 293.

Tarrant, William George (1853–   ), 128, 168, 241, 259, 266, 320.
Taylor, Jeremy (1613–1667), 118.
Teasdale, Sara (1884–   ), 227.
Tennyson, Alfred (1809–1892), 215, 231, 297, 327.
Thalheimer, Elsie, 54.
Theodulph of Orleans (9th century), 116.
Thoburn, Helen, 1.
Thomson, Mary Ann (1834–1923), 306.
Threlfall, Jeannette (1821–1880), 117.
Thring, Godfrey (1823–1903), 94.
Tweedy, Henry Hallam (1868–   ), 66.

Untermeyer, Jean Starr (1886–   ), 173.

Van Dyke, Henry (1852–   ), 43, 191, 272.
Vories, William Merrill (1880–   ), 291.

Walter, Howard Arnold (1883–1918), 177.
Warburton, George A., 309.
Waring, Anna Laetitia (1823–1910), 48.
Warmingham, Osbert Wrightman, 64.
Watt, Lauchlan MacLean (1867–   ), 121.
Wattles, Willard (1888–   ), 123.
Watts, Isaac (1674–1748), 28, 76, 123, 305.
Wesley, Charles (1707–1788), 67, 77, 129, 157.
White, Frederick M., 221.
Whitfield, George (1714–1770), *Hymn Book*, 38, 77.
Whitman, Walt (1819–1892), 211.
Whittier, John Greenleaf (1807–1892), 105, 140, 152, 244, 310, 324, 332.
Wilcox, Ella Wheeler (1855–1919), 239.
Wile, Frances Whitmarch (1878–   ), 326.
Williams, Theodore Chickering (1855–1915), 89, 245.
Wilson, Elizabeth, 1.
Wilson, Sarah Josselyn (1893–   ), 276.
Wilson, Stuart, 224.
Winkworth, Catherine (1829–1878), 35, 85, 325.
Wordsworth, Christopher (1807–1885), 15, 56.

Index of Composers, Arrangers and Sources

Abt, Franz (1819–1885), 225.
Anonymous, 161, 343.
Atkinson, Frederick Cook (1841–1897), 62, 141.

Bach, John Sebastian (1685–1750), 48, 125.
Baker, Henry (1835–1910), 63.
Baker, Henry Williams (1821–1877), 151.
Barnby, Joseph (1838–1896), 2, 13, 23, 145, 330.
Barnes, Archie Fairbairn (1878–   ), 8.
Barnes, Edward Shippen (1887–   ), 123, 234, 319.
Barrington, J. W., 263.
Basque Church Melody, 69.
Bates, William Lester, 308.
Baumbach, Adolph, 338.
Beethoven, Ludwig van (1770–1827), 43, 90, 238, 341.
Berridge, Arthur (1855–   ), 142.
Blanchard, George Frederick (1856–   ), 162, 282.
Bliss, Philip Paul (1838–1876), 253.
Bonner, Carey, 185.
Bonner, Robert, 294.
Booth, Josiah (1852–1929), 58, 288.
Bortniansky, Dmitri Stepanovitch (1752–1825), 16.
Bourgeois, Louis (1500–1561), 334.
Boyd, William (1847–   ), 207, 291.
Branscombe, Gena (1881–   ), 118, 230.
Bullinger, Ethelbert William (1837–1913), 245.
Bunnett, Edward (1834–1923), 138.
Burnap, Uzziah Christopher (1834–1900), 98.
Burney, Charles (1726–1814), 260, 295.
Burnham, John Nicholas, 143.

Calkin, John Baptiste (1827–1905), 267, 304, 324.
Campbell, Leroy B., 114, 236, 332.
Candlyn, Frederick H., 170.
Canzuns Spirituælas, 167.
Chadwick, George Whitfield (1854–   ), 103, 104.
Cheeswright, Frederick Henry, 326.
Coerne, Louis Adolphe (1870–1922), 99.
Conant, Grace Wilbur, 121, 173.
Conkey, Ithamar (1815–1867), 124.
Cramer, John B., 54.
Croft, William (1678–1727), 28.
Cruger, Johann (1598–1662), 325.
Cummings, William Hayman (1831–1918), 77.
Cutler, Henry Stephen (1824–1902), 262, 286.

Daniels, Mabel W. (1878–   ), 91.
Davies, Henry Walford (1869–   ), 80.
Day, George Henry, 110, 166, 200, 232.
Dearle, Edward (1806–1891), 300.
Demuth, John Arthur (1848–1920), 6.
Depew, Arthur, 318.
Douglas, Sallie Hume, 230.
Douglas, Winfred (1867–   ), 204.
Dyer, Samuel (1785–1835), 293.
Dykes, John Bacchus (1823–1876), 4, 50, 56, 115, 139, 147, 157, 159, 176, 179, 193, 216, 244, 246, 266, 333.

Earnshaw, R. H. (1856–   ), 59.
Elvey, George Job (1816–1893), 33, 136, 215, 322.
Emerson, Luther Orlando (1820–1916), 18.
English Melodies, 39, 168, 185, 319.

Fairlamb, J. R., 200.
Fink, Gottfried Wilhelm (1783–1846), 70, 174.
Fowles, Leonard N., 111.
French Folk Song, 277.
French Missal, 75.

Gardiner, William (1770–1853), Sacred Melodies (1815), 10, 255.
Gaul, Alfred R. (1837–1913), 336.
Geistliche Kirchengesang (1623), 45.
Genevan Psalter (1551), 287, 334.
German Folk Song, 171, 293.
Giardini, Felice de (1716–1796), 38.
Gill, W. H., 19.
Gladstone, William Henry (1840–1891), 212.
Godfrey, Nathaniel S. (1817–1883), 198, 214.
Goss, John (1800–1880), 184, 202.
Gottschalk, Louis Moreau (1829–1869), 60.
Gould, John Edgar (1822–1875), 160.
Gower, John Henry (1855–1922), 180, 231.
Greatorex, Henry Wellington (1811–1858), 335.
Greatorex, William, 3.
Gregorian Tone (590), 124.
Grieg, Edward (1844–1907), 261, 281, 292.
Grimley, John T., 274.
Gruber, Franz (1787–1863), 81.
Guidetti Directorium Chori (1582), 11.

Hann, Sidney, 181.
Hamilton, Clarence Grant (1865–   ), 92.
Handel, George Frederick (1685–1759), 76, 195.
Harding, John P., 239.

Index of Composers, Arrangers and Sources

Harrington, Karl Pomeroy (1861–   ), 84.
Hartig's *Vollstandige Sammlung* (1830), 117.
Harts, Harry L., 97.
Harwood, Basil (1859–   ), 307.
Hassler, Hans Leo (1564–1612), 48.
Hatton, John (?–1793), 278, 305.
Haydn, Franz Joseph (1732–1809), 47, 264.
Haydn, Johann Michael (1737–1806), 36.
Helmore, Thomas (1811–1890), 75.
Hemy, Henri Frederic (1818–1888), 49, 256.
Hiles, Henry (1826–1904), 66.
Hodges, Edward (1796–1867), 43.
Holden, Oliver (1765–1844), 135.
Hopkins, Edward John (1818–1901), 24, 73, 250.
Hopkins, John Henry (1820–1891), 96.
Howard, Alonzo P. (1838–1902), 89.
Husband, Edward (1843–1908), 148.
Hyatt, Nathaniel Irving, 229, 237.

Ingram, T. H., 264.
Irish Traditional Melody, 109.

Jackson, Robert (1842–1914), 61.
Jeffery, J. Albert (1851–   ), 1, 34, 247.
Jones, James Edmund, 317.
Jude, William Herbert (1851–1892), 144.

Katholisches Gesangbuch (1774), 22.
Knecht, Justin Heinrich (1752–1817), 148.
Kocher, Conrad (1786–1872), 46, 95.
Koschat, Thomas (1845–1914), 57.
Kucken, F. W. (1810–1882), 227.

La Feillee, Methode du Plain-chant (1782), 26.
Lane, Spencer (1843–1903), 178.
Laufer, Calvin Weiss (1874–   ), 108, 249.
Le Jeune, George Fitz-Curwood (1842–1904), 191.
Lester, Thomas William (1889–   ), 69, 192, 331.
Llawlyfr Moliant (1890), 220.
Lockhart, Charles (1745–1815), 315.
Lowden, Carl Harold (1883–   ), 223.
Loy, Harvey, 5.
Luther, Martin (1483–1546), 210.
Lutkin, Peter Christian (1858–   ), 25, 119, 242, 243.
Lwoff, Alexis Feodorowitch (1799–1871), 284.
Lyra Davidica (1708), 129.

MacDonald, Archibald, 203.
Macfarren, George Alexander (1813–1887), 52.
Maker, Frederick Charles (1844–1927), 21, 51, 120, 152, 165, 255, 314.
Mann, Arthur Henry (1850–1929), 196.
Manx Fishermen's Evening Hymn, 19.
March, F. K., 113.
Marsh, Simeon Butler (1798–1872), 157.
Martin, George Clement (1844–1916), 276.
Mason and Webb's *Cantica Laudis*, 339.

Mason, Harry Silvernail, 205.
Mason, Lowell (1792–1872), 76, 123, 155, 156, 283, 298, 303, 312.
Matthews, Timothy Richard (1826–1910), 41, 101, 175, 206.
Meiningen Gesangbuch (1693), 68.
Mendelssohn-Bartholdy, Felix (1809–1847), 6, 7, 77, 153, 290, 325.
Merrill, William Pierson (1867–   ), 272.
Messiter, Arthur Henry (1831–1889), 27.
Meyer, Sebastion W., 164.
Monk, William Henry (1823–1889), 20, 22, 64, 132.
Morley, Thomas (1845–1892), 213.
Mozart, School of (18th Century), 327.
Murray, J. R., 53.

Naylor, Edward Woodhall (1867–   ), 146.
Netherlands Folk Song (1625), 29.
Newman, Richard Stinson (1850–   ), 321.
Nichol, Henry Ernest (1862–1928), 302.

Oakeley, Herbert Stanley (1830–1903), 218.
Oliver, George Edgar, 221.

Palestrina, Hiovanni Pierluigi da (1525–1594), 64, 132.
Parish Choir, The (1850), 32.
Parry, Charles Hubert Hastings (1848–1918), 269.
Parry, Joseph (1841–1903), 298.
Parker, Edwin Pond (1836–1925), 252.
Parker, Horatio William (1863–1919), 85, 131, 258, 268.
Peace, Albert Lister (1844–1912), 154.
Peek, Joseph Yates, 177.
Peery, Rob Roy (1900–   ), 112.
Perry, E. Cooper, 313.
Pieraccini, E., 37.
Pisani, Umberto, 163, 240.
Plain Song, 11, 26, 75.
Ponsonby, A. B., 226.
Porter, Hugh Boring, 40.

Redner, Lewis Henry (1831–1908), 82.
Reinagle, Alexander Robert (1799–1877), 299.
Reissiger, Carl G. (1798–1859), 316.
Rendle, Lily, 289.
Repper, Charles, 137, 322.
Rimbault, Edward Francis (1816–1876), 248.

Sanderson, Wilfred, 222.
Sandy's *Christmas Carols* (1833), 79.
Schilling, Frederick, 93.
Schleischen Volkslieder (1842), 137.
Schulthes, William August (1816–1879), 72.
Schultz, Johann Abraham Peter (1747–1800), 323.
Schumann, Robert (1810–1856), 251, 309, 340.
Scott-Gatty, Alfred (1847–1919), 310.

Index of Composers, Arrangers and Sources

Shaw, Martin (1876–   ), 211.
Sheppard, Franklin L., 39.
Sherwin, William Fisk (1826–1888), 12, 17, 42, 71, 106.
Shrubsole, William (1760–1806), 135.
Silesian Folk Song (1842), 137.
Simper, Caleb (1856–   ), 44.
Smart, Henry (1813–1879), 88, 127, 199, 329, 337.
Smith, David Stanley (1877–   ), 182.
Smith, Henry Percy (1825–1898), 197.
Smith, Lucia May (1887–   ), 105.
Southgate, Thomas Bishop (1814–1868), 188.
Stainer, John (1840–1901), 86.
Stair, Patty, 169.
Statham, Francis Reginald (1844–   ), 219.
Stebbins, George Waring (1869–   ), 186.
Steffe, William (19th century), 280.
Stocks, George Gilbert (1877–   ), 87.
Stralsund Gesangbuch (1665), 35.
Sullivan, Arthur Seymour (1842–1900), 102, 130, 149, 208, 209, 228.
Sydenham, Edwin Augustus (1847–1891), 183.

Taylor, Virgil Corydon (1817–1891), 31.
Teschner, Melchior (17th century), 116.
Thesaurus Musicus (1740), 279.
Thuringian Folk Song, 54.
Tourjee, Lizzie Estabrook (1858–   ), 55.
Tours, Berthold (1838–1897), 15, 129, 257, 320.
Trembath, Henry Gough (1844–1908), 94, 190.
Turner, Herbert B., 100.

Valerius, Andrianus, Collection of (1625), 29.
Vibbard, Harry, 172.

Wade, James Clifft (1847–   ), 328.
Wade's Cantus Diversi (1751), 74, 83.
Walch, James (1837–1901), 158, 189, 296, 306.
Wallace, William Vincent (1824–1865), 140, 194.
Walton, James George (1821–1905), 49, 256.
Warburton, J. S., 235.
Ward, Samuel Augustus (1847–1903), 271.
Warren, George William (1821–1905), 273.
Watson, Lawrence White (1860–1927), 9, 275.
Webb, George James (1803–1887), 201, 301.
Weber, Carl Maria von (1786–1826), 217.
Welsh Traditional Melody, 18.
Wesley, Samuel Sebastian (1810–1876), 107, 308.
West, John A., 65, 259.
Whelpton, George (1847–   ), 342.
Whitmer, Thomas Carl (1873–   ), 134, 187, 233.
Whitney, Samuel Brenton (1842–1914), 241.
Willcox, John Henry (1827–1875), 30.
Williams, Aaron (1731–1776), 254, 311.
Williams, Ralph Vaughan (1872–   ), 330.
Williams, Thomas John (1869–   ), 220.
Willis, Richard Storrs (1819–1900), 78.
Willis, T. A., 14.
Wostenholm, M. L., 285, 297.

Zundel John (1815–1882), 67.
Ziegler, Charles L., 224.

1

Father of Lights

(ANCIENT OF DAYS. 11, 10, 11, 10)

Elizabeth Wilson and Helen Thoburn, 1913

J. Albert Jeffery, 1886

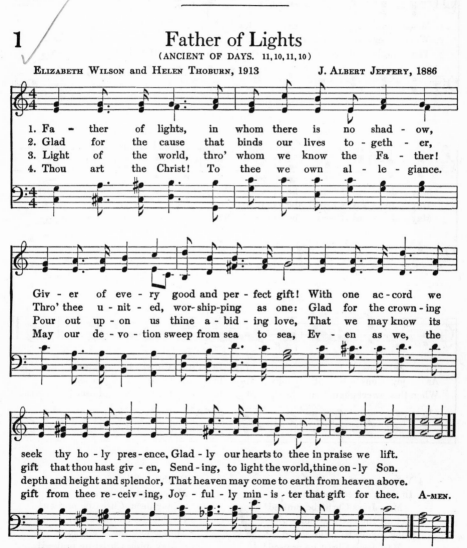

1. Fa - ther of lights, in whom there is no shad - ow,
2. Glad for the cause that binds our lives to - geth - er,
3. Light of the world, thro' whom we know the Fa - ther!
4. Thou art the Christ! To thee we own al - le - giance.

Giv - er of eve - ry good and per - fect gift! With one ac - cord we
Thro' thee u - nit - ed, wor - ship-ping as one: Glad for the crown - ing
Pour out up - on us thine a - bid - ing love, That we may know its
May our de - vo - tion sweep from sea to sea, Ev - en as we, the

seek thy ho - ly pres - ence, Glad - ly our hearts to thee in praise we lift.
gift that thou hast giv - en, Send - ing, to light the world, thine on - ly Son.
depth and height and splendor, That heaven may come to earth from heaven above.
gift from thee re - ceiv - ing, Joy - ful - ly min - is - ter that gift for thee. A-MEN.

When Morning Gilds the Skies

(LAUDES DOMINI. 6, 6, 6, 6, 6, 6)

Anonymous (German) 1800
Translated by EDWARD CASWALL, 1853, 1858

JOSEPH BARNBY, 1868

2

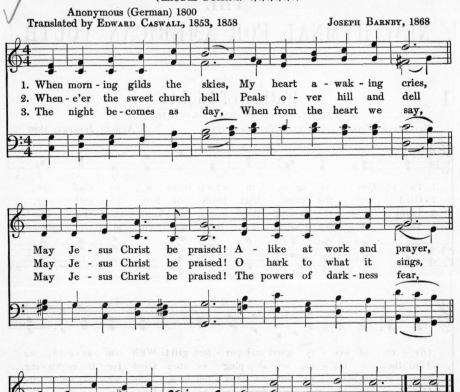

1. When morn - ing gilds the skies, My heart a - wak - ing cries,
   May Je - sus Christ be praised! A - like at work and prayer,
   To Je - sus I re - pair; May Je - sus Christ be praised!

2. When - e'er the sweet church bell Peals o - ver hill and dell
   May Je - sus Christ be praised! O hark to what it sings,
   As joy - ous - ly it rings, May Je - sus Christ be praised!

3. The night be - comes as day, When from the heart we say,
   May Je - sus Christ be praised! The powers of dark - ness fear,
   When this sweet chant they hear, May Je - sus Christ be praised! A - MEN.

4 Ye nations of mankind,
In this your concord find,
   May Jesus Christ be praised!
Let all the earth around
Ring joyous with the sound,
   May Jesus Christ be praised!

5 Be this, while life is mine,
My canticle divine,
   May Jesus Christ be praised!
Be this the eternal song,
Through all the ages long,
   May Jesus Christ be praised!

3 Lift Up Your Hearts

(WOODLANDS. 10, 10, 10, 10)

H. Montagu Butler, 1833–1918

William Greatorex

1. 'Lift up your hearts!' We lift them, Lord, to thee; Here at thy
feet none oth-er may we see: 'Lift up your hearts!' E'en so, with one ac-
cord, We lift them up, we lift them to the Lord.

2. Lift eve-ry gift that thou thy-self hast given; Low lies the
best, till lift-ed up to heaven: Low lie the bound - ing heart, the teem-ing
brain, Till, sent from God, they mount to God a - gain.

3. Then, as the trum - pet-call, in aft-er years, 'Lift up your
hearts!' rings peal-ing in our ears, Still shall those hearts re - spond, with full ac-
cord, 'We lift them up, we lift them to the Lord!' A-men.

4 Holy, Holy, Holy, Lord God Almighty

(NICÆA. 11, 12, 12, 10)

REGINALD HEBER, 1827   JOHN B. DYKES, 1861

1. Ho - ly, ho - ly, ho - ly! Lord God Al - might - y!
2. Ho - ly, ho - ly, ho - ly! all the saints a - dore thee,
3. Ho - ly, ho - ly, ho - ly! tho' the dark-ness hide thee,
4. Ho - ly, ho - ly, ho - ly! Lord God Al - might - y!

Ear - ly in the morn - ing our song shall rise to thee;
Cast - ing down their gold-en crowns a - round the glass - y sea;
Though the eye of sin - ful man thy glo - ry may not see,
All thy works shall praise thy name, in earth, and sky, and sea;

Ho - ly, ho - ly, ho - ly! mer - ci - ful and might - y!
Cher - u - bim and sera - phim fall - ing down be - fore thee,
On - ly thou art ho - ly; there is none be - side thee,
Ho - ly, ho - ly, ho - ly! mer - ci - ful and might - y!

God in three per - sons, bless - ed Trin - i - ty!
Who wert, and art, and ev - er - more shalt be.
Per - fect in power, in love, and pu - ri - ty.
God in three per - sons, bless - ed Trin - i - ty! A-MEN.

4

5 Bring, O Morn, Thy Music

(GANNETT. 12, 13, 12, 10)

WILLIAM C. GANNETT, 1893

HARVEY LOY, 1924

1. Bring, O morn, thy music, night, thy star - lit si - lence;
2. Life and death, thy crea - tures, praise thee, Might - y Giv - er:
3. Light us, lead us, love us! cry thy grop - ing na - tions,
4. Life nor death can part us, O thou Love e - ter - nal,

O - ceans, chant the rap - ture to the storm-winds cours - ing free:
Praise and prayer are ris - ing in thy beast and bird and tree:
Plead - ing in the thou - sand tongues, but nam - ing on - ly thee,
Shep - herd of the wan - dering star, and souls that way - ward flee;

Sun and stars are sing - ing, thou art our Cre - a - tor,
Lo! they praise and van - ish, van - ish at thy bid - ding,
Weav - ing blind - ly out thy ho - ly, hap - py pur - pose,
Home - ward draws our spir - it to thy Spir - it yearn - ing,

Who wert, and art, and ev - er - more shalt be. A - MEN.

6
Still, Still with Thee

(FELIX. 11. 10, 11, 10)

HARRIET BEECHER STOWE, 1855   FELIX MENDELSSOHN–BARTHOLDY, 1809–1847

1. Still, still with thee, when pur - ple morn-ing break-eth, When the bird
2. A - lone with thee, a - mid the mys - tic shad - ows, The sol - emn
3. When sinks the soul, sub-dued by toil, to slum - ber, Its clos - ing
4. So shall it be at last, in that bright morn - ing, When the soul

wak - eth, and the shad - ows flee; Fair - er than morn - ing,
hush of na - ture new - ly born; A - lone with thee in
eye looks up to thee in prayer; Sweet the re - pose be -
wak - eth, and life's shad - ows flee: O in that hour, fair -

love-lier than the day-light, Dawns the sweet con-scious-ness, I am with thee.
breath-less ad-o - ra - tion, In the calm dew and fresh-ness of the morn.
neath thy wings o'ershading, But sweet-er still to wake and find thee there.
er than day-light dawning, Shall rise the glo-rious tho't, I am with thee. A-MEN.

Still, Still with Thee

(OBERLIN. 11, 10, 11, 10) *Second Tune*

HARRIET BEECHER STOWE, 1852   J. ARTHUR DEMUTH, 1900

Still, still with thee, when pur - ple morn-ing break-eth, When the bird

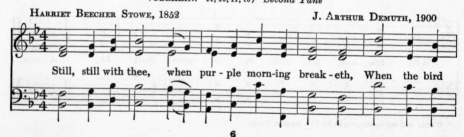

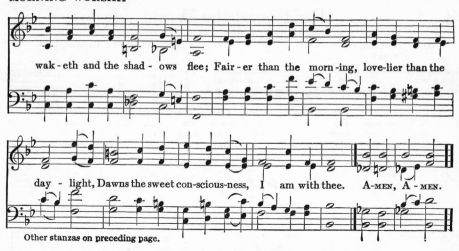

wak-eth and the shad-ows flee; Fair-er than the morn-ing, love-lier than the

day - light, Dawns the sweet con-scious-ness, I am with thee. A-MEN, A - MEN.

Other stanzas on preceding page.

7   The Earth is Hushed in Silence

(LORD'S DAY. 7, 6, 7, 6. With Refrain)

Anonymous, 1897   FELIX MENDELSSOHN-BARTHOLDY, 1809–1847

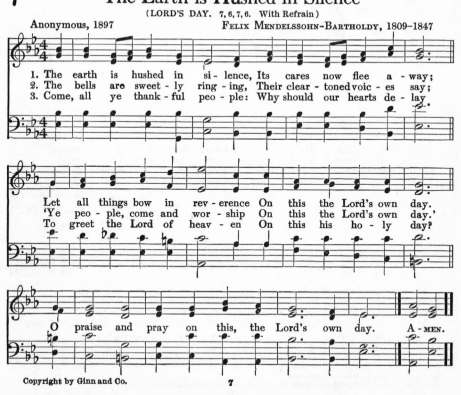

1. The earth is hushed in si - lence, Its cares now flee a - way;
2. The bells are sweet - ly ring - ing, Their clear - toned voic - es say;
3. Come, all ye thank - ful peo - ple: Why should our hearts de - lay

Let all things bow in rev - erence On this the Lord's own day.
'Ye peo - ple, come and wor - ship On this the Lord's own day.'
To greet the Lord of heav - en On this his ho - ly day?

O praise and pray on this, the Lord's own day. A - MEN.

8 Far Round the World

(DUNBLANE CATHEDRAL. 10, 10, 10, 10)

BASIL J. MATHEWS, 1879–   ARCHIE FAIRBAIRN BARNES, 1878–

UNISON

1. Far round the world thy chil - dren sing their song;
2. Where wide thy o - cean, wave on roll - ing wave,
3. Far lands there are where none have seen thy face,
4. Far round the world let chil - dren sing thy song;

HARMONY

From East and West their voic - es rich - ly blend,
Beats through the a - ges, on each is - land shore,
Chil - dren whose hearts have nev - er shared thy joy;
From East and West their voic - es rich - ly blend,

Prais - ing the Lord, in whom young lives are strong,
Praise they their Lord, whose hand a - lone can save,
O wouldst thou pour on these thy ra - diant grace,
Prais - ing the Lord, in whom young lives are strong,

Je - sus, our Guide, our He - ro, and our Friend.
Whose sea of love sur - rounds them ev - er - more.
Give thy glad strength to eve - ry girl and boy.
Je - sus, our Guide, our He - ro, and our Friend. A-MEN.

9 Light of the World, We Hail Thee

(SALVE DOMINE. 7, 6, 7, 6, D.)

John S. B. Monsell, 1863   Lawrence W. Watson, 1909

1. Light of the world, we hail thee, Flush-ing the east-ern skies;
2. Light of the world, thy beau - ty Steals in - to eve - ry heart,
3. Light of the world, il - lu - mine This dark-ened earth of thine,

Nev - er shall dark - ness veil thee A - gain from hu - man eyes;
And glo - ri - fies with du - ty Life's poor - est, hum - blest part;
Till eve - ry - thing that's hu - man Be filled with what's di - vine;

Too long, a - las, with - hold - en, Now spread from shore to shore;
Thou rob - est in thy splen - dor The sim - plest ways of men,
Till eve - ry tongue and na - tion, From sin's do - min - ion free,

Thy light, so glad and gold - en, Shall set on earth no more.
And help - est them to ren - der Light back to thee a - gain.
Rise in the new cre - a - tion Which springs from love and thee. A-men.

10 Now with Creation's Morning Song

(GERMANY. L.M.)

AURELIUS CLEMENS PRUDENTIUS, 348–414
Translated by EDWARD CASWALL, 1849

WILLIAM GARDINER'S
Sacred Melodies, 1815

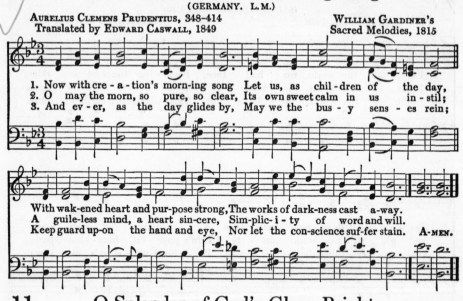

1. Now with cre-a-tion's morn-ing song Let us, as chil-dren of the day,
2. O may the morn, so pure, so clear, Its own sweet calm in us in-stil;
3. And ev-er, as the day glides by, May we the bus-y sens-es rein:

With wak-ened heart and pur-pose strong, The works of dark-ness cast a-way.
A guile-less mind, a heart sin-cere, Sim-plic-i-ty of word and will.
Keep guard up-on the hand and eye, Nor let the con-science suf-fer stain. A-MEN.

11 O Splendor of God's Glory Bright

(AETERNA CHRISTI MUNERA. L.M.)

AMBROSE of Milan, 340–397
Translated by JOHN CHANDLER, 1837
and LOUIS F. BENSON, 1910

Plainsong from GUIDETTI
Directorium Chori, 1582

In free rhythm. UNISON

1. O splen-dor of God's glo - - - - ry bright,
2. Con-firm our will to do the right,
3. O joy-ful be the pass - - - ing day
4. Dawn's glo-ry gilds the earth and skies;

From light e-ter-nal bring-ing light; Thou Light of life, light's
And keep our hearts from en - vy's blight; Let faith her ea - ger
With tho'ts as clear as morn-ing's ray, With faith like noon - tide
Do thou, our per-fect Morn, a - rise; The Fa-ther's help his

liv - ing Spring, True Day, all days il - lu - min - ing.
fires re - new, And hate the false, and love the true.
shin - ing bright, Our souls un - shad - owed by the night.
chil - dren claim, And sing the Fa - ther's glo - rious name. A-MEN.

12 Worship the Lord in the Beauty of Holiness

(MONSELL. 12, 10, 12, 10)

JOHN S. B. MONSELL, 1863 WILLIAM F. SHERWIN, 1826–1887

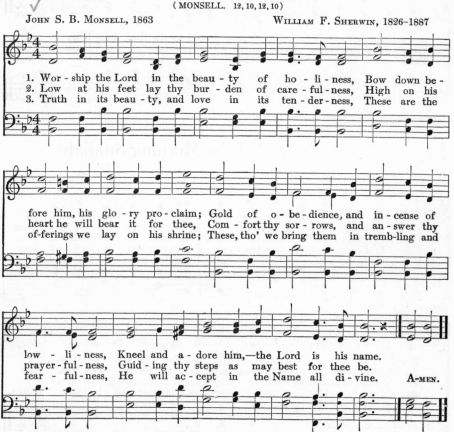

1. Wor - ship the Lord in the beau - ty of ho - li - ness, Bow down be -
2. Low at his feet lay thy bur - den of care - ful - ness, High on his
3. Truth in its beau - ty, and love in its ten - der - ness, These are the

fore him, his glo - ry pro - claim; Gold of o - be - dience, and in - cense of
heart he will bear it for thee, Com - fort thy sor - rows, and an - swer thy
of - ferings we lay on his shrine; These, tho' we bring them in trem - bling and

low - li - ness, Kneel and a - dore him,—the Lord is his name.
prayer - ful - ness, Guid - ing thy steps as may best for thee be.
fear - ful - ness, He will ac - cept in the Name all di - vine. A-MEN.

13 O Lord of Life, Thy Quickening Voice
(SOHO. C. M.)

GEORGE MACDONALD, 1824–1905

JOSEPH BARNBY, 1881

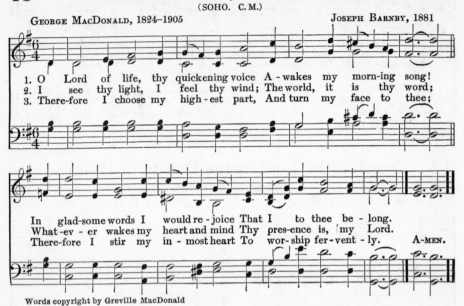

1. O Lord of life, thy quickening voice A-wakes my morn-ing song!
2. I see thy light, I feel thy wind; The world, it is thy word;
3. There-fore I choose my high-est part, And turn my face to thee;

In glad-some words I would re-joice That I to thee be-long.
What-ev-er wakes my heart and mind Thy pres-ence is, my Lord.
There-fore I stir my in-most heart To wor-ship fer-vent-ly. A-MEN.

Words copyright by Greville MacDonald

14 Come, O Lord, Like Morning Sunlight
(LUCERNE. 8, 7, 8, 7)

MILTON S. LITTLEFIELD, 1927

T. A. WILLIS, 1876

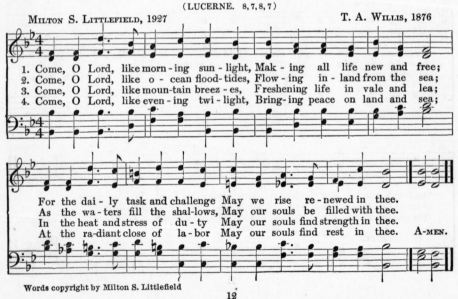

1. Come, O Lord, like morn-ing sun-light, Mak-ing all life new and free;
2. Come, O Lord, like o-cean flood-tides, Flow-ing in-land from the sea;
3. Come, O Lord, like moun-tain breez-es, Freshening life in vale and lea;
4. Come, O Lord, like even-ing twi-light, Bring-ing peace on land and sea;

For the dai-ly task and challenge May we rise re-newed in thee.
As the wa-ters fill the shal-lows, May our souls be filled with thee.
In the heat and stress of du-ty May our souls find strength in thee.
At the ra-diant close of la-bor May our souls find rest in thee. A-MEN.

Words copyright by Milton S. Littlefield

15   O Day of Rest and Gladness

(ROTTERDAM. 7, 6, 7, 6, D.)

CHRISTOPHER WORDSWORTH, 1862   Berthold Tours, 1875

1. O day of rest and glad - ness, O day of joy and light,
2. On thee, at the cre - a - tion, The light first had its birth;
3. To - day on wea - ry na - tions The heaven - ly man - na falls:
4. New gra - ces ev - er gain - ing From this our day of rest,

O balm of care and sad - ness, Most beau - ti - ful, most bright;
On thee, for our sal - va - tion, Christ rose from depths of earth;
To ho - ly con - vo - ca - tions The sil - ver trump - et calls,
We reach the rest re - main - ing To spir - its of the blest.

On thee, the high and low - ly, Through a - ges joined in tune,
On thee, our Lord, vic - to - rious, The Spir - it sent from heaven;
Where gos - pel light is glow - ing With pure and ra - diant beams,
To Ho - ly Ghost be prais - es, To Fa - ther, and to Son;

Sing Ho - ly, Ho - ly, Ho - ly, To the great God Tri - une.
And thus on thee, most glo - rious, A tri - ple light was given.
And liv - ing wa - ter flow - ing With soul - re - fresh - ing streams.
The Church her voice up - rais - es To thee, blest Three in One. A - MEN.

13

16 Hark! the Vesper Hymn is Stealing

(VESPER HYMN. 8, 7, 8, 7, D.)

Thomas Moore, 1779–1852

Dmitri S. Bortniansky, 1818

1. Hark! the ves - per hymn is steal-ing O'er the wa - ters soft and clear;
2. Now like moon-light waves re - treat-ing To the shore it dies a - long;
3. Once a - gain sweet voic - es ring-ing Loud - er still the mu - sic swells;

Near - er yet and near - er peal-ing Soft it breaks up - on the ear.
Now like an - gry surg - es meet-ing Breaks the min-gled tide of song.
While on sum - mer breez - es wing-ing Comes the chime of ves - per bells.

Repeat softly

Ju - bi - la - te! Ju - bi - la - te! Ju - bi - la - te! A - men!

Far - ther now and far - ther steal-ing Soft it fades up - on the ear.
Hark! a-gain like waves re-treat-ing To the shore it dies a - long.
On the sum - mer breez - es wing-ing Fades the chime of ves - per bells. A-men.

17 Day is Dying in the West

(CHAUTAUQUA. 7, 7, 7, 7, 4. With Refrain)

MARY A. LATHBURY, 1877   WILLIAM F. SHERWIN, 1877

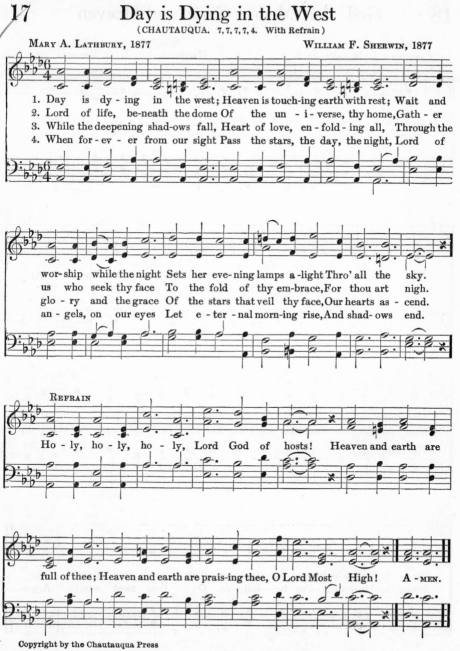

1. Day is dy - ing in the west; Heaven is touch-ing earth with rest; Wait and
2. Lord of life, be-neath the dome Of the un - i - verse, thy home, Gath - er
3. While the deepening shad-ows fall, Heart of love, en - fold - ing all, Through the
4. When for - ev - er from our sight Pass the stars, the day, the night, Lord of

wor-ship while the night Sets her eve-ning lamps a -light Thro' all the sky.
us who seek thy face To the fold of thy em-brace, For thou art nigh.
glo - ry and the grace Of the stars that veil thy face, Our hearts as - cend.
an - gels, on our eyes Let e - ter - nal morn-ing rise, And shad-ows end.

REFRAIN

Ho - ly, ho - ly, ho - ly, Lord God of hosts! Heaven and earth are

full of thee; Heaven and earth are prais-ing thee, O Lord Most High! A - MEN.

18 God, that Madest Earth and Heaven

(AR HYD Y NOS. 8, 4, 8, 4, 8, 8, 8, 4)

REGINALD HEBER, 1827
FREDERICK L. HOSMER, 1912

Welsh Traditional Melody
Harmonized by L. O. EMERSON, 1906

1. God, that mad-est earth and heav-en, Dark-ness and light;
2. When the con-stant sun re-turn-ing Un-seals our eyes,

Who the day for toil hast giv-en, For rest the night;
May we, born a-new like morn-ing, To la-bor rise;

May thine an-gel-guards de-fend us, Slum-ber sweet thy mer-cy send us;
Gird us for the task that calls us, Let not ease and self en-thrall us,

Ho-ly dreams and hopes at-tend us, This live-long night.
Strong thro' thee what-e'er be-fall us, O God most wise! A-MEN.

19 The Day is Past; the Shadows Round

(PEEL CASTLE. 10, 10, 10, 10)

HENRY BURTON, 1924

Manx Fishermen's Evening Hymn
Arranged by W. H. GILL

1. The day is past; the shad - ows round are fall - ing;
2. The toil that pros - pered har - vests for our reap - ing,
3. Thou mak - est, Lord, the eve - ning and the morn - ing;

The light is fad - ing from the west - ern sky;
The plans that failed, a - like were gifts of love;
The dark and light are both a - like to thee;

From the still heavens the eve - ning star is call - ing,
All ways are thine, and thine the glo - rious keep - ing,
And some-where al - ways new the day is dawn - ing,

Bid - ding us rest for night is draw - ing nigh.
In paths of peace all light - ed from a - bove.
Bid - ding thy wak - ing chil - dren, come and see! A - MEN.

17

20 Abide with Me: Fast Falls the Eventide

(EVENTIDE. 10, 10, 10, 10)

HENRY F. LYTE, 1847 WILLIAM H. MONK, 1861

1. A - bide with me: fast falls the e - ven-tide; The dark-ness deep-ens;
2. I need thy pres - ence eve - ry pass-ing hour; What but thy grace can
3. I fear no foe, with thee at hand to bless; Ills have no weight, and
4. Hold thou thy cross be - fore my clos-ing eyes; Shine thro' the gloom, and

Lord, with me a - bide: When oth - er help - ers fail, and com-forts flee,
foil the tempt-er's power? Who like thy - self my guide and stay can be?
tears no bit - ter - ness: Where is death's sting? where, grave, thy vic - to - ry?
point me to the skies: Heaven's morning breaks, and earth's vain shad-ows flee;

Help of the help - less, O a - bide with me.
Through cloud and sun - shine, O a - bide with me.
I tri - umph still, if thou a - bide with me.
In life, in death, O Lord, a - bide with me. A - MEN.

21 Peacefully Round Us the Shadows are Falling

(CURFEW. 11, 10, 11, 10)

AMBROSE N. BLATCHFORD, 1878 FREDERICK C. MAKER, 1844–1928

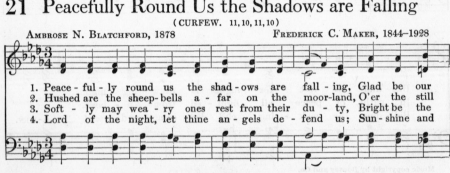

1. Peace - ful - ly round us the shad - ows are fall - ing, Glad be our
2. Hushed are the sheep - bells a - far on the moor-land, O'er the still
3. Soft - ly may wea - ry ones rest from their du - ty, Bright be the
4. Lord of the night, let thine an - gels de - fend us; Sun - shine and

prais - es and trust - ful our prayer: Hear us, O Lord, on thy prov - i - dence
mead-ows the night breez- es sweep, Faint fall the foot-steps in ci - ty and
dreams of the trou -bled and worn, While thro' the shade beam the stars in their
gloom are a - like un - to thee: Lord of the day, let thy Spir- it at -

call - ing, Light-en our dark-ness, and ban - ish our care.
ham - let, Safe - ly the chil - dren are fold - ed in sleep.
beau - ty, Watch-ing the world till the break-ing of morn.
tend us, Bless us and keep us wher - ev - er we be. A - MEN.

22   Sun of my Soul, Thou Saviour Dear

(HURSLEY. L. M.)

Katholisches Gesangbuch, about 1774
Arranged by WILLIAM H. MONK, 1861

JOHN KEBLE, 1820

1. Sun of my soul, thou Sav - iour dear, It is not night if thou be near;
2. A - bide with me from morn till eve, For with-out thee I can - not live;
3. Watch by the sick; en - rich the poor With bless-ings from thy bound-less store:
4. Come near and bless us when we wake, Ere through the world our way we take,

O may no earth-born cloud a-rise To hide thee from thy ser - vant's eyes.
A - bide with me when night is nigh, For with-out thee I dare not die.
Be eve-ry mourn-er's sleep to-night, Like in-fant's slum-bers, pure and light.
Till in the o - cean of thy love We lose our - selves in heaven a - bove. A -MEN.

23

Now the Day is Over

(MERRIAL. 6,5,6,5)

SABINE BARING-GOULD, 1865   JOSEPH BARNBY, 1868

1. Now the day is o - ver, Night is draw - ing nigh;
2. Je - sus, give the wea - ry Calm and sweet re - pose;
3. Grant to lit - tle chil - dren Vis - ions bright of thee;
4. Com - fort eve - ry suf - ferer Watch-ing late in pain;
5. When the morn - ing wak - ens, Then may I a - rise

Shad - ows of the eve - ning Steal a - cross the sky.
With thy ten-derest bless - ing May our eye - lids close.
Guard the sail - ors toss - ing On the deep blue sea.
Those who plan some e - vil From their sins re - strain.
Pure, and fresh, and sin - less In thy ho - ly eyes. A-MEN.

Eve-ning steal a - cross   the sky.

24

Saviour, Again to Thy Dear Name

(ELLERS. 10,10,10,10)

JOHN ELLERTON, 1866   EDWARD J. HOPKINS, 1869

1. Sav - iour, a - gain to thy dear name we raise With one ac - cord our
2. Grant us thy peace, up - on our home-ward way; With thee be - gan, with
3. Grant us thy peace, Lord, thro' the com-ing night; Turn thou for us its
4. Grant us thy peace through-out our earth-ly life, Our balm in sor - row,

part - ing hymn of praise; We stand to bless thee ere our wor-ship cease;
thee shall end the day: Guard thou the lips from sin, the hearts from shame,
dark-ness in - to light; From harm and dan - ger keep thy chil-dren free,
and our stay in strife; Then, when thy voice shall bid our con-flict cease,

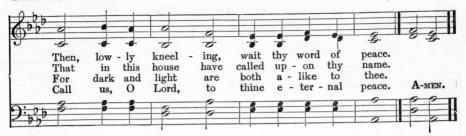

Then, low - ly kneel - ing, wait thy word of peace.
That in this house have called up - on thy name.
For dark and light are both a - like to thee.
Call us, O Lord, to thine e - ter - nal peace. A-MEN.

25 The Lord Bless You and Keep You

(BENEDICTION. Irregular)

Numbers 6: 24–26

PETER C. LUTKIN, 1905

The Lord bless you and keep you, The Lord lift his coun-te-nance upon you, and give you peace, and give you peace; The Lord
and give you peace, ... and give you peace; . . . . . . the Lord

Lord make his face and be gra - - - cious un - to
make his face to shine up - on you. The Lord be gra-cious,
the

you, be gra-cious,
The Lord be gra-cious, The Lord be gra-cious, gra-cious un - to you. A - MEN.

26

Father, We Praise Thee

(CHRISTE SANCTORUM. 11,11,11,5)

GREGORY the Great, 540–604
Translated by PERCY DEARMER, 1906

Melody from LA FEILLÉE
'Méthode du plain-chant,' 1782

UNISON

1. Fa - ther, we praise thee, now the night is o - ver; Ac - tive and
2. Mon - arch of all things, fit us for thy man - sions; Ban - ish our
3. All - ho - ly Fa - ther, Son and e - qual Spir - it, Trin - i - ty

watch - ful, stand we all be - fore thee; Sing - ing, we of - fer
weak - ness, health and whole-ness send - ing; Bring us to heav - en,
bless - ed, send us thy sal - va - tion; Thine is the glo - ry,

prayer and med - i - ta - tion: Thus we a - dore thee.
where thy saints u - nit - ed Joy with-out end - ing.
gleam - ing and re - sound-ing Thro' all cre - a - tion. A - MEN.

27

Rejoice, Ye Pure in Heart

(MARION. S. M. With Refrain)

EDWARD H. PLUMPTRE, 1865

ARTHUR H. MESSITER, 1883

1. Re - joice, ye pure in heart, Re - joice, give thanks and sing;
2. Bright youth and snow-crowned age, Strong men and maid - ens fair,
3. With voice as full and strong As o - cean's surg - ing praise,
4. Yes, on thro' life's long path, Still chant - ing as ye go;
5. Still lift your stan - dard high, Still march in firm ar - ray,

THE MIGHTY GOD

Your fes - tal ban - ner wave on high, — The cross of Christ your King;
Raise high your free, ex - ult - ing song, God's won-drous praise de - clare.
Send forth the hymns our fa - thers loved, The psalms of an - cient days.
From youth to age, by night and day, In glad - ness and in woe.
As war - riors thro' the dark - ness toil Till dawns the gold - en day.

REFRAIN

Re - joice, re - joice, Re - joice, give thanks and sing. A-MEN.
Re - joice, re - joice,

28   Our God, Our Help in Ages Past

(ST. ANNE. C. M.)

ISAAC WATTS, 1719   WILLIAM CROFT, 1708

1. Our God, our help in a - ges past, Our hope for years to come,
2. Be - fore the hills in or - der stood, Or earth re - ceived her frame,
3. A thou - sand a - ges in thy sight Are like an eve - ning gone;
4. Time, like an ev - er - roll-ing stream, Bears all its sons a - way;
5. Our God, our help in a - ges past, Our hope for years to come;

Our shel - ter from the storm - y blast, And our e - ter - nal home:
From ev - er - last - ing thou art God, To end - less years the same.
Short as the watch that ends the night Be - fore the ris - ing sun.
They fly for - got - ten, as a dream Dies at the open - ing day.
Be thou our guard while trou - bles last, And our e - ter - nal home. A-MEN.

23

29 We Praise Thee, O God, Our Redeemer

(KREMSER. 12, 11, 12, 11)

Netherlands Folk Song from
The Collection by ANDRIANUS VALERIUS, 1625

JULIA BULKLEY CADY, 1882–

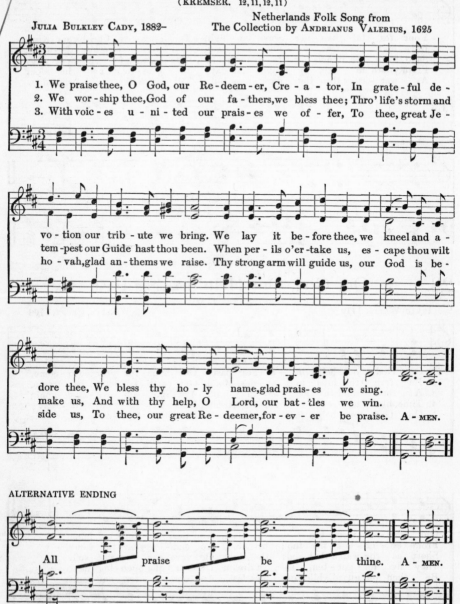

1. We praise thee, O God, our Re-deem-er, Cre-a-tor, In grate-ful de-vo-tion our trib-ute we bring. We lay it be-fore thee, we kneel and a-dore thee, We bless thy ho-ly name, glad prais-es we sing.

2. We wor-ship thee, God of our fa-thers, we bless thee; Thro' life's storm and tem-pest our Guide hast thou been. When per-ils o'er-take us, es-cape thou wilt make us, And with thy help, O Lord, our bat-tles we win.

3. With voic-es u-ni-ted our prais-es we of-fer, To thee, great Je-ho-vah, glad an-thems we raise. Thy strong arm will guide us, our God is be-side us, To thee, our great Re-deem-er, for-ev-er be praise. A-MEN.

ALTERNATIVE ENDING

All praise be thine. A-MEN.

24

30 Praise the Lord, Ye Heavens, Adore Him

(FABEN. 8, 7, 8, 7, D.)

Stanzas 1, 2, Anonymous, 1801
Stanza 3, EDWARD OSLER, 1836

JOHN H. WILLCOX, 1849

1. Praise the Lord, ye heavens, a - dore him; Praise him, an - gels, in the height;
2. Praise the Lord, for he is glo - rious, Nev - er shall his prom-ise fail;
3. Wor - ship, hon - or, glo - ry, bless - ing, Lord, we of - fer un - to thee;

Sun and moon, re - joice be - fore him; Praise him, all ye stars of light.
God hath made his saints vic - to - rious, Sin and death shall not pre - vail.
Young and old, thy praise ex - press - ing, In glad hom - age bend the knee.

Praise the Lord, for he hath spo - ken; Worlds his might - y voice o - beyed;
Praise the God of our sal - va - tion; Hosts on high, his power pro - claim;
All the saints in heaven a - dore thee, We would bow be - fore thy throne;

Laws which nev - er shall be bro - ken, For their guid-ance he hath made.
Heaven and earth and all cre - a - tion, Laud and mag - ni - fy his name.
As thine an - gels serve be - fore thee, So on earth thy will be done. A-MEN.

31 O Lord, All Glorious, Life of Life

(LOUVAN. L. M.)

Harmony in Praise, 1890

VIRGIL C. TAYLOR, 1847

1. O Lord, all glo - rious, Life of life! To thee we
2. Be - low all depths thy mer - cy lies, A - bove all
3. From thee all good de - sires pro - ceed, All ho - ly

raise our grate - ful song; Lift up our souls from tho'ts of
heights thy love as - cends; Thy prov - i - dence our path sur -
thot's we gain from thee; The good we do is thine a -

self To thee, to whom all life be - longs.
rounds, Thy watch - ful care each step at - tends.
lone, Thine shall our heart's thanks - giv - ing be. A - MEN.

32 Let Us with a Gladsome Mind

(INNOCENTS. 7, 7, 7, 7)

JOHN MILTON, 1624

The Parish Choir, 1850

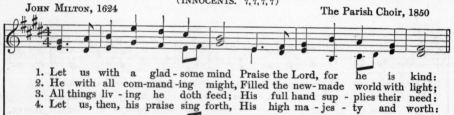

1. Let us with a glad - some mind Praise the Lord, for he is kind:
2. He with all com - mand - ing might, Filled the new - made world with light;
3. All things liv - ing he doth feed; His full hand sup - plies their need:
4. Let us, then, his praise sing forth, His high ma - jes - ty and worth:

26

For his mer-cies aye en-dure, Ev-er faith-ful, ev-er sure. A-men.

33 Lord of All Being, Throned Afar
(ST. CRISPIN. L.M.)

OLIVER WENDELL HOLMES, 1848   GEORGE J. ELVEY, 1862

1. Lord of all be - ing, throned a - far, Thy glo - ry
2. Sun of our life, thy quicken - ing ray Sheds on our
3. Our mid - night is thy smile with - drawn; Our noon - tide
4. Lord of all life, be - low, a - bove, Whose light is
5. Grant us thy truth to make us free, And kin - dling

flames from sun and star; Cen - ter and soul of
path the glow of day; Star of our hope, thy
is thy gra - cious dawn; Our rain - bow arch, thy
truth, whose warmth is love, Be - fore thy ev - er -
hearts that burn for thee; Till all thy liv - ing

eve - ry sphere, Yet to each lov - ing heart how near!
soft - ened light Cheers the long watch - es of the night.
mer - cy's sign; All, save the clouds of sin, are thine.
blaz - ing throne We ask no lus - tre of our own.
al - tars claim One ho - ly light, one heaven - ly flame! A - men.

Alternative Tune, Louvan, No. 81

34

Ancient of Days

(ANCIENT OF DAYS. 11, 10, 11, 10)

WILLIAM C. DOANE, 1886

J. ALBERT JEFFERY, 1886

UNISON

1. An - cient of Days, who sit - test throned in glo - ry,
2. O Ho - ly Fa - ther, who hast led thy chil - dren
3. O Ho - ly Je - sus, Prince of Peace and Sav - iour,
4. O Ho - ly Ghost, the Lord and the Life - giv - er,
5. O Tri - une God, with heart and voice a - dor - ing,

To thee all knees are bent, all voic - es pray; Thy love has blessed the
In all the a - ges, with the fire and cloud, Through seas dry-shod, through
To thee we owe the peace that still pre-vails, Still - ing the rude wills
Thine is the quick-ning power that gives in-crease; From thee have flowed, as
Praise we the good - ness that doth crown our days; Pray we that thou wilt

wide world's won-drous sto-ry With light and life since E- den's dawn-ing day.
wea - ry wastes be-wil-dering; To thee, in rev-er-ent love, our hearts are bowed.
of men's wild be-hav - ior, And calm-ing pas-sion's fierce and storm-y gales.
from a pleas-ant riv - er, Our plen-ty, wealth, pros-per-i - ty and peace.
hear us, still im -plor - ing Thy love and fa - vor kept to us al -ways. A-MEN.

28

35 Praise to the Lord, the Almighty

(LOBE DEN HERREN. 14, 14, 4, 7, 8)

JOACHIM NEANDER, 1680
Translated by CATHERINE WINKWORTH, 1863

Stralsund Gesangbuch, 1665

1. Praise to the Lord, the Al - might - y, the King of cre - a - tion!
2. Praise to the Lord! Who o'er all things so won-drous-ly reign - eth,
3. Praise to the Lord! Who doth pros - per thy work and de - fend . . thee;
4. Praise to the Lord! O let all that is in me a - dore . . him!

O my soul, praise him, for he is thy health and sal - va - tion!
Shield-eth thee gen - tly from harm, or when faint - ing sus - tain - eth;
Sure - ly his good - ness and mer - cy shall dai - ly at - tend . . thee.
All that hath life and breath, come now with prais - es be - fore . . him!

All ye who hear, Now to his tem - ple draw near;
Hast thou not seen How thy heart's wish - es have been
Pon - der a - new What the Al - might - y can do,
Let the A - men Sound from his peo - ple a - gain;

Praise him in glad ad - o - ra - tion.
Grant - ed in what he or - dain - eth?
If with his love he be - friend . . . thee!
Glad - ly for aye we a - dore . . . . him. A - MEN.

29

36 O Worship the King, All-Glorious Above

(LYONS. 10, 10, 11, 11)

ROBERT GRANT, 1833

Arranged from J. MICHAEL HAYDN, 1737–1806

1. O   wor-ship the King, all   glo-rious a - bove,   O   grate-ful - ly
2. O   tell of his   might, O   sing of his grace,   Whose robe is   the
3. Thy boun - ti - ful   care what tongue can re - cite?   It   breathes in the
4. Frail chil - dren of   dust, and fee - ble as frail,   In   thee do we

sing   his   power and his love;   Our Shield and De - fend - er, the An-cient of
light, whose can - o - py space;   His char - iots   of wrath the deep thun-der-clouds
air,   it   shines in   the light;   It streams from the hills,   it   de-scends to the
trust, nor   find thee to   fail;   Thy mer - cies how ten- der, how firm to the

Days,   Pa - vil-ioned in splen-dor, and   gird - ed with praise.
form,   And dark is his path on   the   wings of   the storm.
plain,   And sweet-ly dis - tils in the   dew and the rain.
end,   Our Ma - ker, De - fend - er, Re - deem - er, and Friend.   A - MEN.

37 O Maker of the Sea and Sky

(SANTA TRINITA. L. M.)

HENRY BURTON, 1905

E. PIERACCINI

1. O   Mak - er of   the sea   and sky, Whose word the storm-y winds ful - fill,
2. What if   thy foot -steps are not known? We know thy way is in   the sea;
3. Thou bidd'st the north or   south wind blow; The lone- ly sea - bird is   thy care;
4. The   sun that lights the home-land dear Spreads the new morn-ing o'er the deep;
5. And so,   se - cure from all   a - larms, Thy seas be - neath, thy skies a - bove,

On the wide o - cean thou art nigh, Bidding these hearts of ours be still.
We trace the shadow of thy throne, Constant a - mid in - con - stan - cy.
And in the clouds which come and go, We see thy char - iots eve - ry-where.
And in the dark thy stars ap-pear, Keeping their watches while we sleep.
Clasped in the ev - er -lasting arms, We rest in thine un-slumbering love. A - MEN.

38 Come, Thou Almighty King

(ITALIAN HYMN. 6, 6, 4, 6, 6, 6, 4)

GEORGE WHITFIELD's Hymn Book, 1757 FELICE DE GIARDINI, 1769

1. Come, thou Al - might - y King, Help us thy name to sing,
2. Come, thou In - car - nate Word, Gird on thy might - y sword,
3. Come, Ho - ly Com - fort - er, Thy sa - cred wit - ness bear
4. To the great One in Three, E - ter - nal prais - es be

Help us to praise: Fa - ther, all - glo - ri - ous, O'er all vic -
Our prayer at - tend: Come, and thy peo - ple bless, And give thy
In this glad hour: Thou who al - might - y art, Now rule in
Hence ev - er - more. His sov - ereign ma - jes - ty May we in

to - ri - ous, Come, and reign o - ver us, An - cient of Days.
word suc -cess; Spir - it of ho - li - ness, On us de - scend.
eve - ry heart, And ne'er from us de-part, Spir - it of power.
glo - ry see, And to e - ter - ni - ty Love and a - dore. A - MEN.

31

39

This is My Father's World
(TERRA BEATA. S.M.D.)

MALTBIE D. BABCOCK, 1901

Traditional English Melody
Arranged by FRANKLIN L. SHEPPARD, 1915

1. This is my Fa-ther's world, And to my list-ening ears, All na-ture sings, and round me rings The mu-sic of the spheres. This is my Fa-ther's world, I rest me in the thought Of rocks and trees, of skies and seas— His hand the won-ders wrought.

2. This is my Fa-ther's world, The birds their car-ols raise, The morn-ing light, the lil-y white, De-clare their Ma-ker's praise. This is my Fa-ther's world, He shines in all that's fair; In the rust-ling grass I hear him pass, He speaks to me eve-ry-where.

3. This is my Fa-ther's world, O let me ne'er for-get That tho' the wrong seems oft so strong, God is the Ru-ler yet. This is my Fa-ther's world, Why should my heart be sad? The Lord is King—let the heav-ens ring: God reigns: let the earth be glad. A-MEN.

For other arrangement of this tune, see No. 319

40   O God, I Cried, No Dark Disguise

(RENASCENCE. L. M.)

EDNA ST. VINCENT MILLAY, 1892–   HUGH PORTER, 1927

*1. O God, I cried, no dark dis-guise Can e'er here-aft - er hide from me Thy
2. The world stands out on ei - ther side No wi - der than the heart is wide; A -

ra - di - ant i - den - ti - ty, Thy ra - di - ant i - den - ti - ty!
bove the world is stretched the sky—No high - er than the soul is high.

I know the path that tells the way Thro' the cool eve of eve - ry day.
The heart can push the sea and land Far - ther a - way on ei - ther hand;

God, I can push the grass a - part And lay my fin - ger on thy heart.
The soul can split the sky in two, And let the face of God shine thro'. A-MEN.

* In former printings of this book the first half of this hymn read:
"O God, thou canst not hide from me Thy radiant identity,
Nor speak however silently But my hushed voice will answer thee."

From *Renascence and Other Poems*, published by Harper and Brothers. Copyright, 1917, by Edna St. Vincent Millay
Music copyright by The Century Co.   33

41 The Heavens Declare Thy Glory

(CHENIES. 7, 6, 7, 6, D.)

THOMAS R. BIRKS, 1874   TIMOTHY R. MATTHEWS, 1855

1. The heavens de - clare thy glo - ry, The firm - a - ment thy power;
2. The sun with roy - al splen - dor Goes forth to chant thy praise
3. All heaven on high re - joic - es To do its Ma - ker's will;

Day un - to day the sto - ry Re - peats from hour to hour;
And moon-beams soft and ten - der Their gen - tler an - them raise:
The stars with sol - emn voic - es Re - sound thy prais - es still:

Night un - to night re - ply - ing, Pro - claims in eve - ry land,
O'er eve - ry tribe and na - tion The mu - sic strange is poured;
So let my whole be - hav - ior, Tho'ts, words, and ac - tions be,

O Lord, with voice un - dy - ing, The won - ders of thy hand.
The song of all cre - a - tion To thee, cre - a - tion's Lord.
O Lord, my Strength, my Sav - iour, One cease - less song to thee. A-MEN.

42 God of the Glorious Sunshine

(GOD'S LOVE. 7, 6, 7, 6, D.)

THOMAS PAXTON

WILLIAM F. SHERWIN, 1826–1888

1. God of the glo - rious sun - shine, God of re-fresh-ing rain, Whose
2. God of the hill and moun - tain, Of val - ley and of dale, Whose
3. God of the bus - y day - time, God of the qui - et night, Whose
4. God of the whole cre - a - tion, God of all life be - low, We

voice bids earth a - wak - en And clothe it - self a - gain. With
fin - ger paints the rain - bows; Thy beau-ties nev - er fail To
peace per - vades the dark - ness And greets us with the light, Safe
seek thy near - er pres - ence, Thy grand - er life to know; When

life of rich - est beau - ty In plant, in flower, and tree; Thou
raise our souls in won - der, And turn our thoughts to thee; Thou
with thy pres-ence near us, Wher-ev - er we may be, Thou
we, thy height-ened splen - dor, Thy great - er glo - ries see, Thou

God of light and splen - dor, We rise and wor - ship thee.
God of liv - ing na - ture We stand and wor - ship thee.
God, our great Pro - tect - or, We love and wor - ship thee.
God of all cre - a - tion, We still shall wor - ship thee. A-MEN.

43 Joyful, Joyful, We Adore Thee

(HYMN TO JOY. 8, 7, 8, 7, D.)

HENRY VAN DYKE, 1908

LUDWIG VAN BEETHOVEN, 1826
Arranged by EDWARD HODGES, 1796–1867

1. Joy - ful, joy - ful, we a - dore thee, God of glo - ry, Lord of love;
2. All thy works with joy sur-round thee, Earth and heav'n re - flect thy rays,
3. Thou art giv - ing and for - giv - ing, Ev - er bless - ing, ev - er blest,
4. Mor - tals, join the might - y cho - rus, Which the morn - ing stars be - gan;

Hearts un - fold like flowers be - fore thee, Hail thee as the sun a - bove.
Stars and an - gels sing a - round thee, Cen - ter of un - bro - ken praise;
Well-spring of the joy of liv - ing, O - cean-depth of hap - py rest!
Fa - ther - love is reign - ing o'er us, Broth-er - love binds man to man.

Melt the clouds of sin and sad-ness; Drive the dark of doubt a - way;
Field and for - est, vale and moun-tain, Blossoming mead-ow, flash - ing sea,
Thou our Fa - ther, Christ our Broth-er,— All who live in love are thine:
Ev - er sing - ing march we on - ward, Vic - tors in the midst of strife;

Giv - er of im - mor-tal glad-ness, Fill us with the light of day!
Chant-ing bird and flow-ing foun-tain, Call us to re - joice in thee.
Teach us how to love each oth - er, Lift us to the Joy Di - vine.
Joy - ful mu - sic lifts us sun-ward, In the tri-umph song of life. A-MEN.

36

44 Let the Whole Creation Cry

(ROLAND. 7, 7, 7, 7, D.)

STOPFORD A. BROOKE, 1881   CALEB SIMPER, 1856–

1. Let the whole cre - a - tion cry, Glo - ry to the Lord on high!
2. Chant his hon - or, o - cean fair! Earth, soft rush - ing thro' the air;
3. War - riors fight - ing for the Lord, Proph - ets burn - ing with his word,

Heaven and earth, a - wake and sing, 'God is good, and there - fore King.'
Sun - shine, dark - ness, cloud and storm, Rain and snow, his praise per - form.
Men and wom - en young and old, Raise the an - them man - i - fold.

Praise him, all ye hosts a - bove, Ev - er bright and fair in love!
Let the blos - soms of the earth Join the u - ni - ver - sal mirth;
And let chil - dren's hap - py hearts In this wor - ship bear their parts;

Sun and moon, up - lift your voice; Night and stars in God re - joice.
Birds, with morn and dew e - late, Sing with joy at heav - en's gate.
Ho - ly, Ho - ly, Ho - ly, cry! Glo - ry be to God on high! A-MEN.

45 All Creatures of Our God and King

(LASST UNS ERFREUEN. 8, 8, 4, 4, 8, 8. With Alleluia)

FRANCIS OF ASSISI, 1225

Translated by W. H. DRAPER, 1855–

Geistliche Kirchengesang, Cologne, 1623

UNISON

1. All crea-tures of our God and King, Lift up your voice and with us
2. Thou rush-ing wind that art so strong, Ye clouds that sail in heaven a -
3. Thou flow-ing wa - ter, pure and clear, Make mu - sic for thy Lord to
4. Dear moth-er earth, who day by day Un - fold - est bless-ings on our
5. And all ye men of ten - der heart, For - giv - ing oth - ers, take your

HARMONY — UNISON

sing Al - le - lu - ia, Al - le - lu - ia! Thou burn - ing sun
long, O praise him, Al - le - lu - ia! Thou ris - ing morn,
hear, Al - le - lu - ia, Al - le - lu - ia! Thou fire so mas -
way, O praise him, Al - le - lu - ia! The flowers and fruits
part, O sing ye, Al - le - lu - ia! Praise, praise the Fa -

with gold - en beam, Thou sil - ver moon with sil - ver gleam,
in praise re - joice, Ye lights of eve - ning, find a voice,
ter - ful and bright, That giv - est man both warmth and light,
that in thee grow, Let them his glo - ry al - so show,
ther, praise the Son, And praise the Spir - it, Three in One,

HARMONY

O praise him, O praise him, Al - le - lu - ia,

38

46   For the Beauty of the Earth

(DIX. 7, 7, 7, 7, 7, 7)

Arranged from 'Treur Heiland,'
CONRAD KOCHER, 1838

FOLLIOTT S. PIERPONT, 1864

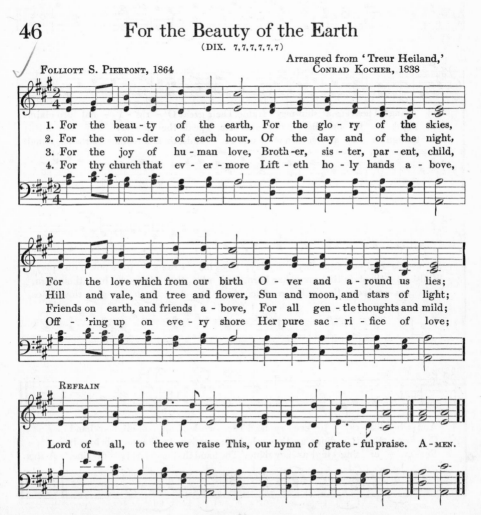

1. For the beau-ty of the earth, For the glo-ry of the skies,
2. For the won-der of each hour, Of the day and of the night,
3. For the joy of hu-man love, Broth-er, sis-ter, par-ent, child,
4. For thy church that ev-er-more Lift-eth ho-ly hands a-bove,

For the love which from our birth O-ver and a-round us lies;
Hill and vale, and tree and flower, Sun and moon, and stars of light;
Friends on earth, and friends a-bove, For all gen-tle thoughts and mild;
Off-'ring up on eve-ry shore Her pure sac-ri-fice of love;

REFRAIN

Lord of all, to thee we raise This, our hymn of grate-ful praise. A-MEN.

47 The Spacious Firmament on High

(CREATION. L. M. D.)

JOSEPH ADDISON, 1712   Arranged from FRANZ JOSEPH HAYDN, 1798

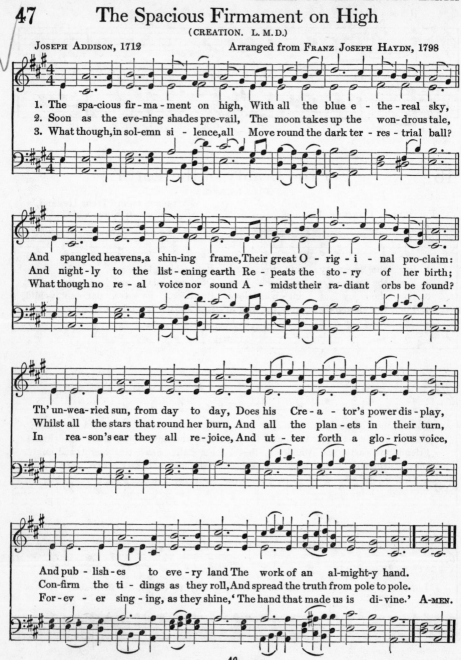

1. The spa-cious fir-ma-ment on high, With all the blue e - the - real sky,
2. Soon as the eve-ning shades pre-vail, The moon takes up the won-drous tale,
3. What though, in sol-emn si - lence, all Move round the dark ter - res - trial ball?

And spangled heavens, a shin-ing frame, Their great O - rig - i - nal pro-claim:
And night-ly to the list-ening earth Re - peats the sto - ry of her birth;
What though no re - al voice nor sound A - midst their ra-diant orbs be found?

Th' un-wea-ried sun, from day to day, Does his Cre - a - tor's power dis-play,
Whilst all the stars that round her burn, And all the plan-ets in their turn,
In rea-son's ear they all re-joice, And ut - ter forth a glo - rious voice,

And pub - lish - es to eve-ry land The work of an al-might-y hand.
Con-firm the ti - dings as they roll, And spread the truth from pole to pole.
For - ev - er sing - ing, as they shine, 'The hand that made us is di-vine.' A-MEN.

48

In Heavenly Love Abiding

(PASSION CHORALE. 7, 6, 7, 6, D.)

Melody by HANS L. HASSLER, c. 1601
Harmonized by JOHN SEBASTIAN BACH, 1719

ANNA L. WARING, 1850

1. In heaven-ly love a - bid - ing No change my heart shall fear;
2. Wher - ev - er he may guide me, No want shall turn me back;
3. Green pas - tures are be - fore me, Which yet I have not seen;

And safe is such con - fid - ing, For noth - ing chang - es here.
My Shep-herd is be - side me, And noth - ing can I lack.
Bright skies will soon be o'er me, Where dark - est clouds have been.

The storm may roar with - out me, My heart may low be laid,
His wis - dom ev - er wak - eth, His sight is nev - er dim,
My hope I can - not meas - ure, My path to life is free,

But God is round a - bout me, And can I be dis - mayed?
He knows the way he tak - eth, And I will walk with him.
My Sav-iour has my treas - ure, And he will walk with me. A-MEN.

49 God of the Earth, the Sky, the Sea

(ST. CATHERINE. 8, 8, 8, 8, 8, 8)

SAMUEL LONGFELLOW, 1864

HENRI F. HEMY, 1864
Arranged by JAMES G. WALTON, 1874

1. God of the earth, the sky, the sea! Mak-er of all a - bove, be - low!
2. Thy love is in the sun-shine's glow, Thy life is in the quick-'ning air;
3. We feel thy calm at eve-ning's hour, Thy gran-deur in the march of night;

Cre - a - tion lives and moves in thee, Thy pres - ent life through all doth flow.
When light-nings flash and storm-winds blow, There is thy power; thy law is there.
And, when thy morn-ing breaks in power, We hear thy word, 'Let there be light.'

REFRAIN

We give thee thanks, thy name we sing, Al-mighty Fa-ther, heaven-ly King. A - MEN.

50 The King of Love My Shepherd Is

(DOMINUS REGIT ME. 8, 7, 8, 7)

HENRY W. BAKER, 1868

JOHN B. DYKES, 1868

1. The King of love my Shep-herd is, Whose good-ness fail - eth nev - er;
2. Where streams of liv - ing wa - ter flow, My ran-somed soul he lead - eth,
3. Per - verse and fool - ish oft I strayed, But yet in love he sought me,
4. In death's dark vale I fear no ill With thee, dear Lord, be - side me;
5. And so through all the length of days, Thy good - ness fail - eth nev - er;

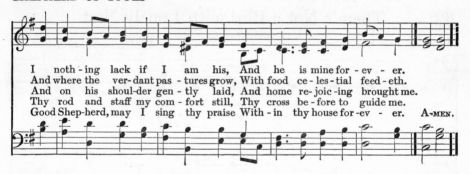

I noth-ing lack if I am his, And he is mine for - ev - er.
And where the ver-dant pas - tures grow, With food ce - les-tial feed-eth.
And on his shoul-der gen - tly laid, And home re-joic-ing brought me.
Thy rod and staff my com - fort still, Thy cross be-fore to guide me.
Good Shep-herd, may I sing thy praise With-in thy house for -ev - er. A-MEN.

51 My God, I Thank Thee Who Hast Made

(WENTWORTH. 8, 4, 8, 4, 8, 4)

ADELAIDE ANNE PROCTER, 1858   FREDERICK C. MAKER, 1876

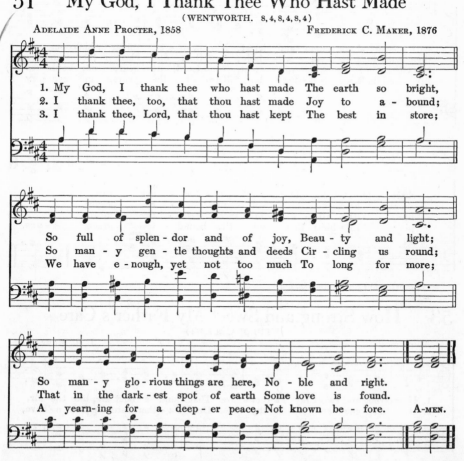

1. My God, I thank thee who hast made The earth so bright,
2. I thank thee, too, that thou hast made Joy to a - bound;
3. I thank thee, Lord, that thou hast kept The best in store;

So full of splen - dor and of joy, Beau - ty and light;
So man - y gen - tle thoughts and deeds Cir - cling us round;
We have e - nough, yet not too much To long for more;

So man - y glo - rious things are here, No - ble and right.
That in the dark - est spot of earth Some love is found.
A yearn-ing for a deep - er peace, Not known be - fore. A-MEN.

52 There's Not a Bird with Lonely Nest

(THANKFULNESS. L. M.)

BAPTIST W. NOEL, 1832

GEORGE A. MACFARREN, 1813~1887

1. There's not a bird with lone - ly nest, In
2. Each bar - ren crag, each des - ert rude, Holds
3. In bus - y mart and crowd - ed street, No
4. And we, wher - e'er our lot is cast, While

path - less wood or moun - tain crest, Nor mean - er thing, which does not
thee with - in its sol - i - tude; And thou dost bless the wan - derer
less than in the still re - treat, Thou, Lord, art near, our souls to
life, and tho't, and feel - ing last, Thro' all the years, in eve - ry

share, O God, in thy pa - ter - nal care.
there, Who makes his sol - i - ta - ry prayer.
bless With all a fa - ther's ten - der - ness.
place, Will bless thee for thy bound - less grace. A - MEN.

53 How Strong and Sweet My Father's Care

(EUDORA. 8, 8, 8, 4)

Anonymous

J. R. MURRAY

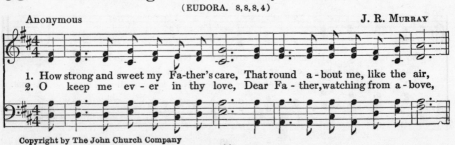

1. How strong and sweet my Fa-ther's care, That round a-bout me, like the air,
2. O keep me ev - er in thy love, Dear Fa - ther, watching from a-bove,

Is with me al - ways, eve - ry - where! He cares for me.
And as through life my steps shall move, O care for me. A-MEN.

54 Thou Art My Shepherd
(LYNDE. 5, 6, 6, 4, 6, 6, 6, 4)

ELSIE THALHEIMER, 1867
MRS. M. SCOTT HAYCROFT, 1904

Thuringian Folk Song
Arranged by JOHN B. CRAMER

1. Thou art my Shep - herd, Car - ing in eve - ry need, Thy lov - ing
2. Or if my way lie Where storms are rag - ing nigh, Noth - ing can
3. Good - ness and mer - cy Ev - er shall fol - low me, Till by thy

lamb to feed, Trust - ing thee still. In the green pas-tures low, Where liv -ing
ter - ri - fy, I trust thee still. How can I be a - fraid, While soft-ly
grace I see Thy ho - ly hill; Lord, in that home with thee, Joy - ful e -

wa - ters flow, Safe by thy side I go, Fear - ing no ill.
on my head Thy ten - der hand is laid; I fear no ill.
ter - nal - ly, Fold - ed thy flock shall be, Safe from all ill. A-MEN.

55 There's a Wideness in God's Mercy

(WELLESLEY. 8,7,8,7)

FREDERICK W. FABER, 1854

LIZZIE S. TOURJEE, 1878

1. There's a wide-ness in God's mer - cy, Like the wide - ness of the sea;
2. There is no place where earth's sor-rows Are more felt than up in heaven;
3. For the love of God is broad - er Than the meas- ure of man's mind;
4. If our love were but more sim - ple, We should take him at his word;

There's a kind -ness in his jus - tice, Which is more than lib - er - ty.
There is no place where earth's failings Have such kind - ly judg-ment given.
And the heart of the E - ter - nal Is most won-der - ful - ly kind.
And our lives would be all sun-shine In the sweet-ness of our Lord. A-MEN.

56 O Lord of Heaven and Earth and Sea

(ALMSGIVING. 8,8,8,4)

CHRISTOPHER WORDSWORTH, 1863

JOHN B. DYKES, 1865

1. O Lord of heaven,and earth,and sea, To thee all praise and glo - ry be;
2. The gold - en sun - shine, ver - nal air, Sweet flowers and fruit,thy love de-clare;
3. For peace-ful homes and health-ful days,For all the bless - ings earth dis-plays,
4. O thou from whom we all de - rive Our life, our gifts, our power to give,

How shall we show our love to thee, Who giv - est all?
Where har-vests ri - pen, thou art there Who giv - est all.
We owe thee thank - ful - ness and praise Who giv - est all.
O may we ev - er live with thee, Who giv - est all. A - MEN.

46

57 The Lord Is My Shepherd

(POLAND. 11, 11, 11, 11)

JAMES MONTGOMERY, 1822

THOMAS KOSCHAT, 1862

1. The Lord is my Shep-herd, no want shall I know, I
2. Thro' the val-ley and shad-ow of death though I stray, Since
3. In the midst of af-flic-tion my ta-ble is spread; With
4. Let good-ness and mer-cy, my boun-ti-ful God, Still

feed in green pas-ture, safe fold-ed I rest; He lead-eth my
thou art my Guard-ian, no e-vil I fear; Thy rod shall de-
bless-ings un-meas-ured my cup run-neth o'er; With per-fume and
fol-low my steps till I meet thee a-bove; I seek by the

soul where the still wa-ters flow, Re - stores me when wan-dering, re-
fend me, thy staff be my stay; No harm can be-fall, with my
oil thou a-noint-est my head; Oh, what shall I ask of thy
path which my fore-fa-thers trod, Thro' the land of their so-journ, thy

deems when op-pressed, Re - stores me when wan-dering, redeems when op-pressed.
Com-fort-er near, No harm can be-fall, with my Com-fort-er near.
prov-i-dence more? Oh, what shall I ask of thy prov-i-dence more?
king-dom of love, Thro' the land of their so-journ, thy king-dom of love. A -MEN.

58 God, Who Made the Earth

(BEECHWOOD. 5, 6, 6, 4)

SARAH B. RHODES, 1870　　　　　　　　　　JOSIAH BOOTH, 1852

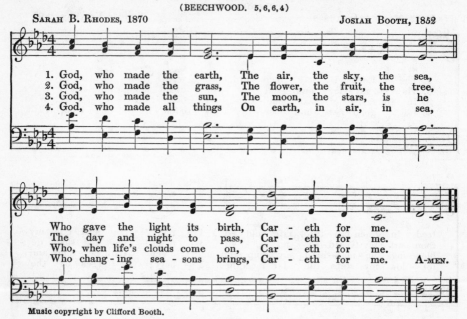

1. God, who made the earth, The air, the sky, the sea,
2. God, who made the grass, The flower, the fruit, the tree,
3. God, who made the sun, The moon, the stars, is he
4. God, who made all things On earth, in air, in sea,

Who gave the light its birth, Car - eth for me.
The day and night to pass, Car - eth for me.
Who, when life's clouds come on, Car - eth for me.
Who chang - ing sea - sons brings, Car - eth for me. A-MEN.

Music copyright by Clifford Booth.

59 The Lone Wild Fowl in Lofty Flight

(ARIZONA. L. M.)

H. R. MACFADYEN, 1926　　　　　　　　　R. H. EARNSHAW, 1856–

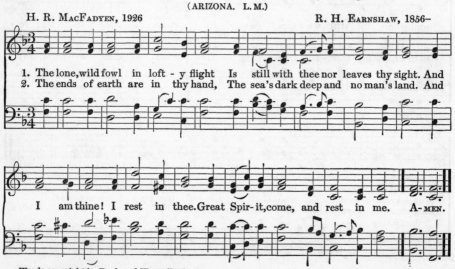

1. The lone, wild fowl in loft - y flight Is still with thee nor leaves thy sight. And
2. The ends of earth are in thy hand, The sea's dark deep and no man's land. And

I am thine! I rest in thee. Great Spir-it, come, and rest in me. A-MEN.

Words copyright by Funk and Wagnalls Co.

48

60 Holy Spirit, Truth Divine

(MERCY. 7, 7, 7, 7)

SAMUEL LONGFELLOW, 1864   LOUIS M. GOTTSCHALK, 1867

1. Ho - ly Spir - it, Truth di - vine, Dawn up - on this soul of mine;
2. Ho - ly Spir - it, Love di - vine, Glow with - in this heart of mine;
3. Ho - ly Spir - it, Power di - vine, Fill and nerve this will of mine;
4. Ho - ly Spir - it, Right di - vine, King with - in my con - science reign;
5. Ho - ly Spir - it, Joy di - vine, Glad - den thou this heart of mine;

Word of God, and in - ward Light, Wake my spir - it, clear my sight.
Kin - dle eve - ry high de - sire; Per - ish self in thy pure fire.
By thee may I strong - ly live, Brave - ly bear, and no - bly strive.
Be my law, and I shall be, Firm - ly bound, for - ev - er free.
In the des - ert ways I sing, 'Spring, O Well, for - ev - er spring.' A-MEN.

61 Breathe on Me, Breath of God

(TRENTHAM. S. M.)

EDWIN HATCH, 1886   ROBERT JACKSON, 1894

1. Breathe on me, Breath of God, Fill me with life a - new, That I may
2. Breathe on me, Breath of God, Un - til my heart is pure, Un - til with
3. Breathe on me, Breath of God, Till I am whol - ly thine, Till all this
4. Breathe on me, Breath of God, So shall I nev - er die, But live with

love what thou dost love, And do what thou wouldst do.
thee I will one will, To do or to en - dure.
earth - ly part of me Glows with thy fire di - vine.
thee the per - fect life Of thine e - ter - ni - ty. A - MEN.

62 Spirit of God, Descend upon My Heart

(MORECAMBE. 10, 10, 10, 10)

GEORGE CROLY, 1854

FREDERICK C. ATKINSON, 1870

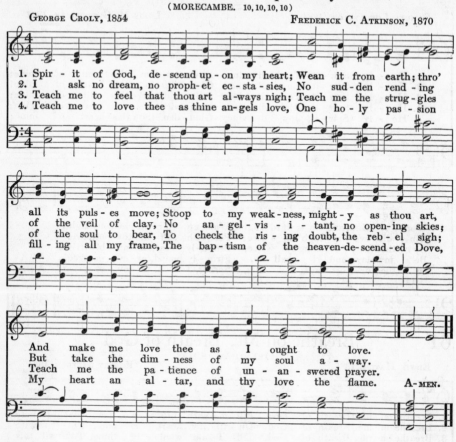

1. Spir - it of God, de - scend up - on my heart; Wean it from earth; thro'
2. I ask no dream, no proph-et ec - sta - sies, No sud - den rend - ing
3. Teach me to feel that thou art al -ways nigh; Teach me the strug - gles
4. Teach me to love thee as thine an-gels love, One ho - ly pas - sion

all its puls - es move; Stoop to my weak -ness, might - y as thou art,
of the veil of clay, No an - gel - vis - i - tant, no open-ing skies;
of the soul to bear, To check the ris - ing doubt, the reb - el sigh;
fill - ing all my frame, The bap - tism of the heaven-de-scend - ed Dove,

And make me love thee as I ought to love.
But take the dim - ness of my soul a - way.
Teach me the pa - tience of un - an - swered prayer.
My heart an al - tar, and thy love the flame. A-MEN.

63 Spirit of Life, in This New Dawn

(HESPERUS. L. M.)

EARL MARLATT, 1926

HENRY BAKER, 1862

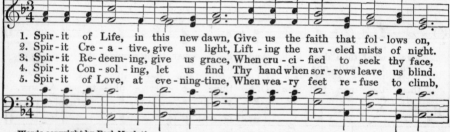

1. Spir - it of Life, in this new dawn, Give us the faith that fol - lows on,
2. Spir - it Cre - a - tive, give us light, Lift - ing the rav - eled mists of night.
3. Spir - it Re - deem-ing, give us grace, When cru - ci - fied to seek thy face,
4. Spir - it Con - sol - ing, let us find Thy hand when sor - rows leave us blind.
5. Spir - it of Love, at eve - ning-time, When wea - ry feet re - fuse to climb,

Let - ting thine all - per -vad - ing power Ful -fill the dream of this high hour.
Touch thou our dust with spir - it hand And make us souls that un - der-stand.
To read for - give-ness in thine eyes— To -day with thee in Par - a - dise.
In the gray val - ley let us hear Thy si-lent Voice:'Lo,I am near.'
Give us thy vi - sion,eyes that see Be-yond the dark,the dawn,and thee. A-MEN.

64   Spirit of God, for Every Good

(VICTORY. 8, 8, 8. With Alleluia)

Arranged from the 'Gloria Patri' of PALESTRINA,1591

OSBERT W. WARMINGHAM, 1929   by WILLIAM H. MONK, 1861

Al - le - lu - ia! Al - le - lu - ia! Al - le - lu - ia!

1. Spir - it of God, for eve - ry good Grant -ed in Sac - ra - men -tal mood,
2. For wood-ed hills in ver-dure dressed,For jew -eled wa - ters, wind-ca-ressed,
3. For beau-ty's ben - e - dic-tive moods,For friend-ship's pure be - at - i -tudes,
4. For childhood's lur-ing po - ten -cies, For youth's in - vig - o - rat -ing dreams,
5. And for thy-self, O Spir-it-Lord, Cre - a - tive Truth and Liv-ing Word,

We raise our song of gra - ti - tude, — Al - le - lu - ia.
For am - ple skies with glo - ries stressed,— Al - le - lu - ia.
For truth's e - ter - nal rec - ti - tudes,— Al - le - lu - ia.
For man-hood's full - er proph-e - cies, — Al - le - lu - ia.
We sing to - day in deep ac - cord, — Al - le - lu - ia. A - MEN.

65 As Comes the Breath of Spring

(GODFREY. 6, 6, 6, 6, D.)

DAVID LAKE RITCHIE

JOHN A. WEST, 1900

1. As comes the breath of spring, With light, and mirth, and song, So
2. He comes like dawn-ing day, With flam-ing truth and love, To
3. He comes like songs at morn, Flood-ing the earth with joy, Till
4. He breathes, and there is health, He moves, and there is power, He

does God's Spir-it bring New days—brave, free, and strong. He
chase all gloom a-way, To brace our wills to prove How
men of him new-born New strength in praise em-ploy. He
whis-pers, there is wealth Of love, his rich-est dower. His

comes with thrill of life, To chase hence win-ter's breath, To
wise, how good to choose The truth and its brave fight; To
comes to rouse the heart From mop-ing and de-spair; Through
pres-ence is to men Like sum-mer in the soul; His

turn to peace the strife Of sin that ends in death.
prize it, win or lose, And live in God's de-light.
high hope to im-part Life, with an am-pler air.
joy shines forth, and then Life blos-soms to its goal. A-MEN.

66   O Gracious Father of Mankind

(ST. LEONARD. C. M. D.)

HENRY HALLAM TWEEDY, 1926   HENRY HILES, 1867

1. O gra-cious Fa-ther of man-kind, Our spir-its' un-seen Friend,
2. Thou hear-est these, the good and ill, Deep bur-ied in each breast;
3. Our best is but thy-self in us, Our high-est thought thy will;
4. Thou seek-est us in love and truth More than our minds seek thee;

High heav-en's Lord, our hearts' dear Guest, To thee our prayers as-cend.
The se-cret thought, the hid-den plan, Wrought out or un-ex-pressed.
To hear thy voice we need but love, And lis-ten, and be still.
Through o-pen gates thy power flows in Like flood tides from the sea.

Thou dost not wait till hu-man speech Thy gifts di-vine im-plore;
O cleanse our prayers from hu-man dross, At-tune our lives to thee,
We would not bend thy will to ours, But blend our wills with thine;
No more we seek thee from a-far, Nor ask thee for a sign,

Our dreams, our aims, our work, our lives Are prayers thou lov-est more.
Un-til we la-bor for those gifts We ask on bend-ed knee.
Not beat with cries on heav-en's doors, But live thy life di-vine.
Con-tent to pray in life and love And toil, till all are thine. A-MEN.

67 Love Divine, All Love Excelling

(BEECHER. 8, 7, 8, 7, D.)

CHARLES WESLEY, 1747

JOHN ZUNDEL, 1870

1. Love divine, all love excelling, Joy of heaven, to earth come down;
2. Breathe, O breathe, thy loving Spirit In - to every troubled breast;
3. Come, almighty to deliver, Let us all thy life receive;
4. Finish, then, thy new creation; Pure and spotless let us be:

Fix in us thy humble dwelling, All thy faithful mercies crown;
Let us all in thee inherit, Let us find the promised rest;
Suddenly return, and never, Never more thy temples leave.
Let us see thy great salvation Perfectly restored in thee;

Jesus, thou art all compassion, Pure, unbounded love thou art;
Take away the love of sinning; Alpha and Omega be;
Thee we would be always blessing, Serve thee as thy hosts above,
Changed from glory into glory Till in heaven we take our place,

Visit us with thy salvation, Enter every trembling heart.
End of faith, as its beginning, Set our hearts at liberty.
Pray and praise thee without ceasing, Glory in thy perfect love.
Till we cast our crowns before thee, Lost in wonder, love and praise. A-MEN.

68 O Word of God Incarnate

(MUNICH. 7, 6, 7, 6, D.)

WILLIAM WALSHAM HOW, 1867   Meiningen Gesangbuch, 1693

1. O Word of God in - car - nate, O Wis - dom from on high,
2. The Church from her dear Mas - ter Re - ceived the gift di - vine,
3. It float - eth like a ban - ner Be - fore God's host un - furled;
4. O make thy Church, dear Sav - iour, A lamp of pur - est gold,

O Truth un-changed, un - chang - ing, O Light of our dark sky;
And still that light she lift - eth O'er all the earth to shine.
It shin - eth like a bea - con A - bove the dark-ling world;
To bear be - fore the na - tions Thy true light, as of old.

We praise thee for the ra - diance That from the hal - lowed page,
It is the gold - en cas - ket, Where gems of truth are stored;
It is the chart and com - pass That o'er life's surg - ing sea,
O teach thy wan-dering pil - grims By this their path to trace,

A lan - tern to our foot - steps, Shines on from age to age.
It is the heaven-drawn pic - ture Of Christ, the liv - ing Word.
'Mid mists and rocks and dark - ness, Still guides, O Christ, to thee.
Till, clouds and dark - ness end - ed, They see thee face to face. A-MEN.

69 Book of Books, Our People's Strength

(SWANSEA. 8, 8, 8, 8, 8, 8)

Basque Church Melody
Harmonized by WILLIAM LESTER, 1929

PERCY DEARMER, 1925

1. Book of books, our peo - ple's strength, States - man's, teach-er's,
2. Thank we those who toiled in thought, Man - y di - verse
3. Praise we God, who hath in - spired Those whose wis - dom

he - ro's treas - ure, Bring - ing free - dom, speed - ing truth,
scrolls com - plet - ing, Po - ets, proph - ets, schol - ars, saints,
still di - rects us; Praise him for the Word made flesh,

Shed - ding light that none can meas - ure; Wis - dom comes to
Each his word from God re - peat - ing; Till they came, who
For the Spir - it who pro - tects us. Light of know - ledge,

those who know thee, All the best we have we owe thee.
told the sto - ry Of the Word, and showed his glo - ry.
ev - er burn - ing, Shed on us thy death-less learn - ing. A-MEN.

70 Thy Word Is Like a Garden, Lord

(GABRIEL. C. M. D.)

EDWIN HODDER, 1868

GOTTFRIED W. FINK, 1842

1. Thy Word is like a gar-den, Lord, With flow-ers bright and fair;
2. Thy Word is like a star-ry host: A thou-sand rays of light

And eve-ry one who seeks may pluck A love-ly clus-ter there.
Are seen to guide the trav-el-er, And make his path-way bright.

Thy Word is like a deep, deep mine; And jew-els rich and rare
O, may I love thy pre-cious Word, May I ex-plore the mine,

Are hid-den in its might-y depths For eve-ry search-er there.
May I its fra-grant flow-ers glean, May light up-on me shine. A-MEN.

71 Break Thou the Bread of Life

(BREAD OF LIFE. 6, 4, 6, 4, D.)

MARY A. LATHBURY, 1877

WILLIAM F. SHERWIN, 1877

1. Break thou the bread of life, Dear Lord, to me, As thou didst
2. Bless thou the truth, dear Lord, To me, to me, As thou didst

break the loaves Be - side the sea; Be - yond the sa - cred page
bless the bread By Gal - i - lee; Then shall all bond - age cease,

I seek thee, Lord; My spir - it pants for thee, O liv - ing Word!
All fet - ters fall; And I shall find my peace, My All - in - all. AMEN.

72 Lamp of Our Feet, Whereby We Trace

(LAMBETH. C. M.)

BERNARD BARTON, 1836

WILLIAM A. F. SCHULTHES, 1871

1. Lamp of our feet, where - by we trace Our path, when wont to stray;
2. Bread of our souls, where - on we feed, True man - na from on high;
3. Pil - lar of fire, through watch - es dark, Or ra - diant cloud by day;
4. Word of the ev - er liv - ing God, Will of his glo - rious Son;

Stream from the fount of heaven-ly grace, Brook by the trav-eler's way.
Our guide and chart, where-in we read Of realms be-yond the sky.
When waves would 'whelm our toss-ing bark Our an - chor and our stay.
With - out thee how could earth be trod, Or heaven it - self be won? A-MEN.

73   Holy Father, Thou Hast Given

(ST. ATHANASIUS. 7, 7, 7, 7, 7, 7)

WILLIAM BRUCE, 1812-1882   EDWARD J. HOPKINS, 1872

1. Ho - ly Fa - ther, thou hast given Ho - ly truth from high - est heaven;
2. Clear - er than the sun at noon, Fair - er than the sil - ver moon,
3. Here the wis - dom from a - bove, Beam-ing ho - li - ness and love,
4. Bless - ed Sav - iour, Light Di - vine, Thou hast bid us rise and shine;

Words of coun - sel wise and pure, Words of prom - ise bright and sure;
Through the clouds and through the night Shin - eth aye this heaven - ly light;
Stir - ring hope, dis - pell - ing fear, Shines to save; for Christ is here:
Grant thy grace, and we shall be Chil - dren of the day in thee,

Light that guides us back to thee, Back to peace and pur - i - ty.
Help us, Lord, to lift our eyes, Take its guid-ance, and be wise.
Know - ing, trust-ing him, we come From our wan-derings glad-ly home.
Show - ing all a - round the road Back to life, and love, and God. A-MEN.

74 How Firm a Foundation

(PORTUGUESE HYMN. 11, 11, 11, 11)

Rippon's Selection, 1787

Wade's Cantus Diversi, 1751

1. How firm a foun - da - tion, ye saints of the Lord, Is laid for your
2. 'Fear not, I am with thee, O be not dis - mayed, For I am thy
3. 'When thro' the deep wa - ters I call thee to go, The riv - ers of
4. 'The soul that on Je - sus hath leaned for re - pose, I will not, I

faith in his ex - cel - lent Word! What more can he say than to
God, I will still give thee aid; I'll strength - en thee, help thee, and
sor - row shall not o - ver - flow; For I will be with thee, thy
will not de - sert to his foes; That soul, tho' all hell should en -

you he hath said, To you who for ref - uge to Je - sus have fled?
cause thee to stand, Up - held by my right - eous, om - nip - o - tent hand,
trou - bles to bless, And sanc - ti - fy to thee thy deep - est dis - tress,
deav - or to shake, I'll nev - er, no, nev - er, no nev - er for - sake,

To you who for ref - uge to Je - sus have fled?
Up - held by my right - eous, om - nip - o - tent hand.
And sanc - ti - fy to thee thy deep - est dis - tress.
I'll nev - er, no, nev - er, no, nev - er for - sake.'

A - men.

75 O Come, O Come, Emmanuel

(VENI EMMANUEL. 8, 8, 8, 8, 8. 8)

From Ancient-Latin Antiphons
Translated by JOHN M. NEALE, 1851
and HENRY SLOANE COFFIN, 1916

Ancient plain Song, from a 'French Missal'
Arranged by THOMAS HELMORE, 1854

1. O come, O come, Em - man - u - el, And ran - som cap - tive
2. O come, thou Wis - dom from on high, And or - der all things,
3. O come, De - sire of na - tions, bind All peo - ples in one

Is - ra - el, That mourns in lone - ly ex - ile here,
far and nigh; To us the path of knowl - edge show,
heart and mind; Bid en - vy, strife and quar - rels cease;

Un - til the Son of God ap - pear. Re - joice! Re - joice! Em -
And cause us in her ways to go. Re - joice! Re - joice! Em -
Fill the whole world with heav - en's peace. Re - joice! Re - joice! Em -

man - u - el Shall come to thee, O Is - ra - el! A-MEN.

76 Joy to the World! the Lord Is Come

(ANTIOCH. C. M.)

Arranged from GEORGE F. HANDEL, 1742
by LOWELL MASON, 1836

ISAAC WATTS, 1719

1. Joy to the world! the Lord is come; Let earth re-ceive her King;
2. Joy to the world! the Sav-iour reigns; Let men their songs em-ploy;
3. He rules the world with truth and grace, And makes the na-tions prove

Let eve-ry heart pre-pare him room,
While fields and floods, rocks, hills, and plains
The glo-ries of his right-eous-ness,

And heaven and na-ture sing, And heaven and na-ture
Re-peat the sound-ing joy, Re-peat the sound-ing
And won-ders of his love, And won-ders of his

And heaven and na-ture sing, And
Re-peat the sound-ing joy, Re-
And won-ders of his love, And

sing, And heaven, and heaven and na-ture sing.
joy, Re-peat, re-peat the sound-ing joy.
love, And won-ders, won-ders of his love. A-MEN.

heaven and na-ture sing,
peat the sound-ing joy,
won-ders of his love,

77 Hark! the Herald Angels Sing

(MENDELSSOHN. 7, 7, 7, 7, D. With Refrain)

CHARLES WESLEY, 1739
Altered by GEORGE WHITEFIELD, 1753
and others

FELIX MENDELSSOHN-BARTHOLDY, 1840
from the ' Festgesang '
Arranged by WILLIAM H. CUMMINGS, 1850

1. Hark! the her - ald an - gels sing, ' Glo - ry to the new-born King;
2. Christ, by high - est heaven a - dored; Christ, the ev - er - last - ing Lord;
3. Hail, the heaven-born Prince of Peace! Hail, the Sun of Right-eous - ness!

Peace on earth, and mer - cy mild, God and sin - ners rec - on- ciled!'
Come, De - sire of Na - tions, come, Fix in us thy hum - ble home.
Light and life to all he brings, Risen with heal - ing in his wings.

Joy - ful all ye na - tions, rise, Join the tri - umph of the skies;
Veiled in flesh the God - head see; Hail th'In-car - nate De - i - ty,
Mild he lays his glo - ry by, Born that man no more may die,

With th'an - gel - ic host pro - claim ' Christ is born in Beth - le - hem.'
Pleased as man with men to dwell; Je - sus, our Em - man - u - el.
Born to raise the sons of earth, Born to give them sec - ond birth.

Hark! the her-ald an - gels sing, ' Glo - ry to the new - born King.' A-MEN.

78 It Came upon the Midnight Clear

(CAROL. C. M. D.)

EDMUND H. SEARS, 1849

RICHARD S. WILLIS, 1850

1. It came up - on the mid-night clear, That glo - rious song of old,
2. Stil' thro' the clo - ven skies they come, With peace-ful wings un - furled;
3. And ye, be - neath life's crush-ing load, Whose forms are bend -ing low,
4. For lo! the days are has -tening on, By proph-et - bards fore - told,

From an - gels bend - ing near the earth, To touch their harps of gold;
And still their heaven-ly mu - sic floats O'er all the wea - ry world:
Who toil a - long the climb-ing way, With pain - ful steps and slow,—
When, with the ev - er - cir - cling years Comes round the age of gold;

'Peace on the earth, good -will to men, From heaven's all - gra- cious King';
A - bove its sad and low - ly plains They bend on heavenly wing,
Look now, for glad and gold - en hours Come swift - ly on the wing;
When peace shall o - ver all the earth Its an - cient splen-dors fling,

The world in sol - emn still -ness lay To hear the an - gels sing.
And ev - er o'er its Ba - bel sounds The bless - ed an - gels sing.
O rest be - side the wea - ry road, And hear the an - gels sing.
And the whole world give back the song Which now the an - gels sing.

A - MEN.

The First Noel the Angel Did Say

79

(THE FIRST NOEL. Irregular)

West of England Carol, 1833

Sandy's Christmas Carols, 1833

1. The first No-el the an-gel did say Was to cer-tain poor shep-herds in fields as they lay; In fields where they lay keep-ing their sheep, On a cold win-ter's night that was so deep.
2. They look-ed up and saw a star Shin-ing in the east, be-yond them far, And to the earth it gave great light, And so it con-tin-ued both day and night.
3. And by the light of that same star, Three wise men came from coun-try far; To seek for a king was their in-tent, And to fol-low the star wher-ev-er it went.
4. This star drew nigh to the north-west, O'er Beth-le-hem it took its rest, And there it did both stop and stay, Right o-ver the place where Je-sus lay.
5. Then en-tered in those wise men three, Full rev-er-ent-ly up-on the knee, And of-fered there, in his pres-ence, Their gold, and myrrh, and frank-in-cense.

REFRAIN

No-el, No-el, No-el, No-el, Born is the King of Is-ra-el. A-MEN.

65

80 The Winter Night Was Dark and Still

(TOWN OF BETHLEHEM. C. M. D.)

Louis F. Benson, 1917

H. Walford Davies, 1869–

1. The win-ter night was dark and still,
2. And now the Yule log glows a-flame,
3. Lord Je-sus, look from heaven a-bove,
4. O Ma-ry's Son, for her sweet sake

The vil-lage lay a-sleep; In mead-ows un-der-neath the hill
And winds with-out run wild, We soft-ly speak the bless-ed Name
And come, Lord Je-sus, here: To fill our home with Christ-mas love,
All wo-man-kind is blest; We praise thy Name when first we wake,

The shep-herds watched their sheep: The shepherds watched their sheep, good Lord,
They gave thee as a child, They gave thee as a child, good Lord;
Our hearts with Christ-mas cheer, Our hearts with Christ-mas cheer, good Lord;
And when we go to rest; And when we go to rest, good Lord,

But an-gels watched o'er thee, While Ma-ry held thee to her heart,
O win-ter winds, be still! O Christ-mas star, shine down a-gain
And hap-py may we be, All lads and maid-ens in our homes
Our night-ly thanks are given For all good moth-ers— some on earth,

And they   sang ju - bi - lee.
On mead - ow and   on hill!
And sail - or boys   at sea.
And some   with thine in heaven.

81   Silent Night, Holy Night
(STILLE NACHT. Irregular)

JOSEPH MOHR, 1818   FRANZ GRUBER, 1818

1. Si - lent night, ho - ly night, All   is calm, all   is bright Round yon Vir - gin
2. Si - lent night, ho - ly night, Dark - ness flies, all   is light; Shep - herds hear the
3. Si - lent night, ho - ly night, Guid - ing Star, lend thy light; See the east - ern
4. Si - lent night, ho - ly night, Won - drous Star, lend thy light; With the an - gels

Moth - er and Child, Ho - ly In - fant so ten - der and mild,
an - gels sing, 'Al - le - lu - ia! hail the King!
wise men bring Gifts and hom - age to our King;
let us sing Al - le - lu - ia to our King!

Sleep in heav - en - ly peace, Sleep in heav - en - ly peace.
Christ the Sav - iour is born, Christ the Sav - iour is born.'
Christ the Sav - iour is born, Christ the Sav - iour is born.
Christ the Sav - iour is born, Christ the Sav - iour is born. A - MEN.

82 O Little Town of Bethlehem

(ST. LOUIS. 8, 6, 8, 6, 7, 6, 8, 6)

PHILLIPS BROOKS, 1868

LEWIS H. REDNER, 1868

1. O lit - tle town of Beth - le - hem, How still we see thee lie!
2. For Christ is born of Ma - ry, And gath - ered all a - bove,
3. How si - lent - ly, how si - lent-ly The won - drous gift is given!
4. O ho - ly Child of Beth - le - hem, De - scend to us, we pray;

A - bove thy deep and dream-less sleep The si - lent stars go by;
While mor - tals sleep, the an - gels keep Their watch of won-dering love.
So God im - parts to hu - man hearts The bless - ings of his heaven.
Cast out our sin, and en - ter in; Be born in us to - day.

Yet in thy dark streets shin - eth The ev - er - last - ing Light;
O morn - ing stars, to - geth - er Pro - claim the ho - ly birth,
No ear may hear his com - ing, But in this world of sin,
We hear the Christ - mas an - gels The great glad ti - dings tell;

The hopes and fears of all the years Are met in thee to - night.
And prais - es sing to God the King, And peace to men on earth!
Where meek souls will re - ceive him, still The dear Christ en - ters in.
O come to us, a - bide with us, Our Lord Em - man - u - el. A-MEN.

83 O Come, All Ye Faithful

(ADESTE FIDELES. Irregular.)

Latin Hymn, 17th Century
Translated by FREDERICK OAKELEY, 1841

WADE's Cantus Diversi, 1751

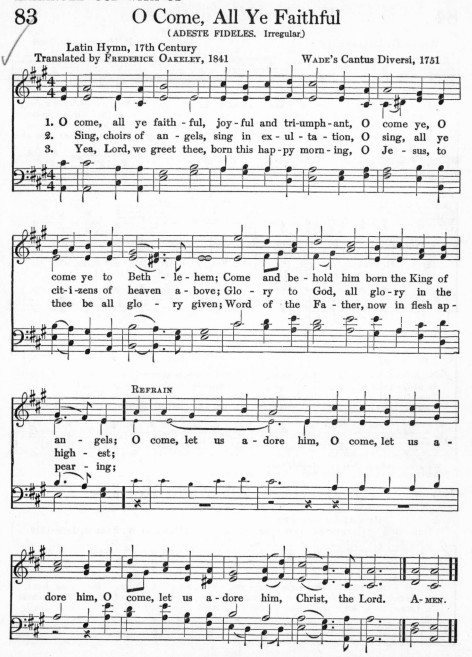

1. O come, all ye faith - ful, joy - ful and tri-umph-ant, O come ye, O
2. Sing, choirs of an - gels, sing in ex - ul - ta - tion, O sing, all ye
3. Yea, Lord, we greet thee, born this hap-py morn-ing, O Je - sus, to

come ye to Beth - le - hem; Come and be - hold him born the King of
cit-i-zens of heaven a - bove; Glo - ry to God, all glo - ry in the
thee be all glo - ry given; Word of the Fa - ther, now in flesh ap -

REFRAIN

an - gels; O come, let us a - dore him, O come, let us a -
high - est;
pear - ing;

dore him, O come, let us a-dore him, Christ, the Lord. A-MEN.

69

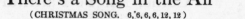

84 There's a Song in the Air

(CHRISTMAS SONG. 6, 6, 6, 6, 12, 12)

JOSIAH G. HOLLAND, 1872   KARL P. HARRINGTON, 1904

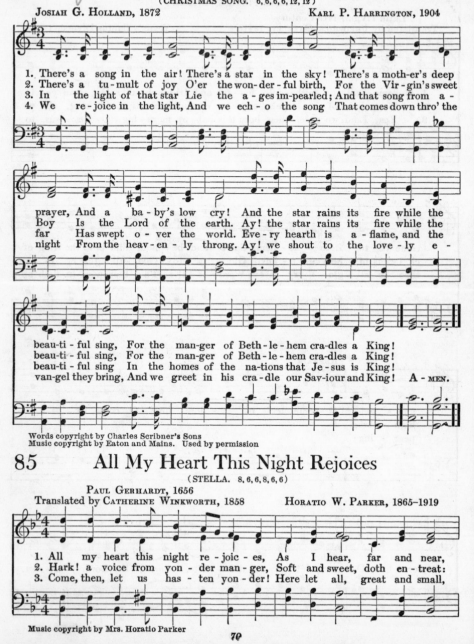

1. There's a song in the air! There's a star in the sky! There's a moth-er's deep
2. There's a tu-mult of joy O'er the won-der-ful birth, For the Vir-gin's sweet
3. In the light of that star Lie the a-ges im-pearled; And that song from a-
4. We re-joice in the light, And we ech-o the song That comes down thro' the

prayer, And a ba-by's low cry! And the star rains its fire while the
Boy Is the Lord of the earth. Ay! the star rains its fire while the
far Has swept o-ver the world. Eve-ry hearth is a-flame, and the
night From the heav-en-ly throng. Ay! we shout to the love-ly e-

beau-ti-ful sing, For the man-ger of Beth-le-hem cra-dles a King!
beau-ti-ful sing, For the man-ger of Beth-le-hem cra-dles a King!
beau-ti-ful sing In the homes of the na-tions that Je-sus is King!
van-gel they bring, And we greet in his cra-dle our Sav-iour and King! A-MEN.

Words copyright by Charles Scribner's Sons
Music copyright by Eaton and Mains. Used by permission

85 All My Heart This Night Rejoices

(STELLA. 8, 6, 6, 8, 6, 6)

PAUL GERHARDT, 1656
Translated by CATHERINE WINKWORTH, 1858   HORATIO W. PARKER, 1865–1919

1. All my heart this night re-joic-es, As I hear, far and near,
2. Hark! a voice from yon-der man-ger, Soft and sweet, doth en-treat:
3. Come, then, let us has-ten yon-der! Here let all, great and small,

Music copyright by Mrs. Horatio Parker

Sweet - est an - gel voic - es; 'Christ is born,' their choirs are sing - ing,
'Flee from woe and dan - ger; Breth - ren, come; from all that grieves you,
Kneel in awe and won - der! Love him who with love is yearn - ing!

Till the air eve - ry - where Now with joy is ring - ing.
You are freed; all you need I will sure - ly give you.'
Hail the Star, that from far Bright with hope is burn - ing! A-MEN.

86 ## Lord Jesus, Son of Mary

(PAROUSIA. 7, 6, 7, 6)

WILLIAM M. CRANE, 1926   JOHN STAINER, 1840–1901

1. Lord Je - sus, Son of Ma - ry, As now we hail thy birth,
2. Thou com - est, walk - ing with us, In those whose fac - es shine
3. Thou com - est, liv - ing tru - ly, In those who nev - er swerve
4. Thou com - est, Lord of na - tions,—Thy prom - ise to ful - fill,—

Give faith to see thy com - ing Each year, each day, to earth.
With joy to know and mir - ror The won - drous life di - vine.
In tho't or hap - py pur - pose To lift and love and serve.
In those with faith to stab - lish The king - dom of good will. A - MEN.

Words copyright by William M. Crane

71

87 The Maker of the Sun and Moon

(VILLAGE. C. M.)

LAURENCE HOUSMAN, 1865–   GEORGE GILBERT STOCKS, 1877–

UNISON

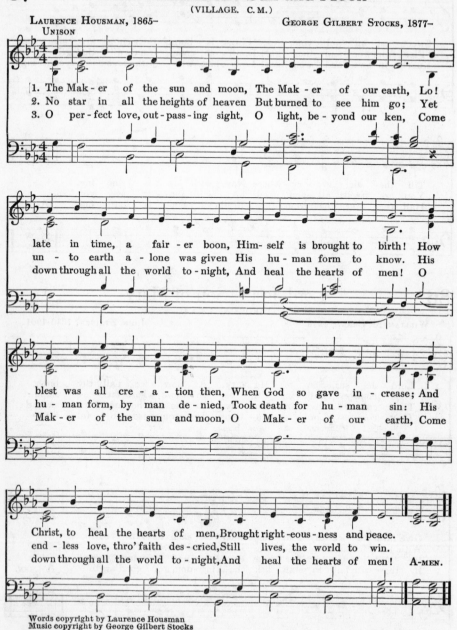

1. The Mak - er of the sun and moon, The Mak - er of our earth, Lo!
2. No star in all the heights of heaven But burned to see him go; Yet
3. O per - fect love, out - pass - ing sight, O light, be - yond our ken, Come

late in time, a fair - er boon, Him- self is brought to birth! How
un - to earth a - lone was given His hu - man form to know. His
down through all the world to - night, And heal the hearts of men! O

blest was all cre - a - tion then, When God so gave in - crease; And
hu - man form, by man de - nied, Took death for hu - man sin: His
Mak - er of the sun and moon, O Mak - er of our earth, Come

Christ, to heal the hearts of men, Brought right - eous - ness and peace.
end - less love, thro' faith des - cried, Still lives, the world to win.
down through all the world to - night, And heal the hearts of men! A-MEN.

Words copyright by Laurence Housman
Music copyright by George Gilbert Stocks

88 Angels, from the Realms of Glory

(REGENT SQUARE. 8, 7, 8, 7. With Refrain)

JAMES MONTGOMERY, 1816   HENRY SMART, 1867

1. An - gels, from the realms of glo - ry, Wing your flight o'er
2. Shep - herds, in the fields a - bid - ing, Watch - ing o'er your
3. Sa - ges, leave your con - tem - pla - tions, Bright - er vi - sions
4. Saints be - fore the al - tar bend - ing, Watch - ing long in

all the earth; Ye who sang cre - a - tion's sto - ry,
flocks by night, God with man is now re - sid - ing,
beam a - far; Seek the great De - sire of na - tions,
hope and fear, Sud - den - ly the Lord, de - scend - ing,

REFRAIN

Now pro - claim Mes - si - ah's birth: Come and wor - ship,
Yon - der shines the in - fant light;
Ye have seen his na - tal star:
In his tem - ple shall ap - pear:

Come and wor - ship, Wor - ship Christ, the new - born King. A - MEN.

89 In the Lonely Midnight

(LONELY MIDNIGHT. 6,5,6,5,D.)

THEODORE CHICKERING WILLIAMS, 1855-1915   ALONZO P. HOWARD, 1838-1902

UNISON

1. In the lone - ly mid-night On the win - try hill, Shep-herds heard the
2. Tho' in Da - vid's cit - y An - gels sing no more, Love makes an - gel
3. Tho' the child of Ma - ry, Sent from heaven on high, In his man-ger

an - gels Sing - ing, 'Peace, good - will.' Lis - ten, O ye wea - ry,
mu - sic On earth's dark - est shore; Tho' no heaven-ly glo - ry
cra - dle May no lon - ger lie, Love is King for - ev - er,

To the an-gels' song, Un - to you the tid - ings Of great joy be-long.
Meet your wondering eyes, Love can make your dwelling Bright as par - a - dise.
Tho' the proud world scorn; If ye tru - ly seek him, Christ your King is born. A-MEN.

Words copyright by The Beacon Press

90 Christians, Lo, the Star Appeareth

(SARDIS. 8,7,8,7)   Arranged from

JAMES A. BLAISDELL, 1900   LUDWIG VAN BEETHOVEN, 1770-1827

1. Chris-tians, lo, the star ap-pear - eth; Lo, 'tis yet Mes - si - ah's day;
2. Where a life is spent in ser - vice Walk-ing where the Mas - ter trod,
3. Who - so bears his broth - er's bur - den, Who - so shares an - oth - er's woe,
4. When we soothe earth's wea - ry chil - dren Tend - ing best the least of them,
5. Chris-tians, lo, the star ap-pear - eth Lead - ing still the an - cient way;

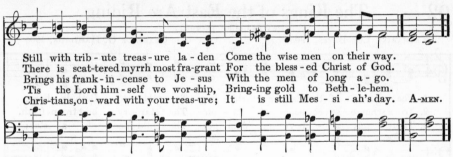

Still with trib-ute treas-ure la-den   Come the wise men on their way.
There is scat-tered myrrh most fra-grant For the bless-ed Christ of God.
Brings his frank-in-cense to Je-sus   With the men of long a-go.
'Tis the Lord him-self we wor-ship,   Bring-ing gold to Beth-le-hem.
Chris-tians, on-ward with your treas-ure; It is still Mes-si-ah's day. A-MEN.

91 Through the Dark the Dreamers Came

(DREAMERS. Irregular)

EARL MARLATT, 1927   MABEL W. DANIELS, 1927

1. Through the dark the dream-ers came, Mel-chi-or, Bal-tha-sar,
2. But the way did not seem Sha-dow-y or long.
3. It was worth the jour-ney-ing To the wea-ry end;

Cas-par, fol-low-ing the flame Of a star. Vi-a,
It was bright-ened by a dream And a song. Glo-ri-a!
For they found their dream, a King And a friend. Max-i-ma,

softly

Vi-a, De pro-fun-dis vi-a!
Glo-ri-a! In ex-cel-sis glo-ri-a!
Max-i-ma, Glo-ria De-i max-i-ma. A-MEN.

92 The Kings of the East Are Riding

(WALLACE. Irregular)

KATHARINE LEE BATES, 1905   CLARENCE G. HAMILTON, 1905

1. The Kings of the East are rid-ing To-night to Beth-le-hem;
2. To a strange sweet song of Zi-on The star-ry host troops forth.
3. There beams a-bove a man-ger The child face of a star;

The sun-set glows di-vid-ing, The Kings of the East are rid-ing,
The gold-en glaived O-ri-on To a strange sweet song of Zi-on
A-mid the stars a stran-ger, It beams a-bove a man-ger.

A star their jour-ney guid-ing, Gleam-ing with gold and gem.
The Arch-er and the Li-on, The watch-ers of the North;
What means this e-ther rang-er To pause where poor folk are?

The Kings of the East are rid-ing To-night to Beth-le-hem.
To a strange sweet song of Zi-on The star-ry host troops forth.
There beams a-bove a man-ger The child face of a star. A-MEN.

93 There's a Beautiful Star

(BEAUTIFUL STAR. Irregular)

ROSSITER W. RAYMOND, 1840–1918

FREDERICK SCHILLING

1. There's a beau-ti-ful star, a beau-ti-ful star, That wea-ry trav-'lers have fol-lowed a-far; Shin-ing so bright-ly all the way, Till it stood o'er the place where the young Child lay.

2. In the land of the East, in the shad-ows of night, We saw the glo-ry of thy new light; Tell-ing to us, in our dis-tant home, The Lord, our Re-deem-er, to earth had come.

3. We have gold for trib-ute and gifts for prayer, Sweet in-cense, myrrh, and spi-ces rare: All that we have we hith-er bring, To lay it with joy at the feet of the King.

REFRAIN

Star, star, beau-ti-ful star! Pil-grims wea-ry we are; To Je-sus, to Je-sus, We fol-low thee from a-far. A-MEN.

94 From the Eastern Mountains

(ROSMORE. 6, 5, 6, 5, D. With Refrain)

GODFREY THRING, 1873   HENRY G. TREMBATH, 1893

1. From the east-ern moun-tains, Press-ing on, they come, Wise men in their
2. Thou who in a man-ger Once hast low-ly lain, Who dost now in
3. Gath-er in the out-casts, All who've gone a-stray; Throw thy ra-diance
4. Un-til eve-ry na-tion, Wheth-er bond or free, 'Neath thy star-lit

wis-dom, To his hum-ble home; Stirred by deep de-vo-tion,
glo-ry O'er all king-doms reign, Gath-er in the peo-ple,
o'er them, Guide them on their way; Those who nev-er knew thee,
ban-ner, Je-sus, fol-lows thee O'er the dis-tant moun-tains

Hast-ing from a-far, Ev-er journey-ing on-ward, Guid-ed by a star.
Who in lands a-far, Ne'er have seen the bright-ness Of thy guid-ing star.
Those who've wandered far, Guide them by the bright-ness Of thy guid-ing star.
To that heavenly home, Where nor sin nor sor-row Ev-er-more shall come.

REFRAIN

Light of life that shin-eth, Ere the worlds be-gan,

Draw thou near, and light - en Eve - ry heart of man. A -MEN.

95 As with Gladness Men of Old
(DIX. 7, 7, 7, 7, 7, 7)

Arranged from 'Treur Heiland'
CONRAD KOCHER, 1838

WILLIAM C. DIX, 1861

1. As with glad-ness men of old Did the guid - ing star be - hold;
2. As with joy - ful steps they sped To that low - ly man - ger - bed,
3. As they of - fered gifts most rare, At that man - ger rude and bare,
4. Ho - ly Je - sus, eve - ry day Keep us in the nar - row way;

As with joy they hailed its light, Lead - ing on - ward, beam-ing bright;
There to bend the knee be - fore Him whom heaven and earth a - dore;
So may we with ho - ly joy, Pure and free from sin's al - loy,
And, when earth - ly things are past, Bring our ran - somed souls at last

So, most gra-cious Lord, may we Ev - er - more be led to thee.
So may we with will-ing feet Ev - er seek thy mer - cy-seat.
All our cost-liest treas-ures bring, Christ, to thee, our heaven -ly King.
Where they need no star to guide, Where no clouds thy glo - ry hide. A -MEN.

96 We Three Kings of Orient Are

(KINGS OF ORIENT. 8,8,8,6. With Refrain)

JOHN H. HOPKINS, 1857   JOHN H. HOPKINS, 1857

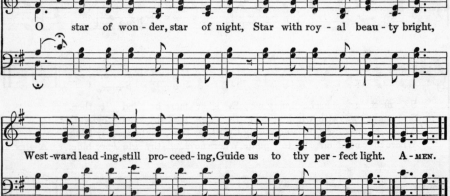

1. We three kings of O - ri - ent are, Bear-ing gifts we trav-erse a - far
2. Born a King on Beth-le-hem's plain, Gold I bring to crown him a - gain,
3. Frank-in-cense to of - fer have I, In - cense owns a De - i - ty nigh;
4. Myrrh is mine: its bit-ter per-fume Breathes a life of gath-er-ing gloom;
5. Glo-rious now be - hold him a - rise, King and God and Sac - ri - fice;

Field and foun - tain, moor and moun-tain, Fol - low-ing yon - der star.
King for - ev - er, ceas-ing nev - er O - ver us all to reign.
Prayer and prais-ing, all men rais-ing, Wor-ship him, God on high.
Sor - rowing, sigh-ing, bleed-ing, dy - ing, Sealed in the stone - cold tomb.
Al - le - lu - ia, Al - le - lu - ia! Sounds thro' the earth and skies.

REFRAIN

O star of won - der, star of night, Star with roy - al beau - ty bright,

West-ward lead-ing, still pro-ceed-ing, Guide us to thy per-fect light. A - MEN.

97 The Hidden Years at Nazareth

(NAZARETH. C. M. D.)

ALLEN EASTMAN CROSS, 1927   HARRY L. HARTS, 1927

1. The hid-den years at Naz-a-reth! How beau-ti-ful they seem, Like
2. The hid-den years at Naz-a-reth! How mar-vel-ous they lie, As
3. The hid-den years at Naz-a-reth! How ra-di-ant they rise, With

foun-tains flow-ing in the dark Or wa-ters in a dream! Like
o-pen to the smile of God As to the Syr-ian sky! As
life and death in bal-ance laid Be-fore a lad's clear eyes! O

wa-ters un-der Syr-ian stars Re-flect-ing lights a-bove, Re-
o-pen to the heart of man As to the ge-nial sun, With
soul of youth, for-ev-er choose For-get-ting fate or fear, To

peat-ing in their si-lent depths The won-der of God's love.
dreams of high ad-ven-tur-ing, And deeds of kind-ness done.
live for truth, or die with God, Who stands be-side thee here. A-MEN.

98 O Master Workman of the Race

(AMESBURY. C.M.D.)

JAY T. STOCKING, 1912   UZZIAH C. BURNAP, 1895

1. O Mas - ter work-man of the race, Thou man of Gal - i - lee,
2. O Car - pen - ter of Naz - a - reth, Build - er of life di - vine,
3. O thou who dost the vis - ion send And gives to each his task,

Who with the eyes of ear - ly youth E - ter - nal things did see;
Who shap - est man to God's own law, Thy -self the fair de - sign,
And with the task suf - fi - cient strength, Show us thy will, we ask;

We thank thee for thy boy - hood faith That shone thy whole life through;
Build us a tower of Christ - like height, That we the land may view,
Give us a con-science bold and good, Give us a pur - pose true,

'Did ye not know it is my work My Fa-ther's work to do?'
And see like thee our no - blest work Our Fa-ther's work to do.
That it may be our high - est joy, Our Fa-ther's work to do. A-MEN.

Alternative tune, Materna, No. 271

82

99 Young and Radiant, He Is Standing

(SON OF MAN. 8, 7, 8, 7, D.)

ALLEN EASTMAN CROSS, 1921　　　　　　LOUIS ADOLPHE COERNE, 1921

1. Young and ra-diant, he is stand-ing As he stood at Sa-lem's shrine;
2. I can see him hum-bly kneel-ing, As he knelt up-on the hill;
3. Like a flame his soul is strik-ing In his wrath at greed and shame;
4. I can see him dy-ing, lov-ing Un-to death on Cal-va-ry;

Just a lad, a lad for-ev-er, With a look and grace di-vine!
While the wa-ters hushed their mu-sic, And the night grew bright and still:
'Ye have made a den of rob-bers Of the tem-ple to his name;
His dear hands still plead-ing, pray-ing, Worn and torn for you and me!

'Tell me, how it is ye sought me? Wist ye not my Fa-ther's plan?
'Brothers, tell me why ye sought me? Wist ye not my Fa-ther's plan?
Know ye not his e-qual jus-tice? Wist ye not my Fa-ther's plan?
'Brothers, will ye scorn and leave me? Wist ye not my Fa-ther's plan?

I must be a-bout his busi-ness, Would I be a Son of Man.'
He must grow in grace and wis-dom, Who would be a Son of Man.'
He must bathe his sword in heav-en Who would be a Son of Man.'
He must wear a crown of sor-row Who would be a Son of Man.' A-MEN.

100 We Would See Jesus

(CUSHMAN. 11, 10, 11. 10)

J. Edgar Park, 1913

Herbert B. Turner, 1905

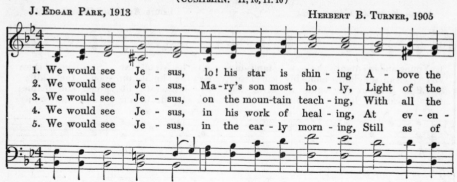

1. We would see Je - sus, lo! his star is shin - ing A - bove the
2. We would see Je - sus, Ma - ry's son most ho - ly, Light of the
3. We would see Je - sus, on the moun-tain teach - ing, With all the
4. We would see Je - sus, in his work of heal - ing, At ev - en -
5. We would see Je - sus, in the ear - ly morn - ing, Still as of

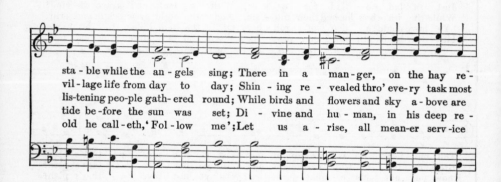

sta - ble while the an - gels sing; There in a man - ger, on the hay re -
vil - lage life from day to day; Shin - ing re - vealed thro' eve - ry task most
lis-tening peo-ple gath- ered round; While birds and flowers and sky a - bove are
tide be - fore the sun was set; Di - vine and hu - man, in his deep re -
old he call - eth, 'Fol - low me'; Let us a - rise, all mean-er serv -ice

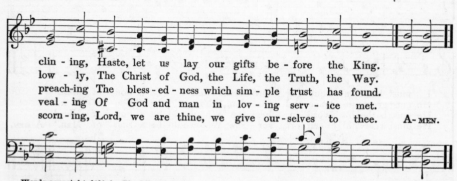

clin - ing, Haste, let us lay our gifts be - fore the King.
low - ly, The Christ of God, the Life, the Truth, the Way.
preach-ing The bless - ed - ness which sim - ple trust has found.
veal - ing Of God and man in lov - ing serv - ice met.
scorn-ing, Lord, we are thine, we give our-selves to thee. A- men.

101 Thou Didst Leave Thy Throne

(MARGARET. Irregular)

EMILY E. S. ELLIOTT, 1864　　　　　　　　　TIMOTHY R. MATTHEWS, 1876

1. Thou didst leave thy throne and thy king-ly crown When thou
2. Heav-en's arch-es rang when the an-gels sang Pro-
3. The fox-es found rest, and the birds their nest In the
4. Thou cam-est, O Lord, with the liv-ing word That should
5. When heaven's arch-es shall ring, and her choirs shall sing At thy

cam-est to earth for me; But in Beth-le-hem's home
claim-ing thy roy-al de-gree; But in low-ly birth
shade of the for-est tree; But thy couch was the sod,
set thy peo-ple free; But with mock-ing scorn,
com-ing to vic-to-ry, Let thy voice call me home,

was there found no room For thy ho-ly na-tiv-i-ty:
didst thou come to earth, And in great hu-mil-i-ty:
O thou Son of God, In the des-ert of Gal-i-lee:
and with crown of thorn, They bore thee to Cal-va-ry:
say-ing, 'Yet there is room, There is room at my side for thee;'

REFRAIN

1-4. O come to my heart, Lord Je-sus, There is room in my heart for thee.
5. And my heart shall re-joice, Lord Je-sus, When thou com-est and callest for me. A-MEN.

Music copyright by Novello and Co., Ltd.

85

102 Ye Fair Green Hills of Galilee

(SAINTS OF GOD. 8,8,8,8,8,8)

EUSTACE R. CONDER, 1887

ARTHUR S. SULLIVAN, 1842–1900

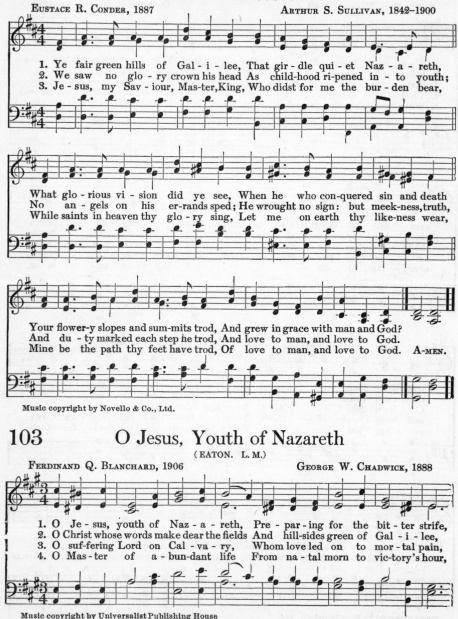

1. Ye fair green hills of Gal - i - lee, That gir - dle qui - et Naz - a - reth,
2. We saw no glo - ry crown his head As child-hood ri-pened in - to youth;
3. Je - sus, my Sav - iour, Mas-ter, King, Who didst for me the bur - den bear,

What glo - rious vi - sion did ye see, When he who con-quered sin and death
No an - gels on his er-rands sped; He wrought no sign: but meek-ness, truth,
While saints in heaven thy glo - ry sing, Let me on earth thy like-ness wear,

Your flower-y slopes and sum-mits trod, And grew in grace with man and God?
And du - ty marked each step he trod, And love to man, and love to God.
Mine be the path thy feet have trod, Of love to man, and love to God. A-MEN.

Music copyright by Novello & Co., Ltd.

103 O Jesus, Youth of Nazareth

(EATON. L. M.)

FERDINAND Q. BLANCHARD, 1906

GEORGE W. CHADWICK, 1888

1. O Je - sus, youth of Naz - a - reth, Pre - par - ing for the bit - ter strife,
2. O Christ whose words make dear the fields And hill-sides green of Gal - i - lee,
3. O suf - fering Lord on Cal - va - ry, Whom love led on to mor - tal pain,
4. O Mas - ter of a - bun-dant life From na - tal morn to vic-tory's hour,

Music copyright by Universalist Publishing House

MASTER AND FRIEND

Wilt thou im-part to eve - ry heart Thy per-fect pu - ri - ty of life?
Grant us to find, with reverent mind, The truth thou saidst should make us free.
We know thy cross is not a loss If we thy love shall tru - ly gain.
We look to thee, heed thou our plea, Teach us to share thy age-less power. A-MEN.

104   When the Lord of Love Was Here

(ARMSTRONG. 7, 7, 5, D.)

STOPFORD A. BROOKE, 1881   GEORGE W. CHADWICK, 1888

1. When the Lord of love was here, Hap - py hearts to him were
2. Meek and low - ly were his ways, From his lov - ing grew his
3. When he walked the fields, he drew From the flowers and birds and
4. And, when in the fields and woods We are filled with Na - ture's

dear, Though his heart was sad; Worn and lone - ly for our sake,
praise, From his giv - ing, prayer: All the out - casts thronged to hear,
dew, Par - a - bles of God; For with - in his heart of love
moods, May the grace be given With my faith - ful heart to say,

Yet he turned a - side to make All the wea - ry glad.
All the sor - row - ful drew near To en - joy his care.
All the soul of man did move, God had his a - bode.
'All I see and feel to - day Is my Fa -ther's heaven.' A - MEN.

87

105 Blest Land of Judea

(ASHLAND. 11, 11, 11, 11)

JOHN GREENLEAF WHITTIER, 1837   LUCIA MAY SMITH, 1918

1. Blest land of Ju - de - a! thrice hal - lowed of song; Where the
2. Blue sea of the hills! in my spir - it I hear Thy
3. O here with his flock the sad Wan - der - er came; These
4. And what if my feet may not tread where he trod, Nor my
5. Yet, loved of the Fa - ther, thy Spir - it is near To the

ho - liest of mem - o - ries pil - grim - like throng; In the
wa - ters, Gen - nes - a - ret, chime on my ear; Where the
hills he toiled o - ver in grief are the same; The
ears hear the dash - ing of Gal - i - lee's flood, Nor my
meek and the low - ly and pen - i - tent here; And the

shade of thy palms, by the shores of thy sea, On the
low - ly and just with the peo - ple sat down, And thy
founts where he drank by the way - side still flow, And the
eyes see the cross which he bowed him to bear, Nor my
voice of thy love is the same e - ven now As at

hills of thy beau - ty, my heart is with thee.
spray on the dust of his san - dals was thrown.
same airs are blow - ing which breathed on his brow.
knees press Geth - sem - a - ne's gar - den of prayer,—
Beth - a - ny's tomb or on Ol - i - vet's brow.   A - MEN.

Music copyright by Lucia May Smith

88

106   Galilee, Bright Galilee

(SHERWIN. 7, 7, 7, 7, D.)

WILLIAM F. SHERWIN, 1880   WILLIAM F. SHERWIN, 1880

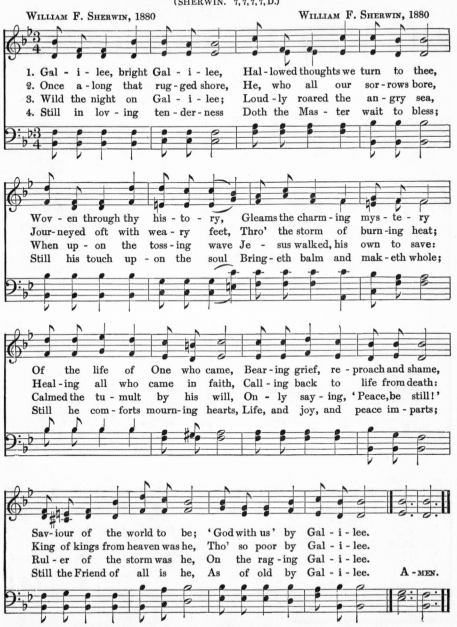

1. Gal - i - lee, bright Gal - i - lee,   Hal - lowed thoughts we turn to thee,
2. Once a - long that rug - ged shore,   He, who all our sor - rows bore,
3. Wild the night on Gal - i - lee;   Loud - ly roared the an - gry sea,
4. Still in lov - ing ten - der - ness   Doth the Mas - ter wait to bless;

Wov - en through thy his - to - ry,   Gleams the charm - ing mys - te - ry
Jour - neyed oft with wea - ry feet,   Thro' the storm of burn - ing heat;
When up - on the toss - ing wave   Je - sus walked, his own to save:
Still his touch up - on the soul   Bring - eth balm and mak - eth whole;

Of the life of One who came,   Bear - ing grief, re - proach and shame,
Heal - ing all who came in faith,   Call - ing back to life from death:
Calmed the tu - mult by his will,   On - ly say - ing, 'Peace, be still!'
Still he com - forts mourn - ing hearts,   Life, and joy, and peace im - parts;

Sav - iour of the world to be;   'God with us' by Gal - i - lee.
King of kings from heaven was he,   Tho' so poor by Gal - i - lee.
Rul - er of the storm was he,   On the rag - ing Gal - i - lee.
Still the Friend of all is he,   As of old by Gal - i - lee.   A - MEN.

107 Holy, Holy, Holy, Lord, Thy Disciples

(TRINITY. 11, 12, 12, 10)

PERCY MACKAYE, 1920 SAMUEL S. WESLEY, 1810–1876

1. Ho - ly, ho - ly, ho - ly, Lord, thy dis - ci - ples
2. Ho - ly, ho - ly, ho - ly, still in the morn - ing
3. Ho - ly, ho - ly, ho - ly, Lord, thy dis - ci - ples

Gath - er in de - vo - tion to sing and dream of thee:
Mend - ing our fish - er nets, we hail thee by the shore;
Ev - er through the a - ges live a - gain be - cause of thee:

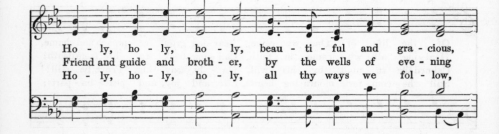

Ho - ly, ho - ly, ho - ly, beau - ti - ful and gra - cious,
Friend and guide and broth - er, by the wells of eve - ning
Ho - ly, ho - ly, ho - ly, all thy ways we fol - low,

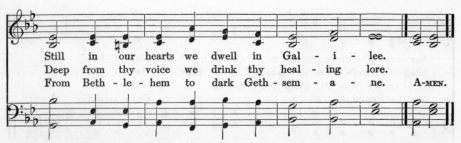

Still in our hearts we dwell in Gal - i - lee.
Deep from thy voice we drink thy heal - ing lore.
From Beth - le - hem to dark Geth - sem - a - ne. A-MEN.

108 When the Golden Evening Gathered

(STOCKWELL NEW. Irregular)

WILLIAM J. DAWSON, 1854–1928   CALVIN W. LAUFER, 1928

1. When the gold-en eve-ning gath-ered On the shore of Gal-i-lee,
2. Not in robes of pur-ple splen-dor, Not in silk-en soft-ness shod,
3. For he healed their sick at e-ven, And he cured the le-per's sore,
4. Not in robes of pur-ple splen-dor, But in lives that do his will,

When the fish-ing boats lay qui-et by the sea,
But in rai-ment worn with trav-el came their God;
So that sin-ful men and wom-en sinned no more;
And in pa-tient acts of kind-ness he comes still;

Long a-go the peo-ple won-dered, Though no sign was in the sky,
And the peo-ple knew his pres-ence By the heart that ceased to sigh
And the world grew mirth-ful-heart-ed, And for-got its mis-er-y
And the peo-ple cry with won-der, Though no sign is in the sky,

For the glo-ry of the Lord was pass-ing by.
When the glo-ry of the Lord was pass-ing by.
When the glo-ry of the Lord was pass-ing by.
That the glo-ry of the Lord is pass-ing by. A-MEN.

109 O Son of Man, Our Hero

(LONDONDERRY. 11, 10, 11, 10, D.)

FRANK FLETCHER, 1926

Old Irish Air

1. O Son of man, our he-ro strong and ten-der, Whose ser-vants
2. Lov-er of chil-dren, boy-hood's in-spi-ra-tion, Of all man-

are the brave in all the earth, Our liv-ing sac-ri-fice to thee we
kind the Ser-vant and the King, O Lord of joy and hope and con-so-

ren-der, Who shar-est all our sor-row, all our mirth.
la-tion, To thee our fears and joys and hopes we bring.

O feet so strong to climb the path of du-ty, O lips di-
O Son of man, our he-ro strong and ten-der, Whose ser-vants

vine that taught the words of truth, Kind eyes that marked the lil-ies in their
are the brave in all the earth, Our liv-ing sac-ri-fice to thee we

beau-ty, And glow-ing heart that kin-dled at the zeal of youth.
ren-der, Who, God-like, shar-est all our sor-row, all our mirth. A-MEN.

110   My Master Was So Very Poor
(MY MASTER. L. M.)

HARRY LEE   GEORGE HENRY DAY, 1929

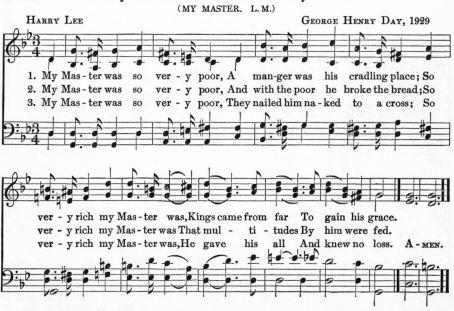

1. My Mas-ter was so ver-y poor, A man-ger was his cradling place; So
2. My Mas-ter was so ver-y poor, And with the poor he broke the bread; So
3. My Mas-ter was so ver-y poor, They nailed him na-ked to a cross; So

ver-y rich my Mas-ter was, Kings came from far To gain his grace.
ver-y rich my Mas-ter was That mul - ti - tudes By him were fed.
ver-y rich my Mas-ter was, He gave his all And knew no loss. A-MEN.

111 Thine Arm, O Lord, in Days of Old

(PHOENIX. C.M,D.)

EDWARD H. PLUMPTRE, 1864   LEONARD N. FOWLES, 1918

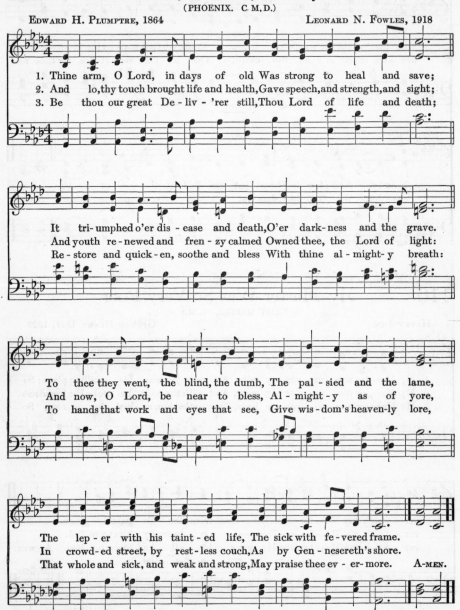

1. Thine arm, O Lord, in days of old Was strong to heal and save;
2. And lo, thy touch brought life and health, Gave speech, and strength, and sight;
3. Be thou our great De-liv-'rer still, Thou Lord of life and death;

It tri-umphed o'er dis-ease and death, O'er dark-ness and the grave.
And youth re-newed and fren-zy calmed Owned thee, the Lord of light:
Re-store and quick-en, soothe and bless With thine al-might-y breath:

To thee they went, the blind, the dumb, The pal-sied and the lame,
And now, O Lord, be near to bless, Al-might-y as of yore,
To hands that work and eyes that see, Give wis-dom's heaven-ly lore,

The lep-er with his taint-ed life, The sick with fe-vered frame.
In crowd-ed street, by rest-less couch, As by Gen-nesereth's shore.
That whole and sick, and weak and strong, May praise thee ev-er-more. A-MEN.

112 Dear Lord, Who Sought at Dawn of Day
(STIREWALT. L. M.)

HARRY WEBB FARRINGTON, 1925   ROB ROY PEERY, 1926

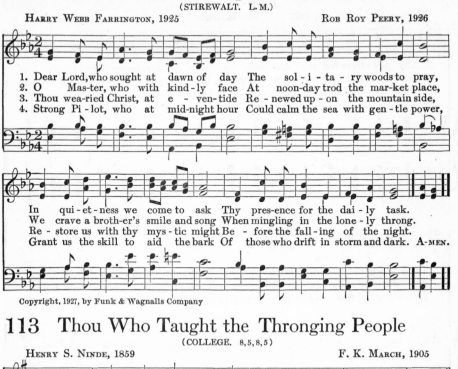

1. Dear Lord, who sought at dawn of day The sol - i - ta - ry woods to pray,
2. O Mas-ter, who with kind-ly face At noon-day trod the mar-ket place,
3. Thou wea-ried Christ, at e - ven-tide Re - newed up - on the mountain side,
4. Strong Pi - lot, who at mid-night hour Could calm the sea with gen - tle power,

In qui - et - ness we come to ask Thy pres-ence for the dai - ly task.
We crave a broth-er's smile and song When mingling in the lone - ly throng.
Re - store us with thy mys - tic might Be - fore the fall-ing of the night.
Grant us the skill to aid the bark Of those who drift in storm and dark. A-MEN.

113 Thou Who Taught the Thronging People
(COLLEGE. 8, 5, 8, 5)

HENRY S. NINDE, 1859   F. K. MARCH, 1905

1. Thou who taught the throng-ing peo - ple By blue Gal - i - lee;
2. Thou whose touch could heal the lep - er, Make the blind to see;
3. Thou whose word could still the tem - pest, Calm the rag - ing sea;
4. Thou who sin - less met the temp - ter; Grant, O Christ, that we

Speak to us, thy err - ing chil - dren, Teach us pu - ri - ty.
Touch our hearts and turn the sin - ning In - to pu - ri - ty.
Hush the storm of hu - man pas - sion, Give us pu - ri - ty.
May o'er - come the bent to e - vil By thy pu - ri - ty. A - MEN.

114 Thy Palm Trees Fed with Dew and Sun

(HOSANNA. Irregular)

KATHARINE LEE BATES, 1921   DORIAN MODE   LEROY B. CAMPBELL, 1929

1. Thy palm-trees fed with dew and sun, Thy ce-dars crown-ing Le-ba-non,
2. Let oaks and elms take up thy praise, Let ma-ples, birch-es, wil-lows raise
3. Thou art the vine, to thee we bring Our-selves thy branch-es, glad with spring;

Thine o-lives of Geth-sem-a-ne, O Lord of Light, all wor-shipped thee.
A-dor-ing branch-es in thy sight, O Lord of Beau-ty, Lord of Light.
By ripen-ing fruit may we be known, O Lord of Light and Love, thine own.

REFRAIN

Ho-san-na! Ho-san-na! To the Son of Da-vid, Ho-san-na! Ho-san-na!

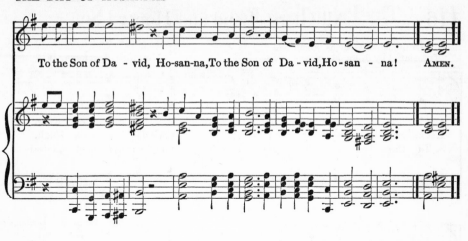

To the Son of Da - vid, Ho-san-na, To the Son of Da - vid, Ho-san - na! AMEN.

115   Ride On, Ride On, in Majesty
(ST. DROSTANE. L. M.)

HENRY H. MILMAN, 1827   JOHN B. DYKES, 1862

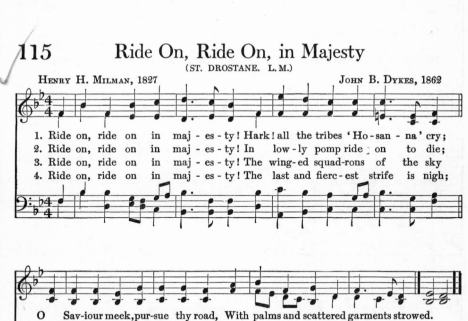

1. Ride on, ride on in maj - es - ty! Hark! all the tribes 'Ho-san - na' cry;
2. Ride on, ride on in maj - es - ty! In low - ly pomp ride on to die;
3. Ride on, ride on in maj - es - ty! The wing-ed squad-rons of the sky
4. Ride on, ride on in maj - es - ty! The last and fierc-est strife is nigh;

O   Sav-iour meek, pur-sue thy road, With palms and scattered garments strowed.
O   Christ, thy tri-umphs now be-gin O'er cap - tive death and conquered sin.
Look down with sad and wondering eyes To   see the approaching sac - ri-fice.
Bow thy meek head to mor-tal pain, Then take, O Christ, thy power and reign. A-MEN.

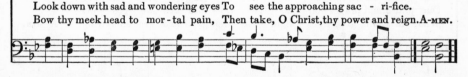

116 All Glory, Laud and Honor

(ST. THEODULPH. 7, 6, 7, 6, D.)

THEODULPH of Orleans, about 820
Translated by JOHN M. NEALE, 1854

MELCHIOR TESCHNER, 1615

1. All glo-ry, laud and hon-or, To thee, Re-deem-er, King,
2. The com-pa-ny of an-gels Are prais-ing thee on high,
3. To thee, be-fore thy pas-sion They sang their hymns of praise;

To whom the lips of chil-dren Made sweet ho-san-nas ring.
And mor-tal men and all things Cre-a-ted make re-ply.
To thee, now high ex-alt-ed, Our mel-o-dy we raise.

Thou art the King of Is-ra-el Thou Da-vid's roy-al Son,
The peo-ple of the He-brews With palms be-fore thee went;
Thou didst ac-cept their prais-es; Ac-cept the praise we bring,

Who in the Lord's name com-est, The King and bless-ed One.
Our praise and prayer and an-thems Be-fore thee we pre-sent.
Who in all good de-light-est, Thou good and gra-cious King. A-MEN.

117 Hosanna, Loud Hosanna

(ELLACOMBE. 7, 6, 7, 6, D.)

JEANNETTE THRELFALL, 1873   HARTIG's Vollstandige Sammlung, 1830

1. Ho - san - na! loud ho - san - na! The lit - tle chil-dren sang;
2. From Ol - i - vet they fol - lowed, 'Midst an ex - ult - ant crowd,
3. Fair leaves of sil - very ol - ive They strewed up - on the ground,
4. 'Ho - san - na in the high - est!' That an - cient song we sing:

Thro' pil - lared court and tem - ple The glo - rious an - them rang:
Wav - ing the vic - tor palm - branch, And shout-ing clear and loud;
Whilst Sa - lem's cir - cling moun - tains Ech - oed the joy - ful sound;
For Christ is our Re - deem - er, The Lord of heaven our King.

To Je - sus who had blessed them, Close fold - ed to his breast,
Bright an - gels joined the cho - rus Be - yond the cloud-less sky—
The Lord of men and an - gels Rode on in low - ly state,
O may we ev - er praise him With heart, and life, and voice,

The chil - dren sang their prais - es, The sim - plest and the best.
'Ho - san - na in the high - est: Glo - ry to God on high!'
Nor scorned that lit - tle chil - dren Should on his bid- ding wait.
And in his ra-diant pres - ence E - ter - nal - ly re - joice. A-MEN.

118 Draw Nigh to Thy Jerusalem, O Lord

(PICTON. 10, 10, 10, 10)

JEREMY TAYLOR, 1613–1667

GENA BRANSCOMBE, 1927

1. Draw nigh to thy Je - ru - sa - lem, O Lord, Thy faith - ful peo - ple cry with one ac - cord: Ride on in tri - umph; Lord, be - hold we lay Our pas - sions, lusts, and proud wills in thy way!

2. Thy road is rea - dy; and thy paths, made straight, With long - ing ex - pec - ta - tion seem to wait The con - se - cra - tion of thy beauteous feet, And si - lent - ly thy prom-ised ad-vent greet!

3. Ho - san - na! wel-come to our hearts! for here Thou hast a tem - ple too, as Zi - on dear; Yes, dear as Zi - on, and as full of sin; How long shall thieves and rob -bers dwell therein!

4. En - ter and chase them forth, and cleanse the floor; O'er - throw them all, that they may nev - er more Pro - fane with traf-fic vile that ho - ly place, Where thou hast cho - sen, Lord, to set thy face. A-MEN.

Music copyright by The Century Co.

119 Into the Woods My Master Went

(LANIER. Irregular)

SIDNEY LANIER, 1880

PETER C. LUTKIN, 1904

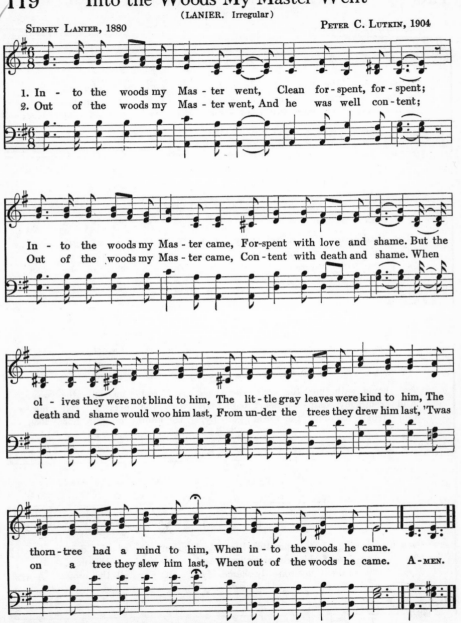

1. In - to the woods my Mas - ter went, Clean for - spent, for - spent;
2. Out of the woods my Mas - ter went, And he was well con - tent;

In - to the woods my Mas - ter came, For-spent with love and shame. But the
Out of the woods my Mas - ter came, Con - tent with death and shame. When

ol - ives they were not blind to him, The lit - tle gray leaves were kind to him, The
death and shame would woo him last, From un-der the trees they drew him last, 'Twas

thorn - tree had a mind to him, When in - to the woods he came.
on a tree they slew him last, When out of the woods he came. A - MEN.

120 Beneath the Cross of Jesus

(ST. CHRISTOPHER. 7, 6, 8, 6, 8, 6, 8, 6)

ELIZABETH C. CLEPHANE, 1868

FREDERICK C. MAKER, 1881

1. Be - neath the cross of Je - sus I fain would take my stand,
2. Up - on that cross of Je - sus Mine eye at times can see
3. I take, O cross, thy shad - ow For my a - bid - ing place;

The shad - ow of a might - y rock With - in a wea - ry land;
The ver - y dy - ing form of One Who suf - fered there for me;
I ask no oth - er sun - shine than The sun - shine of his face;

A home with - in the wil - der - ness, A rest up - on the way,
And from my smit - ten heart with tears Two won - ders I con - fess, —
Con - tent to let the world go by, To know no gain nor loss,

From the burn - ing of the noon - tide heat, And the bur - den of the day.
The won - ders of his glo - rious love And my un - wor - thi - ness.
My sin - ful self my on - ly shame, My glo - ry all the cross. A - MEN.

121   I Bind My Heart This Tide

(FEALTY. 6,7,7,7,6,7,7,7)

LAUCHLAN MacLEAN WATT, 1867–   GRACE WILBUR CONANT, 1927

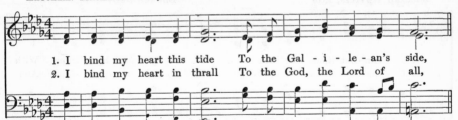

1. I bind my heart this tide   To the Gal - i - le - an's side,
2. I bind my heart in thrall   To the God, the Lord of all,

To the wounds of Cal - va - ry,—   To the Christ who died for me.
To the God, the poor man's Friend, And the Christ whom he did send.

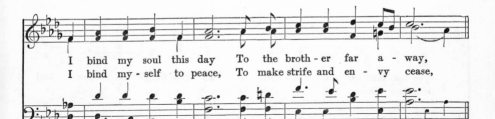

I bind my soul this day   To the broth - er far a - way,
I bind my - self to peace,   To make strife and en - vy cease,

And the broth-er near at hand, In this town, and in this land.
God! knit thou sure the cord Of my thral - dom to my Lord. A - MEN.

122 I Cannot Think or Reason

(COMRADES OF THE CROSS. 7, 6, 7, 6, D.)

WILLARD WATTLES, 1918   EDWARD SHIPPEN BARNES, 1927

1. I can-not think or rea - son, I on - ly know he came With
hands and feet of heal - ing And wild heart all a - flame, With
eyes that dimmed and soft - ened At all the things he saw, And
in his pil - lared sing - ing I read the march - ing law.

2. I on - ly know he loves me, En-folds and un - der - stands—And
oh, his heart that holds me, And oh, his cer - tain hands—The
man, the Christ, the sol - dier, Who from his cross of pain
Cried to a dy - ing com - rade, 'Lad, we shall meet a - gain.'

123 When I Survey the Wondrous Cross

(HAMBURG. L. M.)

From the First Gregorian Tone
Arranged by LOWELL MASON, 1824

ISAAC WATTS, 1707

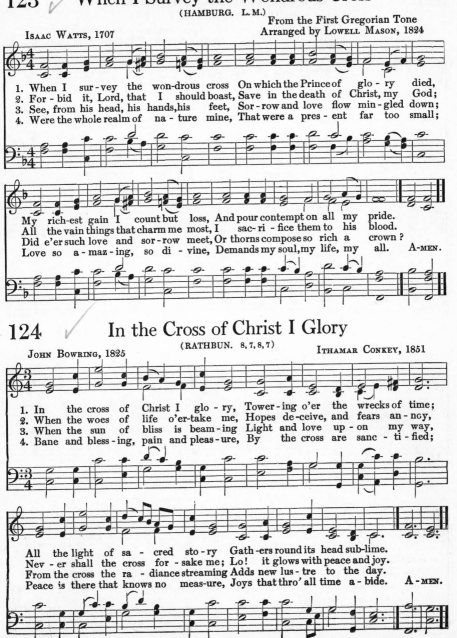

1. When I sur-vey the won-drous cross On which the Prince of glo-ry died,
2. For-bid it, Lord, that I should boast, Save in the death of Christ, my God;
3. See, from his head, his hands, his feet, Sor-row and love flow min-gled down;
4. Were the whole realm of na-ture mine, That were a pres-ent far too small;

My rich-est gain I count but loss, And pour contempt on all my pride.
All the vain things that charm me most, I sac-ri-fice them to his blood.
Did e'er such love and sor-row meet, Or thorns compose so rich a crown?
Love so a-maz-ing, so di-vine, Demands my soul, my life, my all. A-MEN.

124 In the Cross of Christ I Glory

(RATHBUN. 8, 7, 8, 7)

JOHN BOWRING, 1825

ITHAMAR CONKEY, 1851

1. In the cross of Christ I glo-ry, Tower-ing o'er the wrecks of time;
2. When the woes of life o'er-take me, Hopes de-ceive, and fears an-noy,
3. When the sun of bliss is beam-ing Light and love up-on my way,
4. Bane and bless-ing, pain and pleas-ure, By the cross are sanc-ti-fied;

All the light of sa-cred sto-ry Gath-ers round its head sub-lime.
Nev-er shall the cross for-sake me; Lo! it glows with peace and joy.
From the cross the ra-diance streaming Adds new lus-tre to the day.
Peace is there that knows no meas-ure, Joys that thro' all time a-bide. A-MEN.

125 O Joyous Easter Morning

(FAITHFUL. 7, 6, 7, 6, D.)

JOHN SEBASTIAN BACH, 1685-1750
Arranged from 'My Heart Ever Faithful'

Anonymous

1. O joy-ous East-er morn-ing, That saw the Lord of love a-rise!
2. O glad-some East-er morn-ing, Our hearts re-joice a-new to-day,
3. O bless-ed East-er morn-ing, What day so bright and fair as this,

O bright and hap-py morn-ing! The clouds have left the skies.
The grave and death are con-quered, He is of life the way.
When, through his might-y tri-umph, He won the courts of bliss.

The night of grief is end-ed, The smil-ing day has come a-gain,
The hosts of sin are van-quished, He is the Vic-tor, Sav-iour, King;
The doors of heaven are o-pen, The grave no more has power nor dread,

And Christ has won the vic-tory, For all the sons of men.
Then let us all with glad-ness Our thank-ful prais-es sing.
For ris-en is our Sav-iour, The first fruits of the dead. A-MEN.

126 Easter Flowers Are Blooming Bright

(EASTER FLOWERS. 7, 7, 7, 6. With Refrain)

MARY A. NICHOLSON, 1875

G. WARING STEBBINS, 1913

UNISON

1. Eas - ter flowers are bloom-ing bright, Eas - ter skies pour ra - diant light,
2. An - gels car - oled this sweet lay, When in man - ger rude he lay;
3. He, then born to grief and pain, Now to glo - ry born a - gain,
4. As he ris - eth, rise we too, Tune we heart and voice a - new,

Christ our Lord is risen in might, Glo - ry in the high - est!
Now once more cast grief a - way, Glo - ry in the high - est!
Call - eth forth our glad-dest strain, Glo - ry in the high - est!
Offer - ing hom-age glad and true, Glo - ry in the high - est!

REFRAIN

Al - le - lu - ia! Al - le - lu - ia! Christ our Lord is

risen in might, Al - le - lu - ia! A - MEN.

Music copyright by Benjamin Shepard

127 The Day of Resurrection

(LANCASHIRE. 7, 6, 7, 6, D.)

JOHN OF DAMASCUS, 8th Century
Translated by JOHN M. NEALE, 1862

HENRY SMART, 1836

1. The day of res-ur-rec-tion, Earth, tell it out a-broad;
2. Our hearts be pure from e-vil, That we may see a-right
3. Now let the heavens be joy-ful, Let earth her song be-gin;

The pass-o-ver of glad-ness, The pass-o-ver of God.
The Lord in rays e-ter-nal Of res-ur-rec-tion-light;
Let the round world keep tri-umph, And all that is there-in;

From death to life e-ter-nal, From this world to the sky,
And, list-ening to his ac-cents, May hear, so calm and plain,
In-vis-i-ble and vis-i-ble, Their notes let all things blend;

Our Christ hath brought us o-ver With hymns of vic-to-ry.
His own 'All hail!' and, hear-ing, May raise the vic-tor-strain.
For Christ the Lord hath ris-en, Our joy that hath no end. A-MEN.

May be sung to Rotterdam opposite

108

128 ## The Light Along the Ages

(ROTTERDAM. 7, 6, 7, 6, D.)

WILLIAM GEORGE TARRANT, 1890   BERTHOLD TOURS, 1875

1. The Light a - long the a - ges Shines high - er as it goes;
2. But eve - ry gift sur - pass - ing, This won-drous gift we own,—

From age to age more glo - rious Its ra - diant splen - dor grows.
The Son of Man is ris - en To dwell be - fore thy throne.

Man's life, be - gun so low - ly, Now soars to heaven a - bove,
Wher - ev - er good - ness reign - eth The soul of Christ lives on,

To share in life e - ter - nal The joys of end - less love.
And eve - ry Christ-like spir - it Shall rise where he hath gone. A -MEN.

Words copyright by William G. Tarrant

129 Christ the Lord Is Risen To-day

(WORGAN, 7, 7, 7, 7. With Alleluia)

CHARLES WESLEY, 1739

Lyra Davidica, 1708

1. 'Christ the Lord is risen to - day,' Al - - le - lu - ia!
2. Lives a - gain our glo - rious King: Al - - le - lu - ia!
3. Love's re - deem - ing work is done, Al - - le - lu - ia!
4. Soar we now where Christ has led, Al - - le - lu - ia!

Sons of men and an - gels say: Al - - le - lu - ia!
Where, O death, is now thy sting? Al - - le - lu - ia!
Fought the fight, the bat - tle won; Al - - le - lu - ia!
Fol - lowing our ex - alt - ed Head; Al - - le - lu - ia!

Raise your joys and tri - umphs high; Al - - le - lu - ia!
Dy - ing once, he all doth save; Al - - le - lu - ia!
Death in vain for - bids him rise; Al - - le - lu - ia!
Made like him, like him we rise; Al - - le - lu - ia!

Sing, ye heavens, and earth re - ply. Al - - le - lu - ia!
Where thy vic - to - ry, O grave? Al - - le - lu - ia!
Christ has o - pened Par - a - dise. Al - - le - lu - ia!
Ours the cross, the grave, the skies. Al - - le - lu - ia! A-MEN.

130 Welcome, Happy Morning

(FORTUNATUS. 11, 11, 11, 11. With Refrain)

Venantius Fortunatus, 590
Translated by John Ellerton, 1868

Arthur S. Sullivan, 1872

1. Wel-come, hap-py morn-ing! age to age shall say; Hell to-day is van-quished, heaven is won to-day. Lo! the Dead is liv-ing, God for ev-er-more; Him their true Cre-a-tor, all his works a-dore.

2. Earth with joy con-fess-es, cloth-ing for her spring, All fresh gifts re-turned with her re-turn-ing King: Bloom in eve-ry mead-ow, leaves on eve-ry bough, Speak his sor-row end-ed, hail his tri-umph now.

3. Come then, True and Faith-ful, now ful-fil thy word, 'Tis thine own third morn-ing; rise, O bur-ied Lord! Show thy face in bright-ness, bid the na-tions see; Bring a-gain our day-light; day re-turns with thee.

Refrain

Wel-come, hap-py morn-ing! age to age shall say. A-men.

131 On Wings of Living Light

(JUBILATE. 6,6,6,6,8,8)

WILLIAM WALSHAM HOW, 1872, arranged   HORATIO PARKER, 1894

1. On wings of liv-ing light, At ear-liest dawn of day, Came down the
2. The keep-ers watch-ing near, At that dread sight and sound, Fell down with
3. Then rose from death's dark gloom Un-seen by mor-tal eye, Tri-umph-ant
4. Ye chil-dren of the light, A-rise with him, a-rise; See how the

an-gel bright And rolled the stone a-way. **REFRAIN** Lift up your heart, lift
sud-den fear, Like dead men, to the ground.
o'er the tomb, The Lord of earth and sky.
Day-star bright Is burn-ing in the skies!

up your voice; Re-joice, a-gain I say, re-joice. Your voic-es raise with

one ac-cord To bless and praise your ris-en Lord. A-MEN.

132   No Longer, Lord, Thy Sons Shall Sow

(VICTORY. 8, 8, 8. With Alleluia)

Arranged from the 'Gloria Patri' of PALESTRINA, 1591,
by WILLIAM H. MONK, 1861

EARL MARLATT, 1930

Al - le - lu - ia!   Al - le - lu - ia!   Al - le - lu - ia!

1. No lon-ger, Lord, thy sons shall sow   Ha-tred and death where pop - pies blow;
2. No more shall flares and rock-ets rain   Pal-lor on sons and fa - thers slain;
3. Peace-Ma-ker, Christ, whose liv - ing word   Qui-et - ed waves and sheathed the sword,
4. Till souls of all the cru - ci - fied   Wa-ken from sea and moun-tain-side,
5. Then shall we stand as Ma - ry stood,   Know-ing thou liv - est, life is good,

Peace out of har-rowed lives shall grow.   Al - le - lu - ia!
Jus - tice shall van-quish grief and pain.   Al - le - lu - ia!
Show us thy ris - en spir - it, Lord,   Al - le - lu - ia!
Hail - ing the dream for which they died.   Al - le - lu - ia!
Mak - ing all men a broth-er - hood.   Al - le - lu - ia!   A - MEN.

Words copyright by Earl Marlatt

133   The Strife Is O'er, the Battle Done

(VICTORY. No. 132)

1 The strife is o'er, the battle done;
The victory of faith is won;
The song of triumph has begun.
Alleluia!

2 The powers of death have done their worst,
But Christ their legions hath dispersed;
Let shout of holy joy outburst.
Alleluia!

3 The three sad days are quickly sped;
He rises glorious from the dead;
All glory to our risen Head!
Alleluia!

4 Lord, by the stripes which wounded thee,
From death's dread sting thy servants free,
That we may live and sing to thee,
Alleluia! Amen.

Anonymous Latin hymn, translated
by FRANCIS POTT, 1861

134 Blow, Golden Trumpets, Sweet and Clear

(GOLDEN TRUMPETS. L.M.)

MARGARET DELAND, 1887   T. CARL WHITMER, 1930

1. Blow, gold-en trum-pets, sweet and clear, Blow soft up-on the per-fumed air;
2. O, let the winds your mes-sage bear To eve-ry heart of grief and care;
3. On cloud-y wings let glad words fly Thro' the soft blue of echo-ing sky;

Bid the sad earth to join your song, 'To Christ does vic-to-ry be-long.'
Sound thro' the world the joy-ful lay, 'Our Christ has conquered death today.'
Ring out, O trum-pets, sweet and clear, 'Thro' death im-mor-tal life is here.' A-MEN.

135 All Hail the Power of Jesus' Name

(MILES LANE. C.M.)

EDWARD PERRONET, 1779   WILLIAM SHRUBSOLE, 1779

1. All hail the power of Je-sus' name! Let an-gels pros-trate fall;
2. Let eve-ry kin-dred, eve-ry tribe, On this ter-res-trial ball,
3. Oh, that with yon-der sa-cred throng We at his feet may fall,

Bring forth the roy - al di - a - dem, And crown him,
To him all ma - jes - ty as - cribe, And crown him,
Join in the ev - er - last - ing song, And crown him,

crown him, crown him, Crown him Lord of all. A-MEN.

All Hail the Power of Jesus' Name

(CORONATION. C.M.) *Second Tune*

EDWARD PERRONET, 1779

OLIVER HOLDEN, 1793

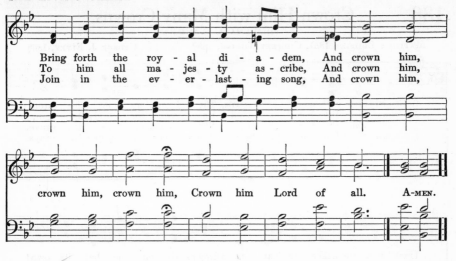

1. All hail the power of Je - sus' name! Let an - gels pros - trate fall;

Bring forth the roy - al di - a - dem, And crown him Lord of all,

Bring forth the roy - al di - a - dem, And crown him Lord of all. A-MEN.

115

136 Crown Him with Many Crowns

(DIADEMATA. S. M. D.)

MATTHEW BRIDGES, 1851, GODFREY THRING, 1882 · GEORGE J. ELVEY, 1868

1. Crown him with man - y crowns, The Lamb up - on his throne;
2. Crown him the Son of God Be - fore the worlds be - gan,
3. Crown him the Lord of Life Who tri - umphed o'er the grave,
4. Crown him the Lord of peace, Whose power a scep - tre sways

Hark! how the heaven - ly an - them drowns All mu - sic but its own!
And ye, who tread where he hath trod Crown him the Son of man,
And rose vic - to - rious in the strife For those he came to save.
From pole to pole, that wars may cease, And all be prayer and praise!

A - wake, my soul, and sing Of him who died for thee,
Who eve - ry grief hath known That wrings the hu - man breast,
His glo - ries now we sing Who died, and rose on high,
Crown him with man - y crowns As thrones be - fore him fall,

And hail him as thy match-less King Thro' all e - ter - ni - ty.
And takes and bears them for his own, That all in him may rest.
Who died, e - ter - nal life to bring, And lives that death may die.
Crown him, ye kings, with man - y crowns For he is King of all. A-MEN.

137 Fairest Lord Jesus

(CRUSADERS' HYMN. Irregular)

Silesian Folk Song,
in Schleischen Volkslieder, Leipzig, 1842
Descant by CHARLES REPPER, 1929

17th Century German Hymn

Descant with 2nd and 3rd stanzas

1. Fair - est Lord Je - sus, Rul - er of all na - ture, O thou of God and man the son! Thee will I cher - ish, Thee will I hon - or Thou, my soul's glo - ry, joy and crown.

2. Fair are the mead - ows, Fair - er still the wood - lands, Robed in the bloom - ing garb of spring; Je - sus is fair - er, Je - sus is pur - er, Who makes the woe - ful heart to sing.

3. Fair is the sun - shine, Fair - er still the moon - light, And all the twink - ling star - ry host; Je - sus shines bright - er, Je - sus shines pur - er Than all the an - gels heaven can boast.

2. Je - sus is fair - er, Je - sus is pur - er, He who makes the heart to sing. A - MEN.

3. Je - sus shines bright - er, Je - sus shines pur - er, Than the an - gels heaven can boast. A - MEN.

Optional Stanzas

4 All fairest beauty,
    Heavenly and earthly,
Wondrously, Jesus, is found in thee:
    None can be nearer,
    Fairer or dearer
Than thou, my Saviour, art to me.

5 Beautiful Saviour;
    Lord of the nations;
Son of God and Son of man.
    Glory and honor,
    Praise, adoration,
Now and evermore be thine.

138 Shepherd of Tender Youth

(KIRBY BEDON. 6, 6, 4, 6, 6, 6, 4)

CLEMENT OF ALEXANDRIA, 220 A. D.
Translated by HENRY M. DEXTER, 1846

EDWARD BUNNETT, 1887

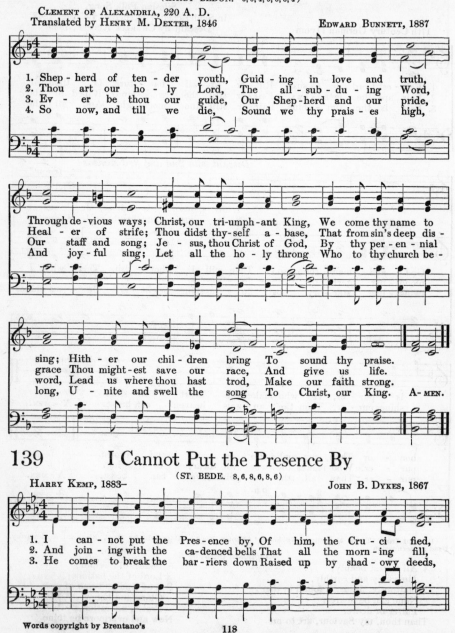

1. Shep-herd of ten-der youth, Guid-ing in love and truth, Through de-vious ways; Christ, our tri-umph-ant King, We come thy name to sing; Hith-er our chil-dren bring To sound thy praise.

2. Thou art our ho-ly Lord, The all-sub-du-ing Word, Heal-er of strife; Thou didst thy-self a-base, That from sin's deep dis-grace Thou might-est save our race, And give us life.

3. Ev-er be thou our guide, Our Shep-herd and our pride, Our staff and song; Je-sus, thou Christ of God, By thy per-en-nial word, Lead us where thou hast trod, Make our faith strong.

4. So now, and till we die, Sound we thy prais-es high, And joy-ful sing; Let all the ho-ly throng Who to thy church be-long, U-nite and swell the song To Christ, our King. A-MEN.

139 I Cannot Put the Presence By

(ST. BEDE. 8, 6, 8, 6, 8, 6)

HARRY KEMP, 1883–

JOHN B. DYKES, 1867

1. I can-not put the Pres-ence by, Of him, the Cru-ci-fied,

2. And join-ing with the ca-denced bells That all the morn-ing fill,

3. He comes to break the bar-riers down Raised up by shad-owy deeds,

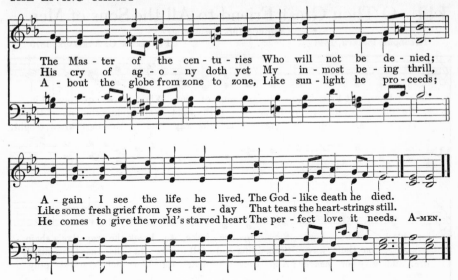

The Mas - ter of the cen - tu - ries Who will not be de - nied;
His cry of ag - o - ny doth yet My in - most be - ing thrill,
A - bout the globe from zone to zone, Like sun - light he pro - ceeds;

A - gain I see the life he lived, The God - like death he died.
Like some fresh grief from yes - ter - day That tears the heart-strings still.
He comes to give the world's starved heart The per - fect love it needs. A-MEN.

140 Immortal Love, Forever Full

(SERENITY. C. M.)

JOHN G. WHITTIER, 1866   Arranged from WILLIAM V. WALLACE, 1855

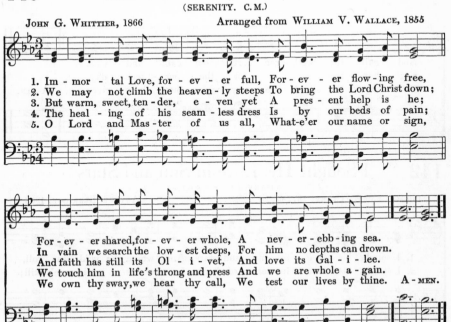

1. Im - mor - tal Love, for - ev - er full, For - ev - er flow - ing free,
2. We may not climb the heaven - ly steeps To bring the Lord Christ down;
3. But warm, sweet, ten - der, e - ven yet A pres - ent help is he;
4. The heal - ing of his seam - less dress Is by our beds of pain;
5. O Lord and Mas - ter of us all, What-e'er our name or sign,

For - ev - er shared, for - ev - er whole, A nev - er - ebb - ing sea.
In vain we search the low - est deeps, For him no depths can drown.
And faith has still its Ol - i - vet, And love its Gal - i - lee.
We touch him in life's throng and press And we are whole a - gain.
We own thy sway, we hear thy call, We test our lives by thine. A - MEN.

141 O Thou Great Friend to All the Sons of Men

(MORECAMBE. 10, 10, 10, 10)

THEODORE PARKER, 1846

FREDERICK C. ATKINSON, 1870

1. O thou great Friend to all the sons of men, Who once ap-peared in
2. We look to thee; thy truth is still the light Which guides the na-tions,
3. Yes, thou art still the life; thou art the way The ho-liest know,—light,

hum-blest guise be - low, Sin to re - buke, to break the cap-tive's chain,
grop-ing on their way, Stum-bling and fall - ing in dis - as-trous night,
life, and way of heaven; And they who dear - est hope and deep-est pray

And call the breth - ren forth from want and woe.
Yet hop - ing ev - er for the per - fect day.
Toil by the light, life, way, which thou hast given. A-MEN.

142 I Sought His Love in Sun and Stars

(HARVARD. 8, 6, 8, 6, 8, 8)

THOMAS CURTIS CLARK, 1877–

ARTHUR BERRIDGE, 1905

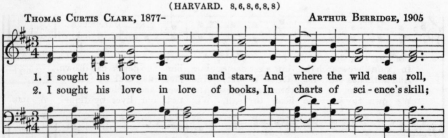

1. I sought his love in sun and stars, And where the wild seas roll,
2. I sought his love in lore of books, In charts of sci - ence's skill;

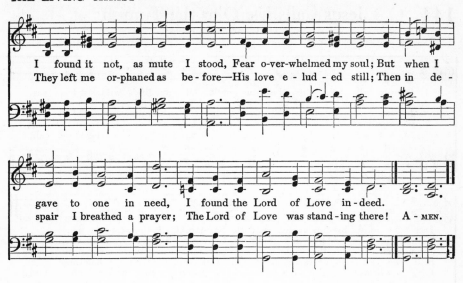

I found it not, as mute I stood, Fear o-ver-whelmed my soul; But when I
They left me or-phaned as be-fore—His love e-lud-ed still; Then in de-

gave to one in need, I found the Lord of Love in-deed.
spair I breathed a prayer; The Lord of Love was stand-ing there! A-MEN.

143 I Know not How that Bethlehem's Babe
(VERITAS. C.M.)

HARRY WEBB FARRINGTON, 1910   JOHN N. BURNHAM, 1923

1. I know not how that Bethlehem's Babe Could in the God-head be;
2. I know not how that Cal-vary's cross A world from sin could free;
3. I know not how that Jos-eph's tomb Could solve death's mys-ter-y;

I on-ly know the Man-ger Child Has brought God's life to me.
I on-ly know its matchless love Has brought God's love to me.
I on-ly know a liv-ing Christ,Our im-mor-tal-i-ty. A-MEN.

144 Jesus Calls Us, O'er the Tumult

(GALILEE. 8, 7, 8, 7)

CECIL F. ALEXANDER, 1852   WILLIAM H. JUDE, 1887

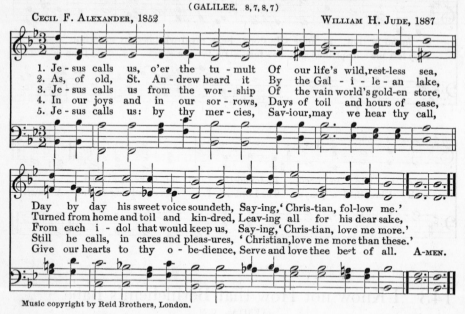

1. Je-sus calls us, o'er the tu-mult Of our life's wild, rest-less sea,
2. As, of old, St. An-drew heard it By the Gal-i-le-an lake,
3. Je-sus calls us from the wor-ship Of the vain world's gold-en store,
4. In our joys and in our sor-rows, Days of toil and hours of ease,
5. Je-sus calls us: by thy mer-cies, Sav-iour, may we hear thy call,

Day by day his sweet voice soundeth, Say-ing, 'Chris-tian, fol-low me.'
Turned from home and toil and kin-dred, Leav-ing all for his dear sake,
From each i-dol that would keep us, Say-ing, 'Chris-tian, love me more.'
Still he calls, in cares and pleas-ures, 'Christian, love me more than these.'
Give our hearts to thy o-be-dience, Serve and love thee best of all. A-MEN.

145 Just As I Am, Thine Own to Be

(JUST AS I AM. 8, 8, 8, 6)

MARIANNE FARNINGHAM, 1887   JOSEPH BARNBY, 1893

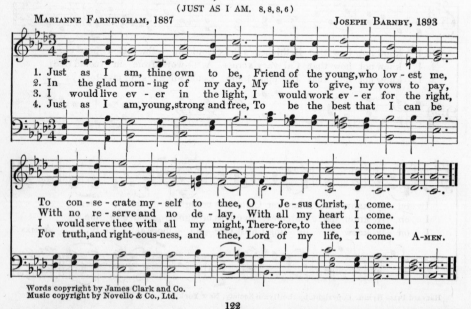

1. Just as I am, thine own to be, Friend of the young, who lov-est me,
2. In the glad morn-ing of my day, My life to give, my vows to pay,
3. I would live ev-er in the light, I would work ev-er for the right,
4. Just as I am, young, strong and free, To be the best that I can be

To con-se-crate my-self to thee, O Je-sus Christ, I come.
With no re-serve and no de-lay, With all my heart I come.
I would serve thee with all my might, There-fore, to thee I come.
For truth, and right-eous-ness, and thee, Lord of my life, I come. A-MEN.

146 Now in the Days of Youth

(FROM STRENGTH TO STRENGTH. S. M. D.)

WALTER J. MATHAMS, 1913   EDWARD WOODALL NAYLOR, 1867–

UNISON

1. Now in the days of youth, When life flows fresh and free,
   Thou Lord of all our hearts and lives, We give our-selves to thee;
   Our fer-vent gift re-ceive, And fit us to ful-fil,
   Thro' all our days, in all our ways, Our heaven-ly Fa-ther's will.

2. Teach us wher-e'er we live, To act as in thy sight,
   And do what thou wouldst have us do With ra-di-ant de-light;
   Not choos-ing what is great, Nor spurn-ing what is small,
   But take as from thy hands our tasks, And glo-ri-fy them all.

3. Teach us to love the true, The beau-ti-ful and pure,
   And let us not for one short hour An e-vil thought en-dure;
   But give us grace to stand De-cid-ed, brave and strong,
   The lov-ers of all ho-ly things, The foes of all things wrong.

4. Spir-it of Christ, do thou Our first bright days in-spire
   That we may live the life of love And loft-i-est de-sire;
   And be by thee pre-pared For larg-er years to come,
   And for the life in-ef-fa-ble With-in the Fa-ther's home. A-MEN.

147 I Heard the Voice of Jesus Say

(VOX DILECTI. C. M. D.)

Horatius Bonar, 1846

John B. Dykes, 1868

1. I heard the voice of Je - sus say, 'Come un - to me and rest;
2. I heard the voice of Je - sus say, 'Be - hold, I free - ly give
3. I heard the voice of Je - sus say, 'I am this dark world's light;

Lay down, thou wea - ry one, lay down Thy head up - on my breast.'
The liv - ing wa - ter, thirst - y one, Stoop down, and drink, and live.'
Look un - to me, thy morn shall rise, And all thy day be bright.'

I came to Je - sus as I was, Wea - ry and worn and sad;
I came to Je - sus and I drank Of that life - giv - ing stream;
I looked to Je - sus, and I found In him my star, my sun;

I found in him a rest - ing place, And he has made me glad.
My thirst was quenched, my soul re - vived, And now I live in him.
And in that light of life I'll walk, Till trav-el-ing days are done. A-MEN.

148 O Jesus, Thou Art Standing

(ST. HILDA. 7, 6, 7, 6, D.)

JUSTIN H. KNECHT, 1799
EDWARD HUSBAND, 1871

WILLIAM WALSHAM HOW, 1867

1. O Je - sus, thou art stand - ing Out - side the fast - closed door,
2. O Je - sus, thou art knock - ing; And lo! that hand is scarred,
3. O Je - sus, thou art plead - ing In ac - cents meek and low,

In low - ly pa - tience wait - ing To pass the thresh - old o'er:
And thorns thy brow en - cir - cle, And tears thy face have marred:
'I died for you, my chil - dren, And will ye treat me so?'

Shame on us, Chris - tian broth - ers, His name and sign we bear,
O love that pass - eth knowl - edge, So pa - tient - ly to wait;
O Lord, with shame and sor - row We o - pen now the door;

O shame, thrice shame up - on us, To keep him stand - ing there.
O sin that hath no e - qual, So fast to bar the gate.
Dear Sav - iour, en - ter, en - ter, And leave us nev - er - more. A-MEN.

149 Draw Thou My Soul, O Christ

(ST. EDMUND. 6, 4, 6, 4, 6, 6, 6, 4)

LUCY LARCOM, 1892

ARTHUR S. SULLIVAN, 1872

1. Draw thou my soul, O Christ, Clos-er to thine; Breathe in-to
2. Lead forth my soul, O Christ, One with thine own, Joy-ful to
3. Not for my-self a-lone May my prayer be; Lift thou thy

eve-ry wish Thy will di-vine: Raised my low self a-bove, Won by thy
fol-low thee Thro' paths un-known: In thee my strength re-new; Give me thy
world, O Christ, Clos-er to thee: Cleanse from its guilt and wrong, Teach it sal-

death-less love, Ev-er, O Christ, through mine Let thy life shine.
work to do; Through me thy truth be shown, Thy love made known.
va-tion's song, Till earth, as heaven, ful-fil God's ho-ly will. A-MEN.

Words copyright by Houghton Mifflin Co.
Music copyright by Novello and Co., Ltd.

150 I Need Thee Every Hour

(NEED. 6, 4, 6, 4. With Refrain)

ANNIE S. HAWKS, 1872

ROBERT LOWRY, 1872

1. I need thee eve-ry hour, Most gra-cious Lord; No ten-der voice like thine
2. I need thee eve-ry hour, Stay thou near by; Temp-ta-tions lose their power
3. I need thee eve-ry hour, In joy or pain; Come quick-ly and a-bide,
4. I need thee eve-ry hour, Teach me thy will; And thy rich prom-is-es

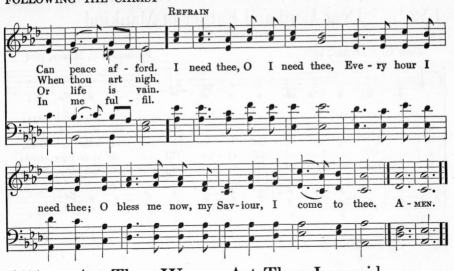

Can peace af - ford.
When thou art nigh.
Or life is vain.
In me ful - fil.

REFRAIN

I need thee, O I need thee, Eve - ry hour I need thee; O bless me now, my Sav-iour, I come to thee. A - MEN.

151 Art Thou Weary, Art Thou Languid

(STEPHANOS. 8, 5, 8, 3)

St. Stephen of Mar Saba, 8th century
Recast by John Mason Neale, 1862

Henry W. Baker, 1868

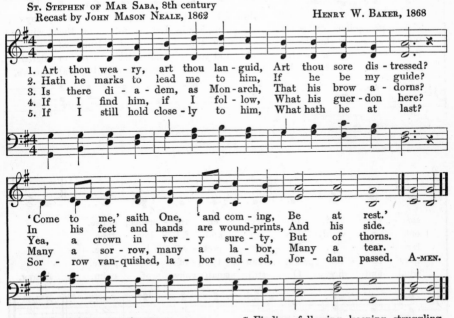

1. Art thou wea - ry, art thou lan - guid, Art thou sore dis - tressed?
2. Hath he marks to lead me to him, If he be my guide?
3. Is there di - a - dem, as Mon - arch, That his brow a - dorns?
4. If I find him, if I fol - low, What his guer - don here?
5. If I still hold close - ly to him, What hath he at last?

'Come to me,' saith One, 'and com - ing, Be at rest.'
In his feet and hands are wound-prints, And his side.
Yea, a crown in ver - y sure - ty, But of thorns.
Many a sor - row, many a la - bor, Many a tear.
Sor - row van-quished, la - bor end - ed, Jor - dan passed. A-MEN.

6 If I ask him to receive me,
Will he say me nay?
Not till earth, and not till heaven
Pass away.

7 Finding, following, keeping, struggling,
Is he sure to bless?
Saints, apostles, prophets, martyrs,
Answer, 'Yes.'

152 Dear Lord and Father of Mankind

(WHITTIER. 8, 6, 8, 8, 6)

John G. Whittier, 1872   Frederick C. Maker, 1887

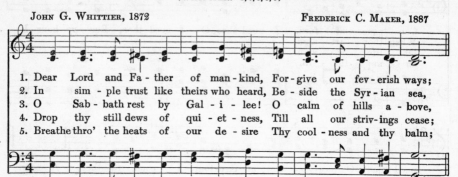

1. Dear Lord and Fa - ther of man - kind, For - give our fev - erish ways;
2. In sim - ple trust like theirs who heard, Be - side the Syr - ian sea,
3. O Sab - bath rest by Gal - i - lee! O calm of hills a - bove,
4. Drop thy still dews of qui - et - ness, Till all our striv - ings cease;
5. Breathe thro' the heats of our de - sire Thy cool - ness and thy balm;

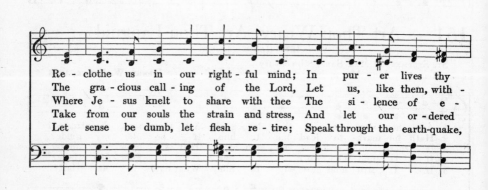

Re - clothe us in our right - ful mind; In pur - er lives thy
The gra - cious call - ing of the Lord, Let us, like them, with -
Where Je - sus knelt to share with thee The si - lence of e -
Take from our souls the strain and stress, And let our or - dered
Let sense be dumb, let flesh re - tire; Speak through the earth-quake,

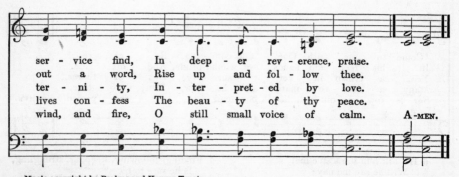

ser - vice find, In deep - er rev - erence, praise.
out a word, Rise up and fol - low thee.
ter - ni - ty, In - ter - pret - ed by love.
lives con - fess The beau - ty of thy peace.
wind, and fire, O still small voice of calm.

A -men.

153 Dear God, Our Father, at Thy Knee

(FELIX. 11, 10, 11, 10)

KATHARINE LEE BATES, 1926   FELIX MENDELSSOHN-BARTHOLDY, 1809–1847

1. Dear God, our Fa - ther, at thy knee con - fess - ing
2. Not for more beau - ty would our eyes en - treat thee,
3. The stars and rain - bows are thy won - drous wear - ing,
4. Not for more love our crav - ing hearts im - plore thee,
5. In souls most sul - len thou art soft - ly dream - ing

Our sins and fol - lies, close in thine em - brace,
Flood - ed with beau - ty, beau - ty eve - ry - where;
Sun - light and shad - ow mov - ing on the hills;
But for more power to love un - til they glow
Of saints and he - roes wrought from thy di - vine

Chil - dren for - giv - en, hap - py in thy bless - ing,
On - ly for keen - er vi - sion that may greet thee
Ho - ly the mead - ow where thy feet are far - ing,
Like hearths of com - fort, ea - ger to re - store thee,
Pit - y and pa - tience, still the lost re - deem - ing;

Deep - en our spir - its to re - ceive thy grace.
In all thy vest - ures of the earth and air.
Ho - ly the brook - let that thy laugh - ter fills.
Hid - den in hu - man wretch - ed - ness and woe.
Deep - en our spir - its for a love like thine. A - MEN.

154 O Love That Wilt Not Let Me Go

(ST. MARGARET. 8, 8, 8, 8, 6)

GEORGE MATHESON, 1882

ALBERT L. PEACE, 1885

1. O Love that wilt not let me go, I rest my wea-ry soul in thee; I give thee back the life I owe, That in thine o-cean depths its flow May rich-er, full-er be.
2. O Light that fol-lowest all my way, I yield my flick-ering torch to thee; My heart re-stores its bor-rowed ray, That in thy sun-shine's blaze its day May bright-er, fair-er be.
3. O Joy that seek-est me through pain, I can-not close my heart to thee; I trace the rain-bow through the rain, And feel the prom-ise is not vain That morn shall tear-less be.
4. O Cross that lift-est up my head, I dare not ask to fly from thee; I lay in dust life's glo-ry dead, And from the ground there blossoms red Life that shall end-less be. A-MEN.

155 My Faith Looks up to Thee

(OLIVET. 6, 6, 4, 6, 6, 4)

RAY PALMER, 1830

LOWELL MASON, 1832

1. My faith looks up to thee, Thou Lamb of Cal-va-ry, Sav-iour di-vine. Now hear me
2. May thy rich grace impart Strength to my fainting heart, My zeal in-spire; As thou hast

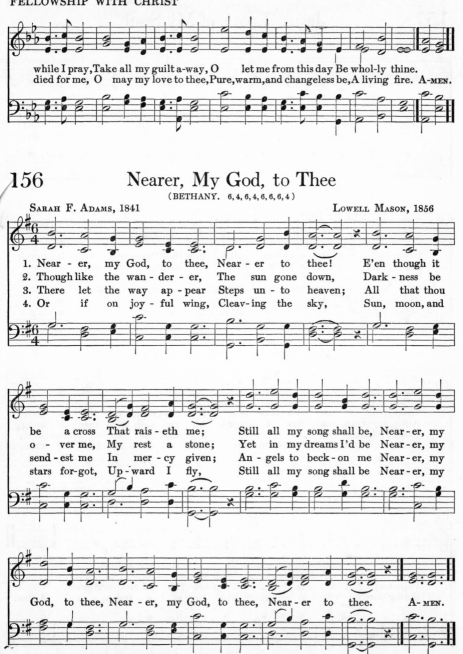

while I pray, Take all my guilt a-way, O   let me from this day Be whol-ly thine. A-MEN.
died for me, O   may my love to thee, Pure, warm, and changeless be, A living fire. A-MEN.

156   Nearer, My God, to Thee

(BETHANY. 6, 4, 6, 4, 6, 6, 6, 4)

SARAH F. ADAMS, 1841   LOWELL MASON, 1856

1. Near - er, my God, to thee, Near - er to thee! E'en though it
2. Though like the wan - der - er, The sun gone down, Dark - ness be
3. There let the way ap - pear Steps un - to heaven; All that thou
4. Or if on joy - ful wing, Cleav-ing the sky, Sun, moon, and

be   a cross That rais - eth me;   Still all my song shall be, Near - er, my
o - ver me, My rest a stone; Yet in my dreams I'd be Near - er, my
send - est me In mer - cy given; An - gels to beck - on me Near - er, my
stars for - got, Up - ward I fly, Still all my song shall be Near - er, my

God, to thee, Near - er, my God, to thee, Near - er to thee. A-MEN.

131

157 Jesus, Lover of My Soul

(HOLLINGSIDE. 7, 7, 7, 7, D.)

CHARLES WESLEY, 1740

JOHN B. DYKES, 1861

1. Je - sus, Lov - er of my soul, Let me to thy bos - om fly,
2. Oth - er ref - uge have I none, Hangs my help - less soul on thee;
3. Thou, O Christ, art all I want, More than all in thee I find;
4. Plen-teous grace with thee is found, Grace to cov - er all my sin;

While the near-er wa - ters roll, While the tem - pest still is high;
Leave, ah, leave me not a - lone, Still sup - port and com - fort me.
Raise the fall - en, cheer the faint, Heal the sick, and lead the blind.
Let the heal-ing streams a - bound; Make and keep me pure with - in.

Hide me, O my Sav - iour, hide, Till the storm of life be past;
All my trust on thee is stayed, All my help from thee I bring;
Just and ho - ly is thy name, I am all un - right-eous - ness;
Thou of life the foun - tain art, Free - ly let me take of thee;

Safe in - to the ha-ven guide, O re - ceive my soul at last.
Cov - er my de - fense-less head With the shad - ow of thy wing.
False and full of sin I am, Thou art full of truth and grace.
Spring thou up with - in my heart, Rise to all e - ter - ni - ty. A-MEN.

Jesus, Lover of My Soul

(MARTYN. 7, 7, 7, 7, D.) *Second Tune*

CHARLES WESLEY, 1740

SIMEON B. MARSH, 1834

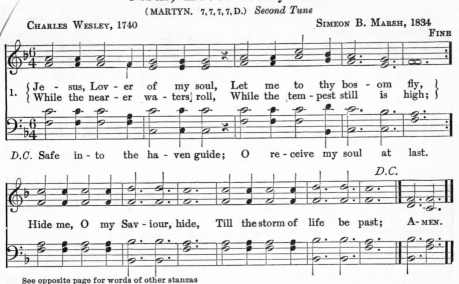

1. Je - sus, Lov - er of my soul, Let me to thy bos - om fly,
   While the near - er wa - ters roll, While the tem - pest still is high;

D.C. Safe in - to the ha - ven guide; O re - ceive my soul at last.

Hide me, O my Sav - iour, hide, Till the storm of life be past; A - MEN.

See opposite page for words of other stanzas

158   Jesus, the Very Thought of Thee

(SAWLEY. C. M.)

Anonymous Latin hymn, 11th century
Translated by EDWARD CASWALL, 1849

JAMES WALCH, 1860

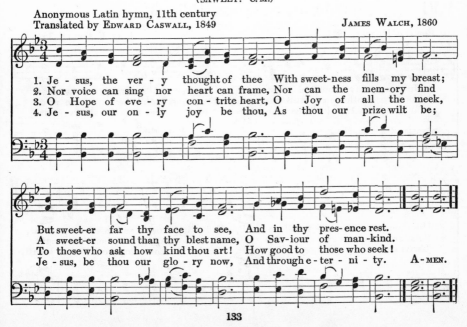

1. Je - sus, the ver - y thought of thee With sweet-ness fills my breast;
2. Nor voice can sing nor heart can frame, Nor can the mem-ory find
3. O Hope of eve - ry con - trite heart, O Joy of all the meek,
4. Je - sus, our on - ly joy be thou, As thou our prize wilt be;

But sweet-er far thy face to see, And in thy pres - ence rest.
A sweet-er sound than thy blest name, O Sav - iour of man - kind.
To those who ask how kind thou art! How good to those who seek!
Je - sus, be thou our glo - ry now, And through e - ter - ni - ty. A - MEN.

133

159 'Mid All the Traffic of the Ways

(ST. AGNES. C.M.)

JOHN OXENHAM, 1917

JOHN B. DYKES, 1866

1. 'Mid all the traf - fic of the ways, Tur - moils with - out, with - in,
2. A lit - tle shrine of qui - et - ness, All sa - cred to thy - self,
3. A lit - tle shel - ter from life's stress, Where I may lay me prone,
4. A lit - tle place of mys - tic grace, Of self and sin swept bare,

Make in my heart a qui - et place, And come and dwell with - in:
Where thou shalt all my soul pos - sess, And I may find my - self:
And bare my soul in lone - li - ness, And know as I am known:
Where I may look up - on thy face, And talk with thee in prayer. A - MEN.

From 'The Vision Splendid.' Copyright, 1917, by George H. Doran Co.

160 Jesus, Saviour, Pilot Me

(PILOT. 7, 7, 7, 7, 7, 7)

EDWARD HOPPER, 1871

JOHN E. GOULD, 1871

1. Je - sus, Sav - iour, pi - lot me, O - ver life's tem - pest - uous sea;
2. As a moth - er stills her child, Thou canst hush the o - cean wild;
3. When at last I near the shore, And the fear - ful break - ers roar

Un - known waves be - fore me roll, Hid - ing rock and treacherous shoal;
Boist - erous waves o - bey thy will When thou sayest to them, 'Be still.'
'Twixt me and the peace - ful rest, Then, while lean - ing on thy breast,

Chart and com-pass came from thee: Je - sus, Sav-iour, pi - lot me.
Won-drous Sov-ereign of the sea, Je - sus, Sav-iour, pi - lot me.
May I hear thee say to me, 'Fear not, I will pi - lot thee.' A - MEN.

161 Father in Heaven, Hear Us Today
(SOUTHAMPTON. Irregular)

CHARLES GORDON AMES, 1828–1912   Anonymous, 1870

1. Fa - ther in heav - en, Hear us to - day; Hal-lowed thy name be,
2. Fa - ther in heav - en, Hear us to - day; Hal-lowed thy name be,
3. Fa - ther in heav - en, Hear us to - day; Hal-lowed thy name be,

Hear us, we pray. O let thy king - dom come, O let thy
Hear us, we pray. Giv - er of dai - ly food, Foun - tain of
Hear us, we pray. Lead us in paths of right, Save us from

will be done, By all be - neath the sun, As in the skies.
truth and good, Be all our hearts im - bued With love like thine.
sin and blight, King of all love and might, Glo - rious for aye. A - MEN.

162 God of Our Youth, to Whom We Yield

(LEST WE FORGET. 8, 8, 8, 8, 8, 8)

WILLIAM BYRON FORBUSH, 1911. Altered   GEORGE F. BLANCHARD, 1898

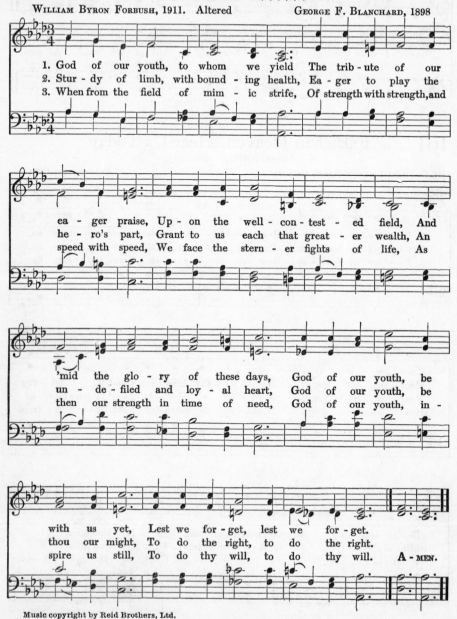

1. God of our youth, to whom we yield The trib-ute of our
2. Stur-dy of limb, with bound-ing health, Ea-ger to play the
3. When from the field of mim-ic strife, Of strength with strength, and

ea-ger praise, Up-on the well-con-test-ed field, And
he-ro's part, Grant to us each that great-er wealth, An
speed with speed, We face the stern-er fights of life, As

'mid the glo-ry of these days, God of our youth, be
un-de-filed and loy-al heart, God of our youth, be
then our strength in time of need, God of our youth, in-

with us yet, Lest we for-get, lest we for-get.
thou our might, To do the right, to do the right.
spire us still, To do thy will, to do thy will. A-MEN.

Music copyright by Reid Brothers, Ltd.

163 Strong of Body, High of Spirit

(PISANI. 8, 7, 8, 7, D.)

RICHARD FELTON

UMBERTO PISANI

1. Strong of bod-y, high of spir-it, Val-iant youth goes strid-ing forth;
2. Lord who liv-eth, youth un-dy-ing, Thou who know-est this our path,

His the sea-sons that in-her-it All the treas-ure trove of earth.
Move a-mong us, still de-fy-ing Nights of fear and gulfs of wrath.

Sky and sun-light, dream and la-bor, Moun-tain crag and spark-ling shore,
Though our years are far and rang-ing, We are young who walk with truth,

Love of God and love of neigh-bor, These are his for-ev-er-more.
Hearts at peace that know no chang-ing, These are thine, im-mor-tal youth. A-MEN.

Music copyright by The American Tract Society

164 The Body, Lord, Is Ours to Keep

(DOLUT. 8, 8, 8, 8, 8, 5)

ELEANOR B. STOCK, 1929

SEBASTIAN W. MEYER, 1909

1. The bod - y, Lord, is ours to keep In glow-ing health and strength for thee,
2. The mind, O Lord, is ours to keep In clean - li - ness and pu - ri - ty,
3. The soul, O Lord, is ours to keep In close com - pan - ion - ship with thee,

That through its life thy life may live, Thy will move strong and swift and free;
That eve - ry tho't and word and deed May own it - self a - kin to thee;
That soul is bod - y, mind and heart, And these are but a u - ni - ty;

My bod - y, Lord, is thine to keep, Strong and swift and free.
My mind, O Lord, is thine to keep, Clean and pure and free.
My soul, O Lord, is thine to keep In com - rade-ship with thee. A-MEN.

Words used by permission of the author. Copyright by Mary S. Dickie, from 'Singing Pathways,' published by Powell and White

165 For Mercy, Courage, Kindness, Mirth

(MELROSE. L. M.)

LAURENCE BINYON, 1869–

FREDERICK C. MAKER, 1844–1927

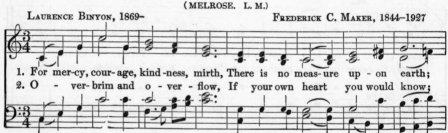

1. For mer-cy, cour-age, kind -ness, mirth, There is no meas-ure up - on earth;
2. O - ver-brim and o - ver - flow, If your own heart you would know;

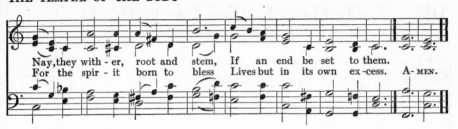

Nay, they with-er, root and stem, If an end be set to them.
For the spir-it born to bless Lives but in its own ex-cess. A-MEN.

166   I Thank Thee, Lord, for Life

(ROCHESTER. 6, 8, 8, 8, 8)

J. WILLIAMS BUTCHER, 1919   GEORGE HENRY DAY, 1929

1. I thank thee, Lord, for life, For thou hast made and dow-ered me With
2. I thank thee, Lord, for health, For day by day the joy of life Runs
3. I thank thee, Lord, for strength, For, as years pass, a full-er sense Of
4. I thank thee, Lord, for hope, What yet shall be I may not know; The

gifts of hear-ing, sight, and speech, With mind a-lert and
through my veins with keen de-light, And I am glad a-
power to dare and do is mine; In ac-tive limb and
un-seen days will chang-es bring: But thro' them all hope's

will that's free: Guard all from harm, I do be-seech.
mid its strife: Keep my tho'ts pure, guide me a-right.
mus-cle tense I feel my strength: let it be thine.
star shall glow, And I shall have my song to sing. A-MEN.

167 Lord of Health, Thou Life Within Us

(IL BUON PASTOR. 8,7,8,7,7)

PERCY DEARMER, 1925   Adapted from a Melody in 'Canzuns Spirituælas,' 1765

UNISON

1. Lord of health, thou life with-in us, Strength of all that
2. Praise for all our work and lei-sure, Mirth and games and
3. Praise for joys, for sor-rows e-ven, All that leads us
4. Help us now, each mo-ment fill-ing, Keep us true to

lives and grows, Love that meets our hearts to win us, Beau-ty that a-
jol-li-ty, Stu-dy, sci-ence, all the treas-ure That is stored for
up to thee; Most of all that out from heav-en Came thy Son to
thee and wise; May our work be keen and will-ing, Power and ser-vice

round us glows, Take the praise that brims and flows.
mem-o-ry, Skill of mind and hand and eye.
set us free, Came to show us what to be.
be our prize, Till to thy far hills we rise. A-MEN.

Words and music from 'Songs of Praise,' copyright by Oxford University Press

168 Welcome, Morning, Bright and Blue

(ENGLAND'S LANE. 7,7,7,7,7,7)

WILLIAM G. TARRANT, 1853–   Arranged from an English Melody, 1925

1. 'Wel-come, morn-ing, bright and blue!' Sings the man with work to do.
2. Hap-py hours, when men com-bined Full-est joys to-geth-er find;
3. When the sun is sink-ing low Back a-gain the toil-ers go,
4. Is there in our na-tive land E-vil heart, or i-dle hand?

Words copyright by William Tarrant
Music from 'Songs of Praise,' copyright by Oxford University Press

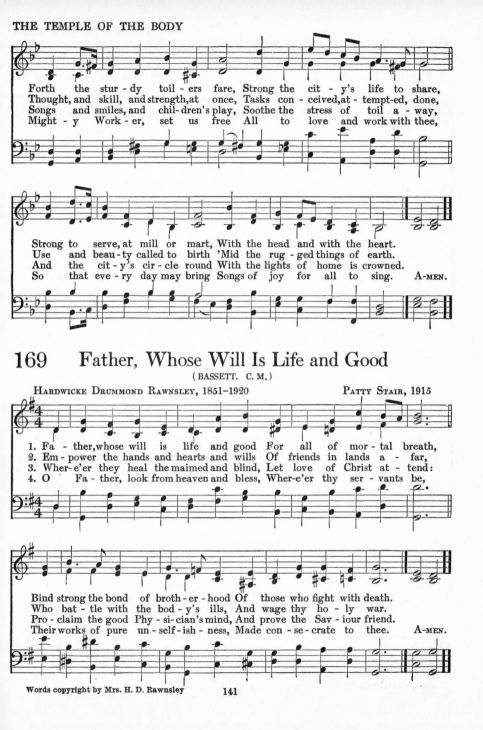

Forth   the   stur - dy   toil - ers   fare, Strong the   cit - y's   life to share,
Thought, and   skill, and strength, at   once, Tasks con - ceived, at - tempt-ed, done,
Songs   and smiles, and   chil-dren's play, Soothe the   stress of   toil a - way,
Might - y   Work - er,   set   us   free   All   to   love   and work with thee,

Strong to   serve, at mill or   mart, With the head and with the heart.
Use   and beau - ty called to   birth 'Mid the rug - ged things of earth.
And   the   cit - y's cir - cle round With the lights of home is crowned.
So   that eve - ry day may bring Songs of joy for all to sing. A-MEN.

169   Father, Whose Will Is Life and Good
(BASSETT. C. M,)

HARDWICKE DRUMMOND RAWNSLEY, 1851–1920   PATTY STAIR, 1915

1. Fa - ther, whose will is   life and good For   all   of   mor - tal breath,
2. Em - power the hands and hearts and wills Of   friends in   lands a - far,
3. Wher - e'er they heal the maimed and blind, Let love   of   Christ at - tend:
4. O   Fa - ther, look from heaven and bless, Wher-e'er thy   ser - vants be,

Bind strong the bond   of broth - er - hood Of   those who fight with death.
Who bat - tle with the bod - y's ills, And wage thy ho - ly   war.
Pro - claim the good Phy - si - cian's mind, And prove the Sav - iour friend.
Their works of pure   un - self - ish - ness, Made con - se - crate to   thee. A-MEN.

Words copyright by Mrs. H. D. Rawnsley   141

170 God, Who Created Me

(RUGBY. 6, 6, 6, 6, D.)

HENRY C. BEECHING, 1895   FREDERICK H. CANDLYN, 1927

1. God, who cre - a - ted me Nim - ble and light of limb,
In three el - e - ments free, To run, to ride, to swim;
Not when the sense is dim, But now from the heart of
joy, I would re - mem - ber him: Take the thanks of a boy.

2. Je - sus, King and Lord, Whose are my foes to fight,
Gird me with thy sword, Swift and sharp and bright.
Thee would I serve if I might, And con - quer if I
can: From day - dawn till night, Take the strength of a man.

3. Spir - it of love and truth, Breath - ing in gross - er clay,
The light and flame of youth, De-light of men in the fray,
Wis - dom in strength's de - cay; From pain, strife, wrong to be
free, This best gift I pray, Take my spir - it to thee. A-MEN.

171 Father, Who on Man Doth Shower

(QUEM PASTORES LAUDAVERE. 8, 8, 8, 7)

PERCY DEARMER, 1906

German Folk Song, 15th Century

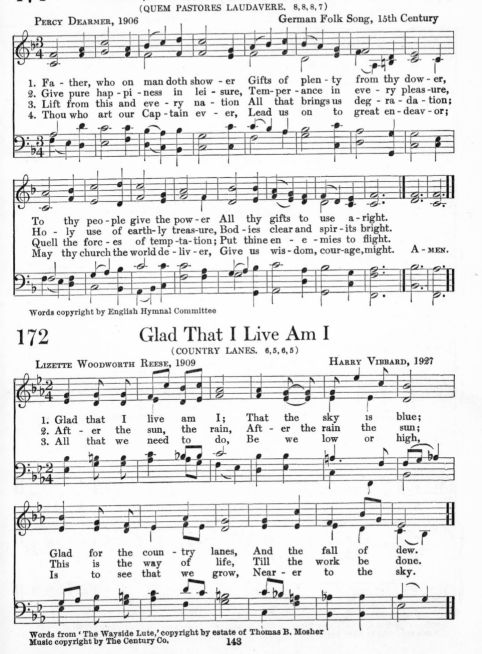

1. Fa - ther, who on man doth show - er Gifts of plen - ty from thy dow - er,
2. Give pure hap - pi - ness in lei - sure, Tem - per - ance in eve - ry pleas - ure,
3. Lift from this and eve - ry na - tion All that brings us deg - ra - da - tion;
4. Thou who art our Cap - tain ev - er, Lead us on to great en - deav - or;

To thy peo - ple give the pow - er All thy gifts to use a - right.
Ho - ly use of earth - ly treas - ure, Bod - ies clear and spir - its bright.
Quell the forc - es of temp - ta - tion; Put thine en - e - mies to flight.
May thy church the world de - liv - er, Give us wis - dom, cour - age, might. A - MEN.

Words copyright by English Hymnal Committee

172 Glad That I Live Am I

(COUNTRY LANES. 6, 5, 6, 5)

LIZETTE WOODWORTH REESE, 1909

HARRY VIBBARD, 1927

1. Glad that I live am I; That the sky is blue;
2. Aft - er the sun, the rain, Aft - er the rain the sun;
3. All that we need to do, Be we low or high,

Glad for the coun - try lanes, And the fall of dew.
This is the way of life, Till the work be done.
Is to see that we grow, Near - er to the sky.

Words from 'The Wayside Lute,' copyright by estate of Thomas B. Mosher
Music copyright by The Century Co.

173   Temper My Spirit, O Lord

(AGNI. Irregular)

JEAN UNTERMEYER, 1921   GRACE WILBUR CONANT, 1927

1. Tem - per my spir - it, O Lord, Keep it long in the fire;

Make it one with the flame, let it share That up - reach-ing de - sire.

Grasp it, thy - self, O my God; Swing it straight-er and high - er!

Tem-per my spir - it, O Lord, Tem-per my spir-it, O Lord. A - MEN.

174   O Jesus, Once a Nazareth Boy

(GABRIEL. C. M. D.)

Anonymous

GOTTFRIED W. FINK, 1842

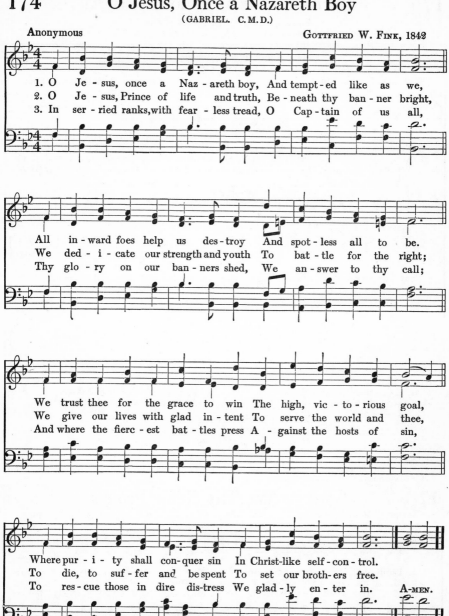

1. O Je - sus, once a Naz - areth boy, And tempt - ed like as we,
2. O Je - sus, Prince of life and truth, Be - neath thy ban - ner bright,
3. In ser - ried ranks, with fear - less tread, O Cap - tain of us all,

All in - ward foes help us des - troy And spot - less all to be.
We ded - i - cate our strength and youth To bat - tle for the right;
Thy glo - ry on our ban - ners shed, We an - swer to thy call;

We trust thee for the grace to win The high, vic - to - rious goal,
We give our lives with glad in - tent To serve the world and thee,
And where the fierc - est bat - tles press A - gainst the hosts of sin,

Where pur - i - ty shall con - quer sin In Christ-like self - con - trol.
To die, to suf - fer and be spent To set our broth - ers free.
To res - cue those in dire dis - tress We glad - ly en - ter in. A-MEN.

175 Father in Heaven, Who Lovest All

Land of our birth, we pledge to thee
Our love and toil in years to be,
When we are grown and take our place
As men and women with our race.

(SAXBY. L. M.)

RUDYARD KIPLING, 1906   TIMOTHY R. MATTHEWS, 1883

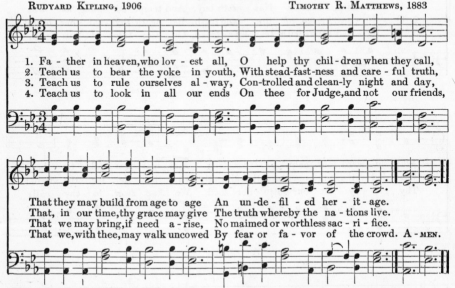

1. Fa - ther in heaven, who lov - est all, O help thy chil - dren when they call,
2. Teach us to bear the yoke in youth, With stead-fast-ness and care - ful truth,
3. Teach us to rule ourselves al - way, Con-trolled and clean-ly night and day,
4. Teach us to look in all our ends On thee for Judge, and not our friends,

That they may build from age to age An un-de - fil - ed her - it - age.
That, in our time, thy grace may give The truth whereby the na - tions live.
That we may bring, if need a - rise, No maimed or worthless sac - ri - fice.
That we, with thee, may walk uncowed By fear or fa - vor of the crowd. A - MEN.

5 Teach us the strength that cannot seek,
By deed or thought, to hurt the weak,
That, under thee, we may possess
Man's strength to comfort man's distress.

6 Teach us delight in simple things,
And mirth that has no bitter springs,
Forgiveness free of evil done,
And love to all men 'neath the sun.

Land of our birth, our faith, our pride,
For whose dear sake our fathers died;
O Motherland, we pledge to thee
Head, heart, and hand through the years to be.

Rudyard Kipling in 'Puck of Pook's Hill,' 1906
Printed by his permission and that of Doubleday, Doran & Co., the publishers
Music copyright by Novello and Co., Ltd.

176 Lord, as We Thy Name Profess

EDWIN P. PARKER, 1890   (ST. BEES. 7, 7, 7, 7)   JOHN B. DYKES, 1862

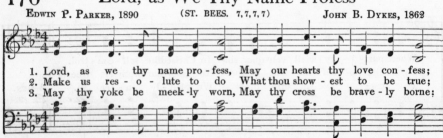

1. Lord, as we thy name pro-fess, May our hearts thy love con-fess;
2. Make us res - o - lute to do What thou show - est to be true;
3. May thy yoke be meek-ly worn, May thy cross be brave - ly borne;

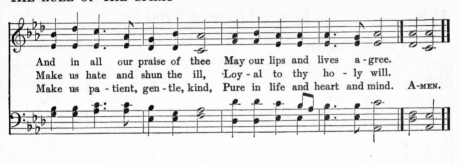

And in all our praise of thee May our lips and lives a-gree.
Make us hate and shun the ill, Loy-al to thy ho-ly will.
Make us pa-tient, gen-tle, kind, Pure in life and heart and mind. A-MEN.

177 I Would Be True

(PEEK. 11, 10, 11, 10)

HOWARD ARNOLD WALTER, 1917   JOSEPH YATES PEEK, 1911

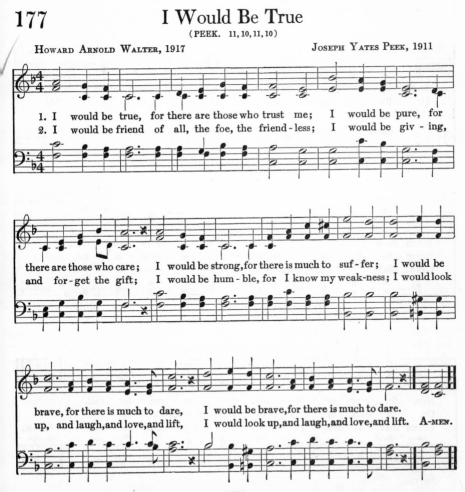

1. I would be true, for there are those who trust me; I would be pure, for
2. I would be friend of all, the foe, the friend-less; I would be giv-ing,

there are those who care; I would be strong, for there is much to suf-fer; I would be
and for-get the gift; I would be hum-ble, for I know my weak-ness; I would look

brave, for there is much to dare, I would be brave, for there is much to dare.
up, and laugh, and love, and lift, I would look up, and laugh, and love, and lift. A-MEN.

178 In the Hour of Trial

(PENITENCE. 6, 5, 6, 5, D.)

JAMES MONTGOMERY, 1834

SPENCER LANE, 1879

1. In the hour of tri - al, Je - sus, plead for me,
2. With for - bid - den pleas - ures Would this vain world charm,
3. Should thy mer - cy send me Sor - row, toil and woe,

Lest by base de - ni - al I de - part from thee;
Or its sor - did treas - ures Spread to work me harm;
Or should pain at - tend me On my path be - low,

When thou see'st me wav - er, With a look re - call,
Bring to my re - mem - brance Sad Geth - sem - a - ne,
Grant that I may nev - er Fail thy hand to see;

Nor, for fear or fa - vor, Suf - fer me to fall.
Or, in dark - er sem - blance, Cross-crowned Cal - va - ry.
Grant that I may ev - er Cast my care on thee. A-MEN.

179 Christian, Dost Thou See Them

(ST. ANDREW OF CRETE. 6, 5, 6, 5, D.)

Andrew of Crete, 660–732
Translated by John M. Neale, 1862

John B. Dykes, 1868

1. Chris - tian, dost thou see them On the ho - ly ground,
2. Chris - tian, dost thou feel them, How they work with - in,
3. Chris - tian, dost thou hear them, How they speak thee fair,
4. 'Well I know thy trou - ble, O my ser - vant true;

How the powers of dark - ness Com - pass thee a - round?
Striv - ing, tempt - ing, lur - ing, Goad - ing in - to sin?
'Al - ways fast and vig - il, Al - ways watch and prayer?'
Thou art ver - y wea - ry, I was wea - ry, too;

Chris - tian, up and smite them, Count - ing gain but loss,
Chris - tian, nev - er trem - ble, Nev - er be down - cast;
Chris - tian, an - swer bold - ly, 'While I breathe I pray,'
But that toil shall make thee Some day all mine own,

In the strength that com - eth By the ho - ly cross.
Gird thee for the bat - tle, Watch and pray and fast.
Peace shall fol - low bat - tle, Night shall end in day.
And the end of sor - row Shall be near my throne.' A-men.

180 Stand Fast for Christ Thy Saviour

(NEILSON. 7, 6, 8, 6, D.)

WALTER J. MATHAMS, 1913

JOHN H. GOWER, 1894

1. Stand fast for Christ thy Sav - iour, Stand fast, what- e'er be - tide;
2. Strong-found-ed like a light - house, That stands the storm and shock,
3. Stout - heart- ed like a sol - dier, Who nev - er leaves the fight,
4. Stand fast for Christ thy Sav - iour, He once stood fast for thee,

Keep thou the faith, un- stained, un-shamed, By keep - ing at his side;
So be thy soul as if it shared The gran - ite of the rock;
But meets the foe - man face to face And meets him with his might;
And stand - eth still, and still shall stand For all e - ter - ni - ty;

Be faith - ful, ev - er faith - ful, Wher-e'er thy lot be cast;
Then far be - yond the break - ers Let thy calm light be cast;
So bear thee in thy bat - tles Un - til the war be past;
Be faith - ful, O be faith - ful To love so true, so vast;

Stand fast for Christ thy Sav- iour, Stand faith - ful to the last. A - MEN.

181 O God of Truth, Whose Living Word

(QUEENSWOOD. C. M. D.)

THOMAS HUGHES, 1859

SIDNEY HANN, 1919

1. O God of truth, whose liv-ing word Up-holds what-e'er hath breath,
2. Fain would we join that blest ar-ray, And fol-low in the might
3. O God of truth, for whom we long, O thou that hear-est prayer,

Look down on thy cre-a-tion, Lord, En-slaved by sin and death.
Of him, the Faith-ful and the True, In rai-ment clean and white.
Do thine own bat-tle in our hearts, And slay the false-hood there.

Set up thy stand-ard, Lord, that we, Who claim a heaven-ly birth,
Yet who can fight for truth and God, En-thralled by lies and sin?
So, tried in thy re-fin-ing fire, From eve-ry lie set free,

May march with thee to smite the lies That vex the groan-ing earth.
He who would wage such war on earth Must first be true with-in.
In us thy per-fect truth shall dwell, And we may fight for thee. A-MEN.

Words and music copyright by Congregational Union of England and Wales

182 Be Strong! We Are Not Here to Play

(FORTITUDE. 2,10,10,10)

MALTBIE D. BABCOCK, 1901   DAVID STANLEY SMITH, 1905

1. Be strong! We are not here to play, to dream, to drift; We
have hard work to do and loads to lift; Shun not the strug-gle,
face it, 'tis God's gift. Be strong, be strong!

2. Be strong! Say not the days are e - vil— who's to blame? And
fold the hands and ac - qui - esce— O shame! Stand up, speak out, and
brave -ly, in God's name, Be strong, be strong!

3. Be strong! It mat - ters not how deep en-trenched the wrong, How
hard the bat -tle goes, the day, how long; Faint not, fight on! To -
mor - row comes the song. Be strong, be strong! A-MEN.

Be strong, be

183 Believe Not Those Who Say

(KING EDWARD. S.M.)

ANNE BRONTE, 1850   EDWIN A. SYDENHAM, 1883

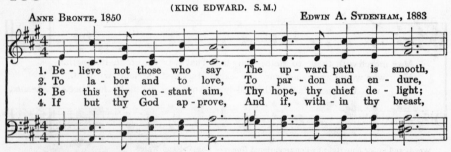

1. Be - lieve not those who say The up - ward path is smooth,
2. To la - bor and to love, To par - don and en - dure,
3. Be this thy con - stant aim, Thy hope, thy chief de - light;
4. If but thy God ap - prove, And if, with - in thy breast,

152

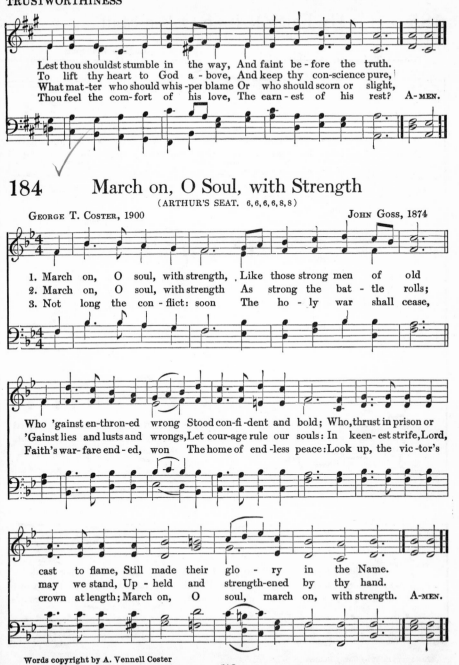

Lest thou shouldst stumble in the way, And faint be - fore the truth.
To lift thy heart to God a - bove, And keep thy con-science pure,
What mat-ter who should whis-per blame Or who should scorn or slight,
Thou feel the com-fort of his love, The earn - est of his rest? A-MEN.

184   March on, O Soul, with Strength

(ARTHUR'S SEAT. 6, 6, 6, 6, 8, 8)

GEORGE T. COSTER, 1900   JOHN GOSS, 1874

1. March on, O soul, with strength, Like those strong men of old
2. March on, O soul, with strength As strong the bat - tle rolls;
3. Not long the con - flict: soon The ho - ly war shall cease,

Who 'gainst en-thron-ed wrong Stood con-fi-dent and bold; Who, thrust in prison or
'Gainst lies and lusts and wrongs, Let cour-age rule our souls: In keen- est strife, Lord,
Faith's war- fare end - ed, won The home of end -less peace: Look up, the vic-tor's

cast to flame, Still made their glo - ry in the Name.
may we stand, Up - held and strength-ened by thy hand.
crown at length; March on, O soul, march on, with strength. A-MEN.

Words copyright by A. Vennell Coster

185 My Faith It Is an Oaken Staff

(MUSWELL HILL. 8, 6, 8, 6, 8, 8, 8, 6)

THOMAS T. LYNCH, 1818–1871

English Folksong
Arranged by CAREY BONNER, 1927

UNISON

1. My faith it is an oak-en staff, The trav-eler's well-loved aid; My faith it is a weap-on stout, The sol-dier's trust-ed blade. I'll trav-el on and still be stirred By si-lent thought or so-cial word, By all my per-ils

2. I have a Guide, and in his steps When trav-elers lone have trod, Wheth-er be-neath was flint-y rock Or yield-ing grass-y sod, They cared not, but with force un-spent, Un-moved by pain they on-ward went, Un-stayed by pleas-ures

3. My faith it is an oak-en staff, O, let me on it lean; My faith it is a trust-y sword, May false-hood find it keen, Thy spir-it, Lord, to me im-part, O, make me what thou ev-er art, Of pa-tient and cour-

154

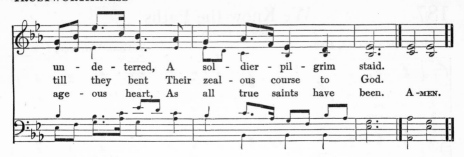

un - de - terred, A sol - dier - pil - grim staid.
till they bent Their zeal - ous course to God.
age - ous heart, As all true saints have been. A -MEN.

186 The Gray Hills Taught Me Patience
(MANCHESTER. 7, 6, 7, 6)

ALLEN EASTMAN CROSS, 1926   G. WARING STEBBINS, 1927

1. The gray hills taught me pa - tience, The wa - ters taught me prayer; The
2. The calm skies made me qui - et, The high stars made me still; The
3. Thy soul is on the tem - pest, Thy cour - age rides the air. Through

flight of birds un - fold - ed The mar - vel of thy care.
bolts of thun - der taught me The light - ning of thy will.
heaven or hell I'll fol - low; I must— and so I dare! A -MEN.

187 We Know the Paths

(DEED. 10, 10, 10, 4)

John Drinkwater, 1882–

T. Carl Whitmer, 1930

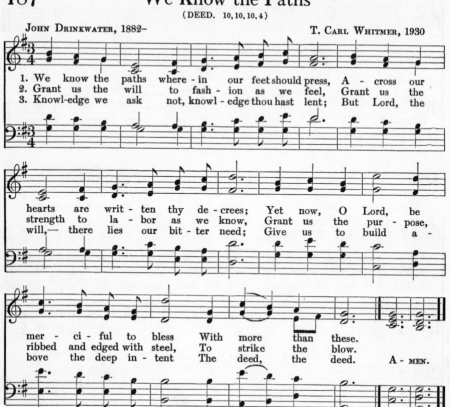

1. We know the paths where-in our feet should press, A - cross our
2. Grant us the will to fash - ion as we feel, Grant us the
3. Knowl-edge we ask not, knowl - edge thou hast lent; But Lord, the

hearts are writ - ten thy de - crees; Yet now, O Lord, be
strength to la - bor as we know, Grant us the pur - pose,
will,— there lies our bit - ter need; Give us to build a -

mer - ci - ful to bless With more than these.
ribbed and edged with steel, To strike the blow.
bove the deep in - tent The deed, the deed. A - men.

Words copyright by Houghton Mifflin Co.
Music copyright by The Century Co.

188 O Son of Man, Thou Madest Known

(BROOKFIELD. L. M.)

Milton S. Littlefield, 1916

Thomas B. Southgate, 1855

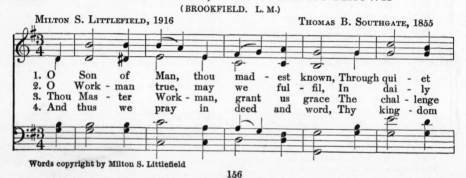

1. O Son of Man, thou mad - est known, Through qui - et
2. O Work - man true, may we ful - fil, In dai - ly
3. Thou Mas - ter Work - man, grant us grace The chal - lenge
4. And thus we pray in deed and word, Thy king - dom

Words copyright by Milton S. Littlefield

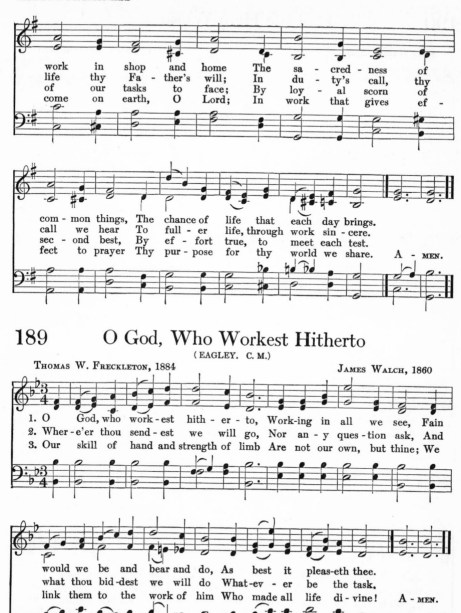

work in shop and home The sa - cred - ness of
life thy Fa - ther's will; In du - ty's call, thy
of our tasks to face; By loy - al scorn of
come on earth, O Lord; In work that gives ef -

com - mon things, The chance of life that each day brings.
call we hear To full - er life, through work sin - cere.
sec - ond best, By ef - fort true, to meet each test.
fect to prayer Thy pur - pose for thy world we share. A - MEN.

189   O God, Who Workest Hitherto
(EAGLEY. C. M.)

THOMAS W. FRECKLETON, 1884

JAMES WALCH, 1860

1. O God, who work - est hith - er - to, Work-ing in all we see, Fain
2. Wher - e'er thou send - est we will go, Nor an - y ques - tion ask, And
3. Our skill of hand and strength of limb Are not our own, but thine; We

would we be and bear and do, As best it pleas-eth thee.
what thou bid - dest we will do What-ev - er be the task.
link them to the work of him Who made all life di - vine! A - MEN.

190 Hail the Hero Workers

(ROSMORE. 6, 5, 6, 5, D. With Refrain)

ANNA GARLIN SPENCER, 1851–   HENRY G. TREMBATH, 1893

1. Hail the he-ro work-ers Of the might-y past! They whose labor build-ed
All the things that last; Tho'ts of wis-est mean-ing, Deeds of no-blest right,
Pa-tient toil in weakness, Struggles in the night; Hail, then, no-ble workers,
Build-ers of the past, All whose lives have blest us With the gains that last.

2. Hail ye, he-ro work-ers, Who to-day do hear Du-ty's myr-iad voic-es,
Sounding high and clear; Ye who quick re-spond-ing, Haste ye to your task,
Be it grand or sim-ple, Ye for-get to ask; Hail ye, no-ble workers,
Build-ers of to-day, Who life's treasure gath-er, That shall last al-way.

3. Hail ye, he-ro work-ers, Ye who yet shall come, When to this world's calling
All our lips are dumb. Ye shall build more no-bly, If our work be true,
As we pass life's treas-ure On from old to new. Hail ye, then, all workers,
Of all lands and time, One brave band of he-roes, With one task sub-lime. A-MEN.

REFRAIN

191 Jesus, Thou Divine Companion

(LOVE DIVINE. 8, 7, 8, 7, D.)

HENRY VAN DYKE, 1909

GEORGE F. LE JEUNE, 1872

1. Je - sus, thou di - vine Com - pan - ion, By thy low - ly hu - man birth
2. They who tread the path of la - bor Fol - low where thy feet have trod;
3. Eve - ry task, how - ev - er sim - ple, Sets the soul that does it free;

Thou hast come to join the work - ers, Bur - den - bear - ers of the earth.
They who work with - out com - plain - ing Do the ho - ly will of God.
Eve - ry deed of love and kind - ness Done to man is done to thee.

Thou, the Car - pen - ter of Naz - areth, Toil - ing for thy dai - ly food,
Thou, the Peace that pass - eth knowl - edge, Dwell - est in the dai - ly strife;
Je - sus, thou di - vine Com - pan - ion, Help us all to work our best;

By thy pa - tience and thy cour - age, Thou hast taught us toil is good.
Thou, the Bread of heaven, art bro - ken In the sac - ra - ment of life.
Bless us in our dai - ly la - bor, Lead us to our Sab - bath rest. A-MEN.

192 When Through the Whirl of Wheels

(INDUSTRY. 11, 10, 11, 10)

G. A. STUDDERT–KENNEDY, 1883–1929   WILLIAM LESTER, 1927

1. When thro' the whirl of wheels, and en-gines hum-ming, Pa-tient-ly
2. When thro' the night the fur-nace fires a-flar-ing, Shoot-ing out
3. When in the depths the pa-tient min-er striv-ing, Feels in his
4. When on the sweat of la-bor and its sor-row, Toil-ing in
5. Then will he come with meek-ness for his glo-ry, God in a

power-ful for the sons of men, Peals like a trum-pet
tongues of flame like leap-ing blood, Speak to the heart of
arms the vig-or of the Lord, Strikes for a king-dom
twi-light flick-er-ing and dim, Flames out the sun-shine
work-man's jack-et as be-fore, Liv-ing a-gain th' e-

prom-ise of his com-ing, Who in the clouds is pledged to come a-gain,
Love, a-live and dar-ing, Sing of the bound-less en-er-gy of God,
and his King's ar-riv-ing, Hold-ing his pick more splen-did than the sword,
of the great to-mor-row, When all the world looks up be-cause of him,
ter-nal gos-pel sto-ry, Sweeping the shavings from his work-shop floor,

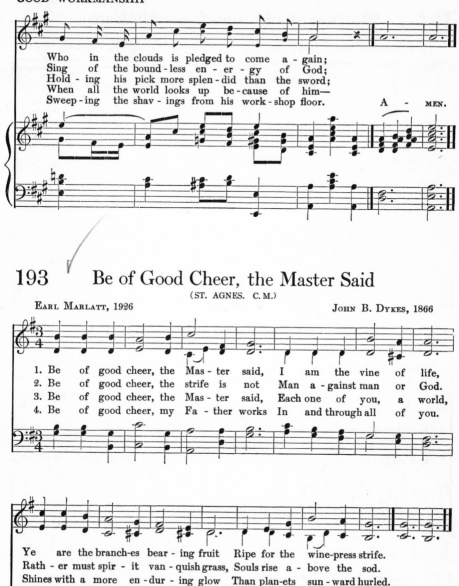

Who in the clouds is pledged to come a - gain;
Sing of the bound - less en - er - gy of God;
Hold - ing his pick more splen - did than the sword;
When all the world looks up be - cause of him—
Sweep - ing the shav - ings from his work - shop floor.   A - MEN.

193   Be of Good Cheer, the Master Said

(ST. AGNES. C.M.)

EARL MARLATT, 1926

JOHN B. DYKES, 1866

1. Be of good cheer, the Mas - ter said, I am the vine of life,
2. Be of good cheer, the strife is not Man a - gainst man or God.
3. Be of good cheer, the Mas - ter said, Each one of you, a world,
4. Be of good cheer, my Fa - ther works In and through all of you.

Ye are the branch - es bear - ing fruit Ripe for the wine - press strife.
Rath - er must spir - it van - quish grass, Souls rise a - bove the sod.
Shines with a more en - dur - ing glow Than plan - ets sun - ward hurled.
I am his Son and ye his sons, Broth - ers in work to do.   A - MEN.

Words copyright by Earl Marlatt

194 We Bear the Strain of Earthly Care

(SERENITY. C. M.)

OZORA STEARNS DAVIS, 1909   Arranged from WILLIAM V. WALLACE, 1855

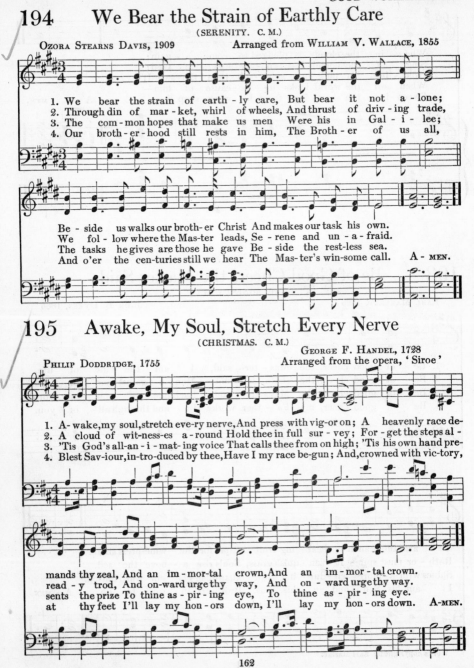

1. We bear the strain of earth-ly care, But bear it not a-lone;
2. Through din of mar-ket, whirl of wheels, And thrust of driv-ing trade,
3. The com-mon hopes that make us men Were his in Gal-i-lee;
4. Our broth-er-hood still rests in him, The Broth-er of us all,

Be-side us walks our broth-er Christ And makes our task his own.
We fol-low where the Mas-ter leads, Se-rene and un-a-fraid.
The tasks he gives are those he gave Be-side the rest-less sea.
And o'er the cen-tur-ies still we hear The Mas-ter's win-some call. A-MEN.

195 Awake, My Soul, Stretch Every Nerve

(CHRISTMAS. C. M.)

PHILIP DODDRIDGE, 1755   GEORGE F. HANDEL, 1728
Arranged from the opera, 'Siroe'

1. A-wake, my soul, stretch eve-ry nerve, And press with vig-or on; A heavenly race de-
2. A cloud of wit-ness-es a-round Hold thee in full sur-vey; For-get the steps al-
3. 'Tis God's all-an-i-mat-ing voice That calls thee from on high; 'Tis his own hand pre-
4. Blest Sav-iour, in-tro-duced by thee, Have I my race be-gun; And, crowned with vic-tory,

mands thy zeal, And an im-mor-tal crown, And an im-mor-tal crown.
read-y trod, And on-ward urge thy way, And on-ward urge thy way.
sents the prize To thine as-pir-ing eye, To thine as-pir-ing eye.
at thy feet I'll lay my hon-ors down, I'll lay my hon-ors down. A-MEN.

O Jesus, I Have Promised

(ANGEL'S STORY. 7, 6, 7, 6, D.)

JOHN E. BODE, 1868

ARTHUR H. MANN, 1883

1. O Je - sus, I have prom - ised To serve thee to the end;
2. O let me feel thee near me, The world is ev - er near;
3. O let me hear thee speak - ing In ac - cents clear and still,
4. O Je - sus, thou hast prom - ised To all who fol - low thee,

Be thou for - ev - er near me, My Mas - ter and my Friend;
I see the sights that daz - zle, The tempt - ing sounds I hear:
A - bove the storms of pas - sion, The mur - murs of self - will:
That where thou art in glo - ry There shall thy ser - vant be;

I shall not fear the bat - tle If thou art by my side,
My foes are ev - er near me, A - round me and with - in;
O speak to re - as - sure me, To has - ten or con - trol;
And, Je - sus, I have prom - ised To serve thee to the end;

Nor wan - der from the path - way, If thou wilt be my Guide.
But, Je - sus, draw thou near - er, And shield my soul from sin.
O speak, and make me lis - ten, Thou Guard-ian of my soul.
O give me grace to fol - low, My Mas - ter and my Friend. A-MEN.

Music copyright by A. H. Mann

163

197 O Master, Let Me Walk with Thee
(MARYTON. L. M.)

Washington Gladden, 1879

Henry Percy Smith, 1874

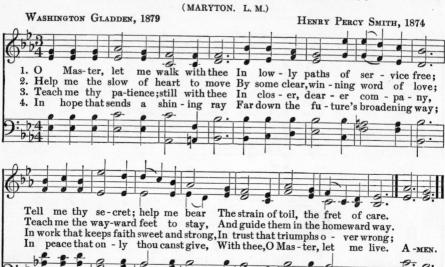

1. O Mas-ter, let me walk with thee In low - ly paths of ser - vice free;
2. Help me the slow of heart to move By some clear, win - ning word of love;
3. Teach me thy pa-tience; still with thee In clos - er, dear - er com - pa - ny,
4. In hope that sends a shin - ing ray Far down the fu - ture's broadening way;

Tell me thy se - cret; help me bear The strain of toil, the fret of care.
Teach me the way-ward feet to stay, And guide them in the homeward way.
In work that keeps faith sweet and strong, In trust that triumphs o - ver wrong;
In peace that on - ly thou canst give, With thee, O Mas - ter, let me live. A - men.

198 Take My Life, and Let It Be
(ELLINGHAM. 7, 7, 7, 7)

Frances R. Havergal, 1874

Nathaniel S. Godfrey, 1881

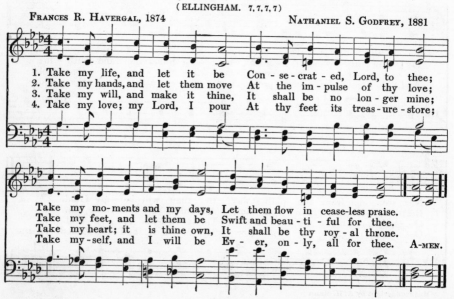

1. Take my life, and let it be Con - se - crat - ed, Lord, to thee;
2. Take my hands, and let them move At the im - pulse of thy love;
3. Take my will, and make it thine, It shall be no lon - ger mine;
4. Take my love; my Lord, I pour At thy feet its treas - ure - store;

Take my mo - ments and my days, Let them flow in cease-less praise.
Take my feet, and let them be Swift and beau - ti - ful for thee.
Take my heart; it is thine own, It shall be thy roy - al throne.
Take my-self, and I will be Ev - er, on - ly, all for thee. A - men.

199 Lead On, O King Eternal

(LANCASHIRE. 7, 6, 7, 6, D.)

ERNEST W. SHURTLEFF, 1888

HENRY SMART, 1836

1. Lead on, O King E - ter - nal, The day of march has come;
2. Lead on, O King E - ter - nal, Till sin's fierce war shall cease,
3. Lead on, O King E - ter - nal, We fol - low, not with fears,

Hence-forth in fields of con - quest Thy tents shall be our home.
And ho - li - ness shall whis - per The sweet A - men of peace.
For glad - ness breaks like morn - ing Wher - e'er thy face ap - pears.

Through days of prep - a - ra - tion Thy grace has made us strong,
For not with swords, loud clash - ing, Nor roll of stir - ring drums,
Thy cross is lift - ed o'er us, We jour - ney in its light;

And now, O King E - ter - nal, We lift our bat - tle - song.
With deeds of love and mer - cy, The heaven-ly king - dom comes.
The crown a - waits the con - quest; Lead on, O God of might. A-MEN.

200   O Star of Truth, Down-Shining

(MARTINEAU. 7, 6, 7, 6, D.)

MINOT J. SAVAGE, 1841–1918

J. R. FAIRLAMB, 1886
Harmonized by GEORGE HENRY DAY, 1930

UNISON

1. O star of truth, down - shin - ing, Thro' clouds of doubt and fear,
2. I know thy bless - ed ra - diance Can nev - er lead a - stray,
3. The bleed - ing feet of mar - tyrs Thy toil - some road have trod;

I ask but 'neath thy guid - ance My path - way may ap - pear.
How - ev - er an - cient cus - tom May tread some oth - er way.
But fires of hu - man pas - sion May light the way to God.

HARMONY

How - ev - er long the jour - ney, How hard so - e'er it be,
E'en if through un - trod des - erts, Or o - ver track - less sea,
Then to my high al - le - giance I must not faith - less be:

Though I be lone and wea - ry, Lead on, I'll fol - low thee.
Though I be lone and wea - ry, Lead on, I'll fol - low thee.
Thro' life or death, for - ev - er, Lead on, I'll fol - low thee.   A - MEN.

201 Stand Up, Stand Up for Jesus

(WEBB. 7, 6, 7, 6, D.)

GEORGE DUFFIELD, 1858

GEORGE J. WEBB, 1837

1. Stand up, stand up for Je - sus, Ye sol - diers of the cross;
2. Stand up, stand up for Je - sus, The trum - pet call o - bey;
3. Stand up, stand up for Je - sus, Stand in his strength a - lone;
4. Stand up, stand up for Je - sus, The strife will not be long;

Lift high his roy - al ban - ner, It must not suf - fer loss;
Forth to the might - y con - flict In this his glo - rious day:
The arm of flesh will fail you, Ye dare not trust your own;
This day the noise of bat - tle, The next the vic - tor's song:

From vic - tory un - to vic - tory His ar - my he shall lead,
Ye that are men now serve him A - gainst un - num-bered foes;
Put on the gos - pel ar - mor, Each piece put on with prayer;
To him that o - ver - com - eth A crown of life shall be;

Till eve - ry foe is van-quished, And Christ is Lord in - deed.
Let cour - age rise with dan - ger, And strength to strength op - pose.
Where du - ty calls, or dan - ger, Be nev - er want - ing there.
He with the King of Glo - ry Shall reign e - ter - nal - ly. A-MEN.

202
Who is On the Lord's Side

(ARMAGEDDON. 6,5,6,5, D. With Refrain)

FRANCES R. HAVERGAL, 1877. Altered

Arranged by JOHN GOSS, 1871

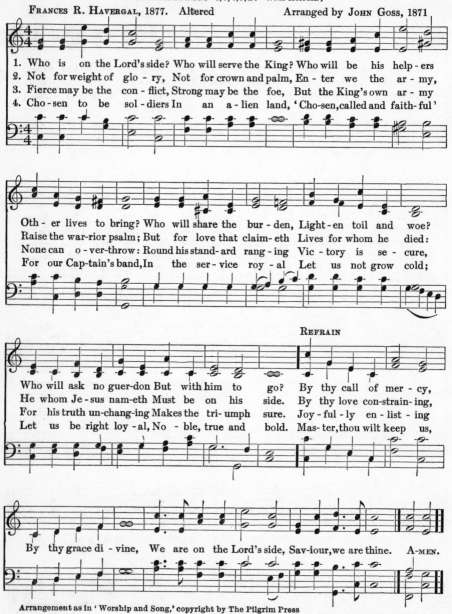

1. Who is on the Lord's side? Who will serve the King? Who will be his help-ers
2. Not for weight of glo-ry, Not for crown and palm, En-ter we the ar-my,
3. Fierce may be the con-flict, Strong may be the foe, But the King's own ar-my
4. Cho-sen to be sol-diers In an a-lien land, 'Cho-sen, called and faith-ful'

Oth-er lives to bring? Who will share the bur-den, Light-en toil and woe?
Raise the war-rior psalm; But for love that claim-eth Lives for whom he died:
None can o-ver-throw: Round his stand-ard rang-ing Vic-tory is se-cure,
For our Cap-tain's band, In the ser-vice roy-al Let us not grow cold;

REFRAIN

Who will ask no guer-don But with him to go? By thy call of mer-cy,
He whom Je-sus nam-eth Must be on his side. By thy love con-strain-ing,
For his truth un-chang-ing Makes the tri-umph sure. Joy-ful-ly en-list-ing
Let us be right loy-al, No-ble, true and bold. Mas-ter, thou wilt keep us,

By thy grace di-vine, We are on the Lord's side, Sav-iour, we are thine. A-MEN.

Arrangement as in 'Worship and Song,' copyright by The Pilgrim Press

203 God's Trumpet Wakes the Slumbering World

(WARRIOR. C. M. D.)

SAMUEL LONGFELLOW, 1864   ARCHIBALD MacDONALD, 1875

1. God's trum-pet wakes the slum-bering world; Now, each man to his post.
2. He who, no an - ger on his tongue, Nor an - y i - dle boast,
3. He who is read - y for the cross, The cause de-spised loves most,

The red-cross ban - ner is un - furled; Who joins the glo - rious host?
Bears stead-fast wit - ness 'gainst the wrong, He joins the sa - cred host;
And shuns not pain or shame or loss, He joins the mar - tyr host.

He who, in feal - ty to the truth, And count-ing all the cost,
He who, with calm un - daunt-ed will, Ne'er counts the bat - tle lost,
God's trum-pet wakes the slumbering world; Now, each man to his post;

Doth con - se-crate his gen-erous youth; He joins the no - ble host.
But, though de-feat - ed, bat - tles still, He joins the faith - ful host.
The red - cross ban - ner is un-furled; We join the glo - rious host. A-MEN.

204 He Who Would Valiant Be

(ST. DUNSTAN'S. 6, 5, 6, 5, 6, 6, 6, 5)

JOHN BUNYAN, 1628–1688. Altered   WINFRED DOUGLAS, 1917

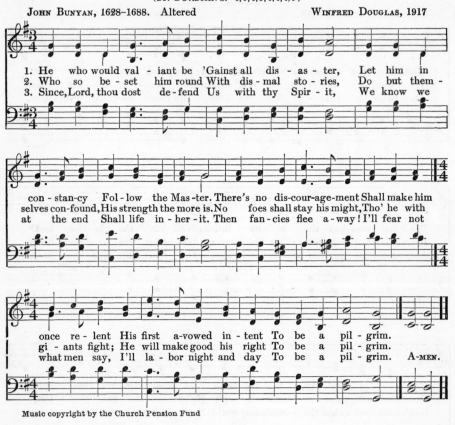

1. He who would val - iant be 'Gainst all dis - as - ter, Let him in
2. Who so be - set him round With dis - mal sto - ries, Do but them -
3. Since, Lord, thou dost de - fend Us with thy Spir - it, We know we

con - stan - cy Fol - low the Mas - ter. There's no dis - cour - age - ment Shall make him
selves con - found, His strength the more is. No foes shall stay his might, Tho' he with
at the end Shall life in - her - it. Then fan - cies flee a - way! I'll fear not

once re - lent His first a - vowed in - tent To be a pil - grim.
gi - ants fight; He will make good his right To be a pil - grim.
what men say, I'll la - bor night and day To be a pil - grim. A-MEN.

Music copyright by the Church Pension Fund

205 Are Ye Able, Said the Master

(BEACON HILL. Irregular)

EARL MARLATT, 1926   HARRY S. MASON, 1926

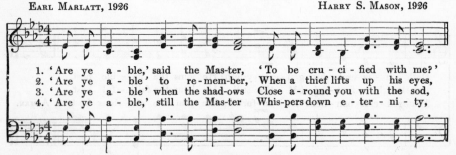

1. 'Are ye a - ble,' said the Mas-ter, 'To be cru - ci - fied with me?'
2. 'Are ye a - ble' to re-mem-ber, When a thief lifts up his eyes,
3. 'Are ye a - ble' when the shad-ows Close a-round you with the sod,
4. 'Are ye a - ble,' still the Mas-ter Whis-pers down e - ter - ni - ty,

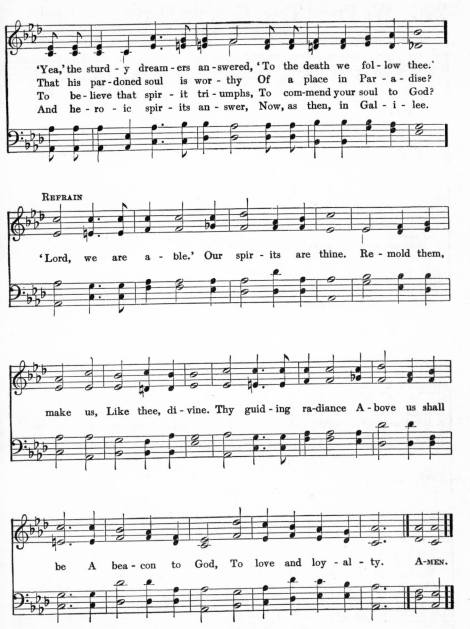

'Yea,' the sturd - y dream - ers an - swered, 'To the death we fol - low thee.'
That his par - doned soul is wor - thy Of a place in Par - a - dise?
To be - lieve that spir - it tri - umphs, To com - mend your soul to God?
And he - ro - ic spir - its an - swer, Now, as then, in Gal - i - lee.

REFRAIN

'Lord, we are a - ble.' Our spir - its are thine. Re - mold them,

make us, Like thee, di - vine. Thy guid - ing ra - diance A - bove us shall

be A bea - con to God, To love and loy - al - ty. A-MEN.

206 We Praise Thee, God, for Harvests Earned
(SAXBY. L. M.)

John C. Adams, 1849–   Timothy R. Matthews, 1883

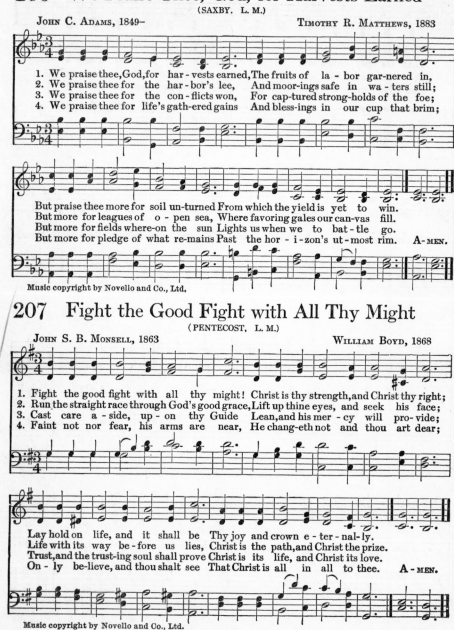

1. We praise thee, God, for har-vests earned, The fruits of la-bor gar-nered in,
2. We praise thee for the har-bor's lee, And moor-ings safe in wa-ters still,
3. We praise thee for the con-flicts won, For cap-tured strong-holds of the foe;
4. We praise thee for life's gath-ered gains And bless-ings in our cup that brim;

But praise thee more for soil un-turned From which the yield is yet to win.
But more for leagues of o-pen sea, Where favoring gales our can-vas fill.
But more for fields where-on the sun Lights us when we to bat-tle go.
But more for pledge of what re-mains Past the hor-i-zon's ut-most rim.   A-men.

Music copyright by Novello and Co., Ltd.

207 Fight the Good Fight with All Thy Might
(PENTECOST, L. M.)

John S. B. Monsell, 1863   William Boyd, 1868

1. Fight the good fight with all thy might! Christ is thy strength, and Christ thy right;
2. Run the straight race through God's good grace, Lift up thine eyes, and seek his face;
3. Cast care a-side, up-on thy Guide Lean, and his mer-cy will pro-vide;
4. Faint not nor fear, his arms are near, He chang-eth not and thou art dear;

Lay hold on life, and it shall be Thy joy and crown e-ter-nal-ly.
Life with its way be-fore us lies, Christ is the path, and Christ the prize.
Trust, and the trust-ing soul shall prove Christ is its life, and Christ its love.
On-ly be-lieve, and thou shalt see That Christ is all in all to thee.   A-men.

Music copyright by Novello and Co., Ltd.

208
Brightly Gleams Our Banner

(ST. THERESA. 6,5,6,5,D. With Refrain)

THOMAS J. POTTER, 1860
Revised and abridged

ARTHUR S. SULLIVAN, 1874

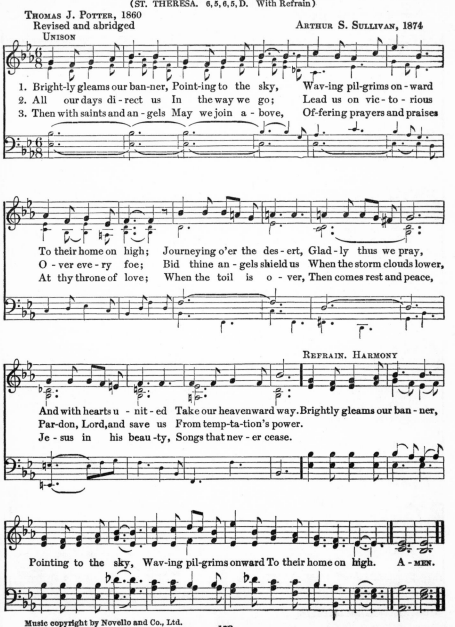

1. Bright-ly gleams our ban-ner, Point-ing to the sky, Wav-ing pil-grims on-ward
2. All our days di-rect us In the way we go; Lead us on vic-to-rious
3. Then with saints and an-gels May we join a-bove, Of-fering prayers and praises

To their home on high; Journeying o'er the des-ert, Glad-ly thus we pray,
O-ver eve-ry foe; Bid thine an-gels shield us When the storm clouds lower,
At thy throne of love; When the toil is o-ver, Then comes rest and peace,

REFRAIN. HARMONY

And with hearts u-nit-ed Take our heavenward way. Brightly gleams our ban-ner,
Par-don, Lord, and save us From temp-ta-tion's power.
Je-sus in his beau-ty, Songs that nev-er cease.

Pointing to the sky, Wav-ing pil-grims onward To their home on high. A-MEN.

209 Onward, Christian Soldiers

(ST. GERTRUDE. 6,5,6,5,D. With Refrain)

Sabine Baring-Gould, 1865   Arthur S. Sullivan, 1871

1. On - ward, Christian sol - diers, Marching as to war, With the cross of Je - sus
2. Like a might-y ar - my Moves the Church of God; Brothers, we are tread - ing
3. Crowns and thrones may perish, Kingdoms rise and wane, But the Church of Je - sus
4. On - ward, then, ye peo - ple, Join our hap-py throng; Blend with ours your voic-es

Go - ing on be - fore; Christ, the roy - al Mas-ter, Leads a-gainst the foe;
Where the saints have trod; We are not di - vid-ed, All one bod-y we,
Con - stant will re - main; Gates of hell can nev - er 'Gainst that Church pre-vail;
In the tri-umph song; Glo - ry, laud, and hon - or, Un - to Christ the King;

REFRAIN

For-ward in - to bat - tle, See, his ban-ners go. On-ward, Christian sol - diers,
One in hope and doc - trine, One in char - i - ty.
We have Christ's own prom-ise, And that can-not fail.
This, thro' countless a - ges Men and an-gels sing.

March-ing as to war, With the cross of Je - sus Go-ing on be-fore. A-men.

210 A Mighty Fortress Is Our God

(EIN FESTE BURG. 8, 7, 8, 7, 6, 6, 6, 7)

MARTIN LUTHER, 1529
Translated by FREDERICK H. HEDGE, 1853

MARTIN LUTHER, 1529

1. A might-y fort-ress is our God, A bul-wark nev-er fail-ing;
2. Did we in our own strength con-fide, Our striv-ing would be los-ing;
3. And tho' this world, with dev-ils filled, Should threaten to un-do us;
4. That word a-bove all earth-ly powers, No thanks to them, a-bid-eth;

Our help-er, he, a-mid the flood Of mor-tal ills pre-vail-ing.
Were not the right man on our side, The man of God's own choos-ing.
We will not fear, for God hath willed His truth to tri-umph through us.
The Spir-it and the gifts are ours Thro' him who with us sid-eth.

For still our an-cient foe Doth seek to work us woe; His craft and power are
Dost ask who that may be? Christ Je-sus, it is he, Lord Sab-a-oth his
The Prince of dark-ness grim, We trem-ble not for him; His rage we can en-
Let goods and kin-dred go, This mor-tal life al-so; The bod-y they may

great; And, armed with cru-el hate, On earth is not his e-qual.
name, From age to age the same, And he must win the bat-tle.
dure, For lo, his doom is sure, One lit-tle word shall fell him.
kill; God's truth a-bid-eth still, His king-dom is for-ev-er. A-MEN.

211 All the Past We Leave Behind

(PIONEERS. 7, 8, 8, 8, 8, 7)

WALT WHITMAN, 1819–1892   MARTIN SHAW, 1925

1. All the past we leave be-hind: We take
2. Not for de-lec-ta-tions sweet, Not the
3. All the puls-es of the world, All the
4. On and on the com-pact ranks, With ac-

up the task e-ter-nal, And the bur-den, and the les-son, Conquering,
rich-es safe and pall-ing, Not for us the tame en-joy-ment; Nev-er
joy-ous, all the sorrowing, These are of us, they are with us; We to-
ces-sions ev-er wait-ing, We must nev-er yield or fal-ter, Through the

hold-ing, dar-ing, venturing, So we go the un-known ways,
must you be di-vid-ed, In our ranks you move u-nit-ed,
day's pro-ces-sion head-ing, We the route for trav-el clear-ing,
bat-tle, through de-feat, Mov-ing yet and nev-er stop-ping,

Pi - on - eers! O pi - on - eers!

212   God of the Strong, God of the Weak

(OMBERSLEY. L. M.)

RICHARD WATSON GILDER, 1903   W. H. GLADSTONE, 1840–1891

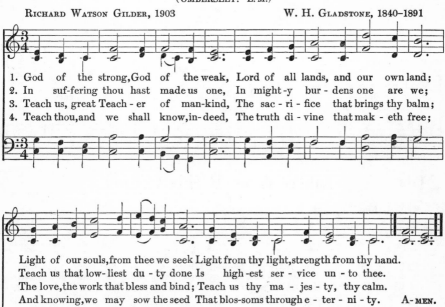

1. God of the strong, God of the weak, Lord of all lands, and our own land;
2. In suf-fering thou hast made us one, In might-y bur - dens one are we;
3. Teach us, great Teach - er of man-kind, The sac - ri - fice that brings thy balm;
4. Teach thou, and we shall know, in-deed, The truth di - vine that mak - eth free;

Light of our souls, from thee we seek Light from thy light, strength from thy hand.
Teach us that low-liest du - ty done Is high-est ser - vice un - to thee.
The love, the work that bless and bind; Teach us thy ma - jes - ty, thy calm.
And knowing, we may sow the seed That blos-soms through e - ter - ni - ty. A-MEN.

213 In Life's Earnest Morning

(MORLEY. 6, 5, 6, 5, D.)

EBENEZER S. OAKLEY, 1885

THOMAS MORLEY, 1867

1. In life's ear-nest morn-ing, When our hope was high, Came thy voice in
2. Teach us, Lord, thy wis-dom, While we seek men's lore; May the mind be
3. Should thy face be cloud-ed To our spir-its' sight, Speak thro' hu-man

sum-mons Not to be put by: Nor in toil nor sor-row,
hum-bled As we know thee more; Let the lar-ger vi-sion
kind-ness, Shine thro' na-ture's light, In the face of loved ones,

Weak-ness nor dis-may, Need we ev-er fal-ter, Art not thou our stay?
Bring the child-like heart, And our deep-er knowl-edge Ho-lier zeal im-part.
Or the ties of home, On-ly, gra-cious Fa-ther, To thy chil-dren come. A-MEN.

214 Life of Ages, Richly Poured

(ELLINGHAM. 7, 7, 7, 7)

SAMUEL JOHNSON, 1864

NATHANIEL S. GODFREY, 1881

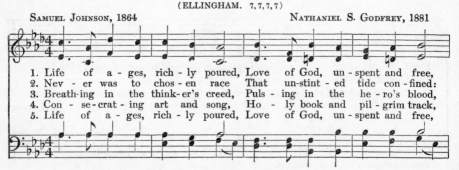

1. Life of a-ges, rich-ly poured, Love of God, un-spent and free,
2. Nev-er was to chos-en race That un-stint-ed tide con-fined:
3. Breath-ing in the think-er's creed, Puls-ing in the he-ro's blood,
4. Con-se-crat-ing art and song, Ho-ly book and pil-grim track,
5. Life of a-ges, rich-ly poured, Love of God, un-spent and free,

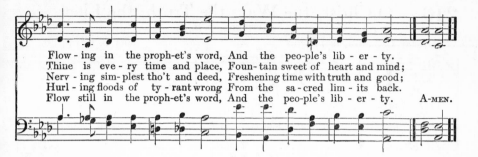

Flow - ing in the proph-et's word, And the peo-ple's lib - er - ty.
Thine is eve - ry time and place, Foun- tain sweet of heart and mind;
Nerv - ing sim- plest tho't and deed, Freshening time with truth and good;
Hurl - ing floods of ty - rant wrong From the sa - cred lim - its back.
Flow still in the proph-et's word, And the peo-ple's lib - er - ty. A-MEN.

215   Strong Son of God, Immortal Love

(ST. CRISPIN. L. M.)

ALFRED TENNYSON, 1850   GEORGE J. ELVEY, 1862

1. Strong Son of God, im - mor - tal Love, Whom we, that
2. Thou seem - est hu - man and di - vine, The high - est,
3. Our lit - tle sys - tems have their day; They have their
4. Let knowl - edge grow from more to more, But more of

have not seen thy face, By faith, and faith a -
ho - liest man - hood, thou: Our wills are ours, we
day and cease to be; They are but bro - ken
rev - erence in us dwell; That mind and soul, ac -

lone, em - brace, Be - liev - ing where we can - not prove;
know not how; Our wills are ours, to make them thine.
lights of thee, And thou, O Lord, art more than they.
cord - ing well, May make one mu - sic as be - fore. A - MEN.

216 O Christ, the Way, the Truth, the Life
(BEATITUDO. C. M.)

GEORGE L. SQUIER, 1907

JOHN B. DYKES, 1875

1. O Christ, the way, the truth, the life, Show me the liv-ing way,
2. Teach me thy truth, O Christ, my light, The truth that makes me free,
3. The life that thou a-lone canst give, Im-part in love to me,

That in the tu-mult and the strife, I may not go a-stray.
That in the dark-ness and the night, My trust shall be in thee.
That I may in thy pres-ence live, And ev-er be like thee. A-MEN.

217 Slowly, by Thy Hand Unfurled
(SEYMOUR, 7, 7, 7, 7)

CARL M. VON WEBER, 1826
Arranged from 'Oberon'

WILLIAM H. FURNESS, 1823

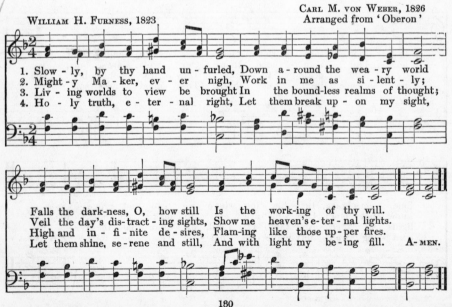

1. Slow-ly, by thy hand un-furled, Down a-round the wea-ry world
2. Might-y Ma-ker, ev-er nigh, Work in me as si-lent-ly;
3. Liv-ing worlds to view be brought In the bound-less realms of thought;
4. Ho-ly truth, e-ter-nal right, Let them break up-on my sight,

Falls the dark-ness, O, how still Is the work-ing of thy will.
Veil the day's dis-tract-ing sights, Show me heaven's e-ter-nal lights.
High and in-fi-nite de-sires, Flam-ing like those up-per fires.
Let them shine, se-rene and still, And with light my be-ing fill. A-MEN.

218   O Lord, Thy Benediction Give

(ABENDS. L. M.)

JOHN ARMSTRONG, 1847   HERBERT S. OAKELEY, 1874

1. O   Lord, thy ben - e - dic - tion give On   all who teach, on all   who learn,
2. Give those that teach pure hearts and wise, Faith, hope, and love, all warmed by prayer:
3. Give those that learn the will - ing ear, The   spir - it meek, the guile - less mind;
4. O   bless the shep-herd, bless the sheep, That guide and guid - ed both   be   one;

That all thy church may ho - lier live, And eve - ry lamp more brightly burn.
Themselves first training for the skies, They best will raise their peo-ple there.
Such gifts will make the low-liest here Far bet - ter than a   kingdom find.
One in the faith-ful watch they keep, One in the joy of   work well done. A-MEN.

219   O Life That Maketh All Things New

(THANKSGIVING. L. M.)

SAMUEL LONGFELLOW, 1874   FRANCIS REGINALD STATHAM, 1844–

1. O   Life that mak - eth all things new, The   blooming earth, the tho'ts of men;
2. From hand to hand the greet - ing flows, From eye to   eye the sig - nals run,
3. One in the free - dom of the truth, One in the joy of paths un - trod,
4. The fre - er step, the full - er breath, The   wide ho - ri - zon's grand - er view,

Our   pil-grim feet, wet with thy dew, In   gladness hith-er turn a-gain.
From heart to heart the bright hope glows; The seek-ers of the Light are one.
One in the soul's per - en - nial youth, One in the larg-er tho't of God;
The sense of life that knows no death,—The Life that maketh all things new. A-MEN.

     181

220 Once to Every Man and Nation

(EBENEZER (TON-Y-BOTEL.) 8, 7, 8, 7, D.)

JAMES RUSSELL LOWELL, 1845

THOMAS J. WILLIAMS, 1890
From Llawlyfr Moliant

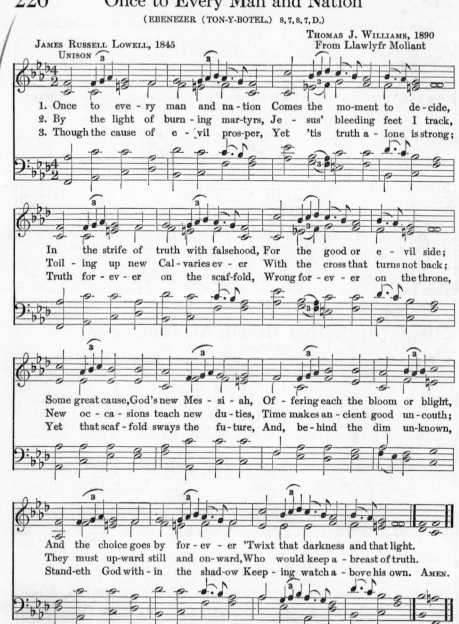

1. Once to eve-ry man and na-tion Comes the mo-ment to de-cide,
2. By the light of burn-ing mar-tyrs, Je-sus' bleeding feet I track,
3. Though the cause of e-vil pros-per, Yet 'tis truth a-lone is strong;

In the strife of truth with falsehood, For the good or e-vil side;
Toil-ing up new Cal-varies ev-er With the cross that turns not back;
Truth for-ev-er on the scaf-fold, Wrong for-ev-er on the throne,

Some great cause, God's new Mes-si-ah, Of-fering each the bloom or blight,
New oc-ca-sions teach new du-ties, Time makes an-cient good un-couth;
Yet that scaf-fold sways the fu-ture, And, be-hind the dim un-known,

And the choice goes by for-ev-er 'Twixt that darkness and that light.
They must up-ward still and on-ward, Who would keep a-breast of truth.
Stand-eth God with-in the shad-ow Keep-ing watch a-bove his own. AMEN.

Music copyright by W. Gwenlyn Evans and Son, Carnarvon

221 We Bless Thee, Lord

(OLIVER. 10, 10, 10, 10)

FREDERICK M. WHITE, 1873

GEORGE EDGAR OLIVER

1. We bless thee, Lord, for all this com - mon life
2. For Pis - gah - gleams of new - er, fair - er truth,
3. For each a - chieve - ment hu - man toil can reach;

Can give of rest and joy a - midst its strife;
Which ev - er ripen - ing still re - news our youth;
For all the pa - triots win, and po - ets teach;

For earth and trees and seas and clouds and springs;
The fel - low - ship with no - ble souls and wise,
For the old light that gleams on his - tory's page,

For work, and all the les - sons that it brings.
Whose hearts beat time to mu - sic of the skies.
For the new hope that shines on each new age. A-MEN.

222

Great Master, Touch Us

(CONISBOROUGH. 10, 10, 10, 10)

HORATIUS BONAR, 1808–1889

WILFRID SANDERSON, 1919

1. Great Mas - ter, touch us with thy skil - ful hands; Let not the
2. Spare not the stroke; do with us what thou wilt; Let there be

mu - sic that is in us die: Great Sculp-tor, hew and pol - ish us, nor
naught un -fin-ished, bro - ken, marred; Com - plete thy pur - pose that we may be -

let, Hid - den and lost, thy form with - in us lie.
come Thy per - fect im - age—thou our God and Lord. A-MEN.

Music copyright by the Wesleyan Methodist Sunday School Department

223

God Who Touchest Earth with Beauty

(GENEVA. 8, 5, 8, 5)

MARY S. EDGAR

C. HAROLD LOWDEN

1. God, who touch - est earth with beau - ty, Make me love - ly too,
2. Like thy springs and run - ning wa - ters, Make me crys - tal pure,
3. Like thy danc - ing waves in sun - light, Make me glad and free,
4. Like the arch - ing of the heav - ens, Lift my thoughts a - bove,
5. God, who touch - est earth with beau - ty, Make me love - ly too,

Words copyright by Mary S. Edgar
Music copyright by C. Harold Lowden. Used by permission

With thy Spir - it re - cre - ate me, Make my heart a - new.
Like thy rocks of tow-ring grand-eur Make me strong and sure.
Like the straightness of the pine trees, Let me up-right be.
Turn my dreams to no - ble ac - tion, Min - is - tries of love.
Keep me ev - er, by thy Spir - it, Pure and strong and true.   A - MEN.

224 Praise We the Lord Who Made All Beauty

(CHURCH VIGILANT. 9, 8, 9, 8)

STUART WILSON, 1928   CHARLES L. ZIEGLER, 1902

1. Praise we the Lord who made all beau - ty For all our
2. Praise him who makes our life a pleas - ure, Send - ing us
3. Praise him who by a sim - ple flow - er Lifts up our

sen - ses to en - joy; Owe we our hum - ble thanks and
things which bless our eyes; Thank him who gives us wel - come
hearts to things a - bove; Thank him who gives to each one

du - ty That sim - ple pleas - ures nev - er cloy.
lei - sure, That in our hearts sweet tho'ts may rise.
pow - er To find a friend to know and love.   A - MEN.

225 Seek Not Afar for Beauty

(WILLINGHAM. 10, 10, 10, 10)

Minot J. Savage, 1841–1918   Franz Abt, 1825–1885

1. Seek not a-far for beauty: lo, it glows
In dew-wet grass-es all a-bout thy feet;
In birds, in sun-shine, child-ish fac-es sweet,
In stars and moun-tain sum-mits topped with snows.

2. Go not a-broad for hap-pi-ness: for see,
It is a flow-er bloom-ing at thy door.
Bring love and jus-tice home, and then no more
Thou'lt won-der in what dwell-ing joy may be.

3. Dream not of no-ble ser-vice else-where wrought;
The sim-ple du-ty that a-waits thy hand
Is God's voice ut-ter-ing a di-vine com-mand,
Life's com-mon deeds build all that saints have thought.

4. In won-der-work-ings, or some bush a-flame,
Men look for God and fan-cy him con-cealed;
But in earth's com-mon things he stands re-vealed,
While grass and flowers and stars spell out his name.   A-MEN.

226 The Ships Glide in at the Harbor's Mouth

(DEO GRATIAS. 10, 7, 10, 7)

Margaret E. Sangster, 1893

A. B. Ponsonby, 1913

1. The ships glide in at the har-bor's mouth, And the ships sail out to sea,
2. The har-vest waves in the breez-y morn, And the men go forth to reap;

And the wind that sweeps from the sun-ny south Is sweet as sweet can be.
The full-ness comes to the tas-selled corn, Wheth-er we wake or sleep.

There's a world of toil and a world of pains, And a world of trou-ble and care,
And far on the hills by feet un-trod There are blos-soms that scent the air,

But O in a world where our Fa-ther reigns, There is glad-ness eve-ry-where.
For O in this world of our Fa-ther, God, There is beau-ty eve-ry-where. A-men.

227 Life Has Loveliness to Sell

(KUCKEN. 7, 7, 7, 7, 7, 7)

SARA TEASDALE, 1884–

F. W. KUCKEN, 1810–1882

1. Life has love - li - ness to sell, All beau - ti - ful and splen-did things,
2. Life has love - li - ness to sell, Mu - sic like a curve of gold,
3. Spend all you have for love - li - ness, Buy it and nev - er count the cost; For

Blue waves whit-ened on a cliff, Soar - ing fire that sways and sings, And
Scent of pine trees in the rain, Eyes that love you, arms that hold, And
one white sing - ing hour of peace Count man-y a year of strife well lost, And

chil-dren's fa - ces look-ing up, Hold-ing won - der like a cup.
for your spir - it's still de - light, Ho - ly tho'ts that star the night.
for a breath of ec - sta - sy Give all you have been or could be.

Words from 'Love Songs,' 1917, copyright by The Macmillan Co.

228 Angel Voices Ever Singing

(ANGEL VOICES. 8, 5, 8, 5, 8, 4, 3)

FRANCIS POTT, 1861

ARTHUR S. SULLIVAN, 1872

1. An - gel voic - es ev - er sing - ing Round thy throne of light,
2. Yea, we know thy love re - joic - es O'er each work of thine;
3. Here, great God, to - day we of - fer, Of thine own to thee;
4. Hon - or, glo - ry, might and mer - it, Thine shall ev - er be,

Music copyright by Novello and Co., Ltd.

188

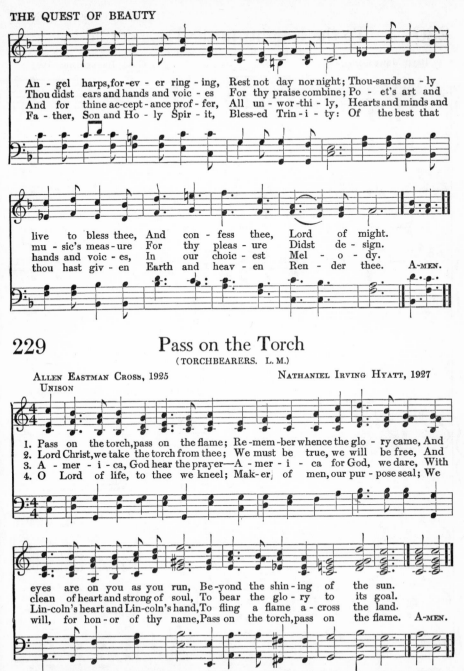

An - gel harps, for -ev - er ring - ing, Rest not day nor night; Thou-sands on - ly
Thou didst ears and hands and voic - es For thy praise combine; Po - et's art and
And for thine ac-cept-ance prof- fer, All un - wor -thi - ly, Hearts and minds and
Fa - ther, Son and Ho - ly Spir - it, Bless-ed Trin - i - ty: Of the best that

live to bless thee, And con - fess thee, Lord of might.
mu - sic's meas- ure For thy pleas - ure Didst de - sign.
hands and voic - es, In our choic - est Mel - o - dy.
thou hast giv - en Earth and heav - en Ren - der thee. A-men.

229 Pass on the Torch
(TORCHBEARERS. L. M.)

Allen Eastman Cross, 1925   Nathaniel Irving Hyatt, 1927
Unison

1. Pass on the torch, pass on the flame; Re -mem -ber whence the glo - ry came, And
2. Lord Christ, we take the torch from thee; We must be true, we will be free, And
3. A - mer - i - ca, God hear the prayer—A - mer - i - ca for God, we dare, With
4. O Lord of life, to thee we kneel; Mak-er, of men, our pur - pose seal; We

eyes are on you as you run, Be-yond the shin - ing of the sun.
clean of heart and strong of soul, To bear the glo - ry to its goal.
Lin-coln's heart and Lin-coln's hand, To fling a flame a - cross the land.
will, for hon - or of thy name, Pass on the torch, pass on the flame. A-men.

230 To the Knights in the Days of Old

(CHALICE. Irregular.) *Second Tune*

Bryn Mawr College

GENA BRANSCOMBE, 1927

1. To the knights in the days of old, Keep-ing watch on the mountain
2. And we who would serve the King And loy-al-ly him o-

heights, Came a vis-ion of Ho-ly Grail, And a
bey, In the con-se-crate si-lence know That the

voice thro' the wait-ing night. Fol-low, fol-low the
chal-lenge still holds to-day. Fol-low, fol-low the

REFRAIN

gleam, Fol-low, fol-low the gleam, Ban-ners un-
gleam, Fol-low, fol-low the gleam, Stan-dards of

'furled o'er all the world. Fol-low, fol-low the
worth o'er all the world. Fol-low, fol-low the

gleam, Fol-low, fol-low the gleam, Fol-low the gleam of the
gleam, Fol-low, fol-low the gleam, Fol-low the gleam of the

cha-lice— the cha-lice that is the Grail.
light— the light that shall bring the dawn.

To the Knights in the Days of Old

(FOLLOW THE GLEAM. Irregular.) *First Tune*

Bryn Mawr College   SALLIE HUME DOUGLAS

1. To the knights in the days of old, Keep-ing watch on the moun-tain heights, Came a vi-sion of Ho-ly Grail, And a voice thro' the wait-ing night. Fol-low, fol-low, fol-low the gleam, Ban-ners un-furled o'er all the world. Fol-low, fol-low, fol-low the gleam Of the chal-ice that is the Grail.

2. And we who would serve the King And loy-al-ly him o-bey, In the con-se-crate si-lence know That the chal-lenge still holds to-day. Fol-low, fol-low, fol-low the gleam, Standards of worth o'er all the earth, Fol-low, fol-low, fol-low the gleam Of the light that shall bring the dawn.

231 O Young Mariner

(SUNDOWN. Irregular)

ALFRED TENNYSON, 1809–1892

JOHN H. GOWER, 1890

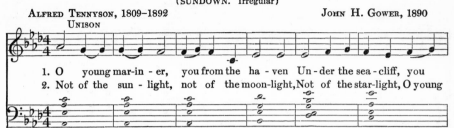

UNISON

1. O young mar-in - er, you from the ha - ven Un - der the sea - cliff, you
2. Not of the sun - light, not of the moon-light, Not of the star-light, O young

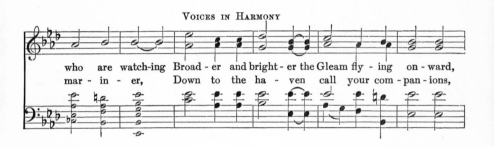

VOICES IN HARMONY

who are watch-ing Broad - er and bright - er the Gleam fly - ing on - ward,
mar - in - er, Down to the ha - ven call your com - pan - ions,

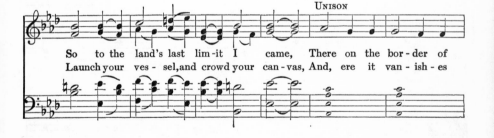

UNISON

So to the land's last lim-it I came, There on the bor - der of
Launch your ves - sel, and crowd your can - vas, And, ere it van - ish - es

HARMONY

bound-less o - cean, And all but in heav - en, hov-ers the Gleam.
o - ver the mar - gin, Af - ter it, fol - low it, fol-low the Gleam. A-MEN.

232 To Every Man There Openeth

(DECISION. Irregular)

John Oxenham

George Henry Day, 1929

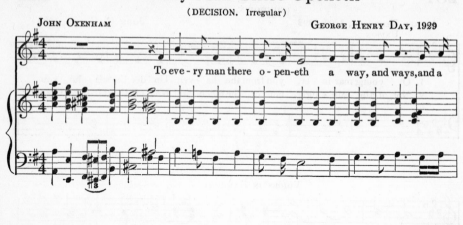

To eve-ry man there o-pen-eth a way, and ways,and a

way, And the high soul climbs the high way, And the

low soul gropes the low. And in be-tween, on the

From 'Bees in Amber.' Copyright by The American Tract Society. Used by permission
Music copyright by The Century Co.

194

mist - y flats, the rest drift to and fro. But to eve - ry man there o - pen-eth a high way and a low; And eve - ry man de -

cid - eth the way his soul shall go.

233 Backward We Look, O God of All Our Days

(GRATITUDE. 10, 10, 10, 10)

ROBERT FREEMAN, 1878–
T. CARL WHITMER, 1929

UNISON

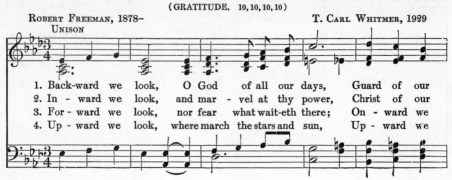

1. Back-ward we look, O God of all our days, Guard of our
2. In - ward we look, and mar - vel at thy power, Christ of our
3. For - ward we look, nor fear what wait-eth there; On - ward we
4. Up - ward we look, where march the stars and sun, Up - ward we

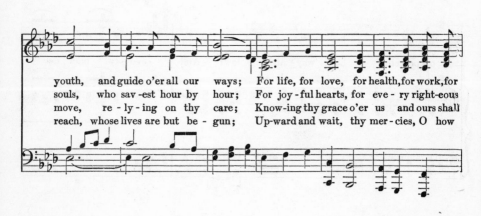

youth, and guide o'er all our ways; For life, for love, for health, for work, for
souls, who sav -est hour by hour; For joy -ful hearts, for eve - ry right-eous
move, re - ly - ing on thy care; Know-ing thy grace o'er us and ours shall
reach, whose lives are but be - gun; Up-ward and wait, thy mer - cies, O how

food, Lord of our lives, we sing our grat - i - tude.
mood, Lord of our lives, we sing our grat - i - tude.
brood, Lord of our lives, we sing our grat - i - tude.
good! Up - ward and sing, O Lord, our grat - i - tude. A-MEN.

234   O Christ, Who Holds the Open Gate

(QUI TENET. L. M.)

JOHN MASEFIELD, 1874–
UNISON

EDWARD SHIPPEN BARNES, 1927

1. O Christ, who holds the o - pen gate, O Christ, who drives the fur - row straight, O Christ, the plough, O Christ, the laugh-ter Of ho - ly white birds fly - ing aft - er,

2. Lo, all my heart's field red and torn, And thou wilt bring the young green corn, The young green corn di - vine - ly spring-ing, The young green corn for - ev - er sing-ing;

3. And when the field is fresh and fair Thy bless - ed feet shall glit - ter there, And we will walk the weed - ed field, And tell the gold-en har - vest's yield,

4. The corn that makes the ho - ly bread By which the soul of man is fed, The ho - ly bread, the food un-priced, Thy ev - er - last-ing mer - cy, Christ.

A-MEN.

Reprinted by permission of Mr. John Masefield, The Macmillan Company of New York, and Messrs. Sidgwick
& Jackson of London.
Music copyright by The Century Co.   **197**

235 Christ of the Upward Way

(SPES MEA IN DEO. 10, 10, 10, 10)

WALTER J. MATHAMS, 1851–   J. S. WARBURTON

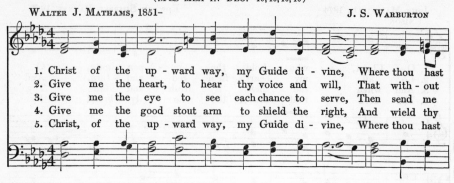

1. Christ of the up-ward way, my Guide di-vine, Where thou hast
2. Give me the heart, to hear thy voice and will, That with-out
3. Give me the eye to see each chance to serve, Then send me
4. Give me the good stout arm to shield the right, And wield thy
5. Christ, of the up-ward way, my Guide di-vine, Where thou hast

set thy feet may I place mine; And move and march wher-ev-er
fault or fear I may ful-fill Thy pur-pose with a glad and
strength to rise with stead-y nerve, And leap at once with kind and
sword of truth with all my might, That, in the war-fare I must
set thy feet, may I place mine; And when thy last call comes se-

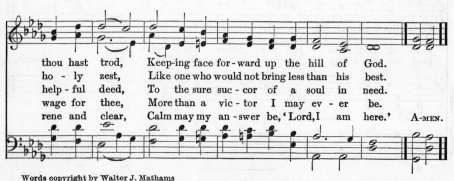

thou hast trod, Keep-ing face for-ward up the hill of God.
ho - ly zest, Like one who would not bring less than his best.
help - ful deed, To the sure suc-cor of a soul in need.
wage for thee, More than a vic-tor I may ev-er be.
rene and clear, Calm may my an-swer be, 'Lord, I am here.' A-MEN.

236 Be Thou My Vision

(VISION. 10, 10, 9, 10)

Ancient Irish
Arranged by MARY BYRNE and ELEANOR HULL

LEROY B. CAMPBELL, 1929

1. Be thou my vis - ion, O Lord of my heart;
2. Be thou my wis - dom, O thou my true word;
3. Be thou my bat - tle - shield, sword for the fight;
4. Rich - es I heed not, nor man's emp - ty praise,

Naught be all else to me, save that thou art,—
I ev - er with thee, and thou with me, Lord;
Be thou my dig - ni - ty, thou my de - light,
Thou mine in - her - i - tance, now and al - ways;

Thou my best thought, by day or by night,
Thou my great Fa - ther, I thy true son;
Thou my soul's shel - ter, thou my high tower:
Thou and thou on - ly, first in my heart,

Wak - ing or sleep - ing, thy pres - ence my light.
Thou in me dwell - ing, and I with thee one.
Raise thou me heav - en - ward, power of my power.
High King of heav - en, my treas - ure thou art. A - MEN.

FRIENDSHIP

237 The Touch of Human Hands

(COMRADE HEART. 6, 6, 6, 6, D.)

THOMAS CURTIS CLARK, 1915　　　　NATHANIEL IRVING HYATT, 1927

1. The touch of hu-man hands—That is the boon we ask; For
2. The touch of hu-man hands—Not vain, un-think-ing words, Nor
3. The touch of hu-man hands—Such care as was in him Who

grop - ing, day by day, A - long the sto - ny way, We need the comrade heart That
that cold char - i - ty Which shuns our mis-er - y; We seek a loy - al friend Who
walked in Gal - i - lee Be - side the sil - ver sea; We need a pa-tient guide Who

un - der-stands, And the warmth, the liv - ing warmth Of hu - man hands.
un - der-stands, And the warmth, the puls - ing warmth Of hu - man hands.
un - der-stands, And the warmth, the lov - ing warmth Of hu - man hands. A-MEN.

Words copyright by Thomas Curtis Clark
Music copyright by The Century Co.

238 Comrades, Known in Marches Many

(SARDIS. 8, 8, 8, 7,)

CHARLES G. HALPINE, 1829–1868　　Arranged from LUDWIG VAN BEETHOVEN'S
Romance for Violin, 1770–1827

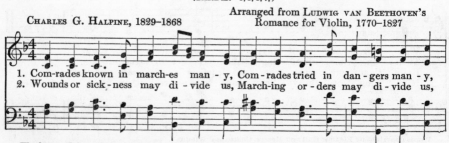

1. Com-rades known in march-es man - y, Com-rades tried in dan-gers man - y,
2. Wounds or sick-ness may di-vide us, March-ing or-ders may di-vide us,

Words copyright by Harper Brothers

Com-rades bound by memo-ries man - y, Broth-ers ev - er let us be.
But, what - ev - er fate be - tide us, Broth-ers of the heart are we. A-MEN.

239

Love Thyself Last

(MORNING STAR. 11, 10, 11, 10)

ELLA WHEELER WILCOX, 1855–1919   JOHN P. HARDING, 1861–

1. Love thy - self last; look near, be - hold thy du - ty To those who
2. Love thy - self last; look far, and find the stran - ger Who stag-gers
3. Love thy - self last; the vast - ness - es a - bove thee Are filled with
4. Love thy - self last; and thou shalt grow in spir - it To see, to

walk be - side thee down life's road; Make glad their days by
'neath his sin and his des - pair; Go, lend a hand and
spir - it for - ces, strong and pure; And fer - vent - ly these
hear, to know and un - der - stand; The mes - sage of the

lit - tle acts of beau - ty, And help them bear the bur-den of earth's load.
lead him out of dan - ger To heights where he may see the world is fair.
faith-ful friends shall love thee, Keep thy watch o - ver oth - ers and en-dure.
stars, lo, thou shalt hear it, And all God's joys shall be at thy com-mand. A-MEN.

Words from *Poems of Power*, copyright by W. B. Conkey Co.

240 Heaven Is Here, Where Hymns of Gladness

(ARMONIA BIBLICA. 8, 7, 8, 7, D.)

JOHN GREENLEAF ADAMS, 1846

UMBERTO PISANI

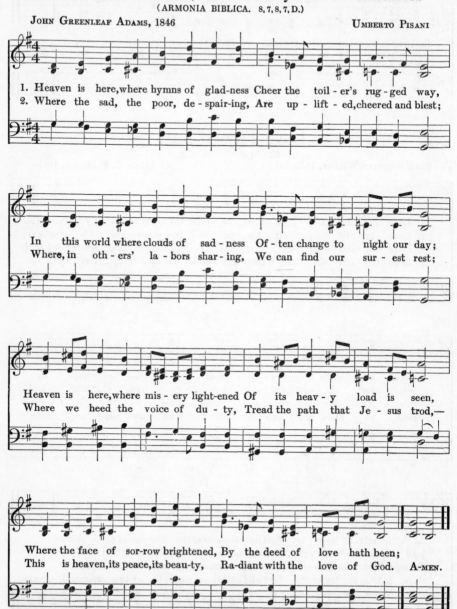

1. Heaven is here, where hymns of glad-ness Cheer the toil-er's rug-ged way,
2. Where the sad, the poor, de-spair-ing, Are up-lift-ed, cheered and blest;

In this world where clouds of sad-ness Of-ten change to night our day;
Where, in oth-ers' la-bors shar-ing, We can find our sur-est rest;

Heaven is here, where mis-er-y light-ened Of its heav-y load is seen,
Where we heed the voice of du-ty, Tread the path that Je-sus trod,—

Where the face of sor-row brightened, By the deed of love hath been;
This is heaven, its peace, its beau-ty, Ra-diant with the love of God. A-MEN.

241 Come, Let Us Join with Faithful Souls

(CRUSADER. C. M. D.)

WILLIAM G. TARRANT, 1892   SAMUEL B. WHITNEY, 1889

1. Come, let us join with faith-ful souls Our song of faith to sing;
2. And faith-ful are the gen-tle hearts To whom the power is given,
3. From step to step it wins its way A-gainst the hosts of sin;

One broth-er-hood in heart are we, And one our Lord and King.
Of eve-ry hearth to make a home, Of eve-ry home a heaven.
Part of the bat-tle-field is won, And part is yet to win.

One broth-er-hood!   One Lord and King!

One   broth-er-hood!   One   Lord and King!

Faith-ful are those who love the truth, And dare the truth to tell;
O might-y host! no tongue can tell The num-bers of its throng;
O Lord of hosts, our faith re-new, And grant us, in thy love,

Who stead-fast stand at God's right hand, And strive to serve him well.
No words can sound the mu-sic vast Of its grand bat-tle song.
To sing the songs of vic-to-ry With faith-ful souls a-bove.

A-MEN.

242 If I Can Stop One Heart from Breaking

(CHARITY. Irregular)

EMILY DICKINSON, 1830–1886   PETER C. LUTKIN, 1927

If I can stop one heart from break-ing, I shall not live in vain,

If I can ease one life the ach - ing, Or cool one pain,

Or help one faint-ing rob - in Un - to his nest a - gain,

I shall not live in vain, I shall not live in vain. A - MEN.

Optional stanza

If I can keep one spirit singing,
I shall not live in vain,
Or send one twinkling vision winging
Through mist and rain,
Or lead one groping pilgrim
Into the light again,
I shall not live in vain.

EARL MARLATT, 1927

243 Little Things That Run and Quail

(DUBLIN. Irregular)

James Stephens, 1882–

Peter C. Lutkin, 1927

Lit - tle things that run and quail And die in si - lence and de - spair;

Lit - tle things that fight and fail And fall on sea and earth and air; All

trapped and fright-ened lit - tle things, The mouse, the co - ney hear our prayer: As

we for - give those done to us, The lamb, the lin - net and the hare, For -

give us all our tres - pass - es, Lit - tle crea - tures eve - ry - where.

244 O Brother Man, Fold to Thy Heart

(STRENGTH AND STAY. 11, 10, 11, 10)

JOHN G. WHITTIER, 1848

JOHN B. DYKES, 1875

1. O broth-er man, fold to thy heart thy broth-er;
2. Fol-low with rev-erent steps the great ex-am-ple
3. Then shall all shac-kles fall; the storm-y clang-or

Where pit-y dwells, the peace of God is there;
Of him whose ho-ly work was 'do-ing good';
Of wild war mu-sic o'er the earth shall cease;

To wor-ship right-ly is to love each oth-er,
So shall the wide earth seem our Fa-ther's tem-ple,
Love shall tread out the bale-ful fire of an-ger,

Each smile a hymn, each kind-ly deed a prayer.
Each lov-ing life a psalm of grat-i-tude.
And in its ash-es plant the tree of peace. A-MEN.

245 When Thy Heart, with Joy O'erflowing

(BULLINGER. 8,5,8,3)

THEODORE CHICKERING WILLIAMS, 1891

ETHELBERT W. BULLINGER, 1874

1. When thy heart, with joy o'er-flow-ing, Sings a thank-ful prayer,
2. When the har-vest sheaves in-gath-ered Fill thy barns with store,
3. If thy soul, with power up-lift-ed, Yearn for glo-rious deed,
4. Share with him thy bread of bless-ing, Sor-row's bur-den share;

In thy joy, O let thy broth-er With thee share.
To thy God and to thy broth-er Give the more.
Give thy strength to serve thy broth-er In his need.
When thy heart en-folds a broth-er, God is there. A - MEN.

Words copyright by Mrs. T. C. Williams

246 Gird Us, O God, with Humble Might

(BEATITUDO. C.M.)

WILLIAM HIRAM FOULKES, 1924

JOHN B. DYKES, 1875

1. Gird us, O God, with hum-ble might To serve the souls who tire;
2. Guide us, O God, with swift-winged feet To find the souls a - stray;
3. Guard us, O God, with con-quering light To hedge a-bout our way;
4. Grant us, O God, thy death-less love To set our spir-its free;

Give us stout hearts a-blaze with right To kin-dle far its fire.
Give us thy pa-tience, we en-treat, To fol-low all the way.
Give us sure faith in dark-est night To see the dawn-ing day.
Give us thy Spir-it from a-bove To bind our souls to thee. A - MEN.

Words copyright by William Hiram Foulkes

247 Lord God of Hosts, Whose Purpose

(ANCIENT OF DAYS. 11, 10, 11, 10)

SHEPHERD KNAPP, 1907

J. ALBERT JEFFERY, 1886

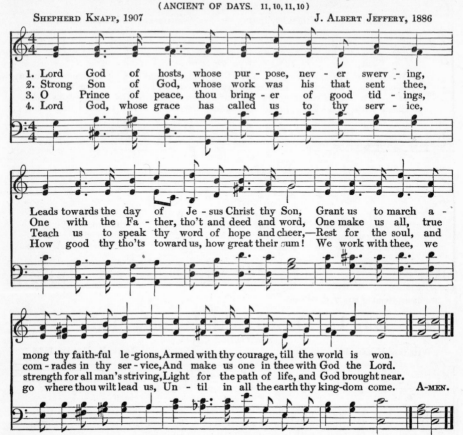

1. Lord God of hosts, whose pur - pose, nev - er swerv - ing,
2. Strong Son of God, whose work was his that sent thee,
3. O Prince of peace, thou bring - er of good tid - ings,
4. Lord God, whose grace has called us to thy serv - ice,

Leads towards the day of Je - sus Christ thy Son, Grant us to march a -
One with the Fa - ther, tho't and deed and word, One make us all, true
Teach us to speak thy word of hope and cheer,—Rest for the soul, and
How good thy tho'ts toward us, how great their sum! We work with thee, we

mong thy faith-ful le - gions, Armed with thy courage, till the world is won.
com - rades in thy ser - vice, And make us one in thee with God the Lord.
strength for all man's striving, Light for the path of life, and God brought near.
go where thou wilt lead us, Un - til in all the earth thy king-dom come. A - MEN.

248 O Ye Who Taste That Love Is Sweet

(DELHI. 8, 8, 8)

CHRISTINA ROSSETTI, 1830-1894

EDWARD FRANCIS RIMBAULT, 1816-1876

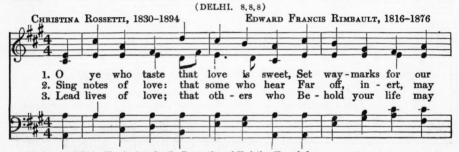

1. O ye who taste that love is sweet, Set way - marks for our
2. Sing notes of love: that some who hear Far off, in - ert, may
3. Lead lives of love; that oth - ers who Be - hold your life may

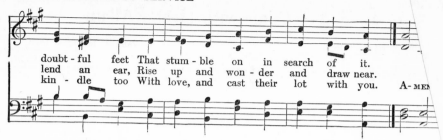

doubt - ful feet That stum - ble on in search of it.
lend an ear, Rise up and won - der and draw near.
kin - dle too With love, and cast their lot with you. A- MEN

249 We Thank Thee, Lord, Thy Paths of Service

(FIELD. 10, 10, 10, 10)

CALVIN W. LAUFER, 1919

CALVIN W. LAUFER, 1919

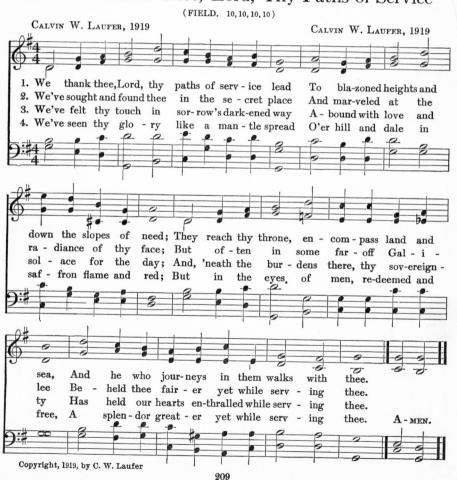

1. We thank thee, Lord, thy paths of serv - ice lead To bla-zoned heights and
2. We've sought and found thee in the se - cret place And mar-veled at the
3. We've felt thy touch in sor - row's dark-ened way A - bound with love and
4. We've seen thy glo - ry like a man - tle spread O'er hill and dale in

down the slopes of need; They reach thy throne, en - com - pass land and
ra - diance of thy face; But of - ten in some far - off Gal - i -
sol - ace for the day; And, 'neath the bur - dens there, thy sov-ereign -
saf - fron flame and red; But in the eyes of men, re-deemed and

sea, And he who jour-neys in them walks with thee.
lee Be - held thee fair - er yet while serv - ing thee.
ty Has held our hearts en-thralled while serv - ing thee.
free, A splen - dor great - er yet while serv - ing thee. A - MEN.

250 Lord, We Come with Hearts Aflame

(ST. ATHANASIUS. 7,7,7,7,7,7)

BERTON BRALEY, 1882–   EDWARD J. HOPKINS, 1872

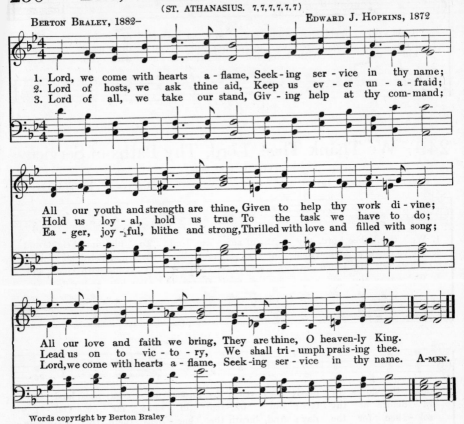

1. Lord, we come with hearts a-flame, Seek-ing ser-vice in thy name;
2. Lord of hosts, we ask thine aid, Keep us ev-er un-a-fraid;
3. Lord of all, we take our stand, Giv-ing help at thy com-mand;

All our youth and strength are thine, Given to help thy work di-vine;
Hold us loy-al, hold us true To the task we have to do;
Ea-ger, joy-ful, blithe and strong, Thrilled with love and filled with song;

All our love and faith we bring, They are thine, O heaven-ly King.
Lead us on to vic-to-ry, We shall tri-umph prais-ing thee.
Lord, we come with hearts a-flame, Seek-ing ser-vice in thy name. A-MEN.

Words copyright by Berton Braley

251 Lord, Speak to Me That I May Speak

(CANONBURY. L. M.)

FRANCES R. HAVERGAL, 1872   ROBERT SCHUMANN, 1833

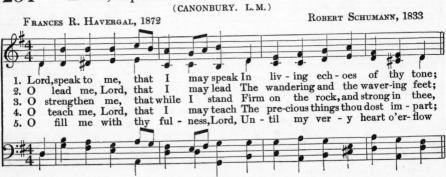

1. Lord, speak to me, that I may speak In liv-ing ech-oes of thy tone;
2. O lead me, Lord, that I may lead The wandering and the waver-ing feet;
3. O strengthen me, that while I stand Firm on the rock, and strong in thee,
4. O teach me, Lord, that I may teach The pre-cious things thou dost im-part;
5. O fill me with thy ful-ness, Lord, Un-til my ver-y heart o'er-flow

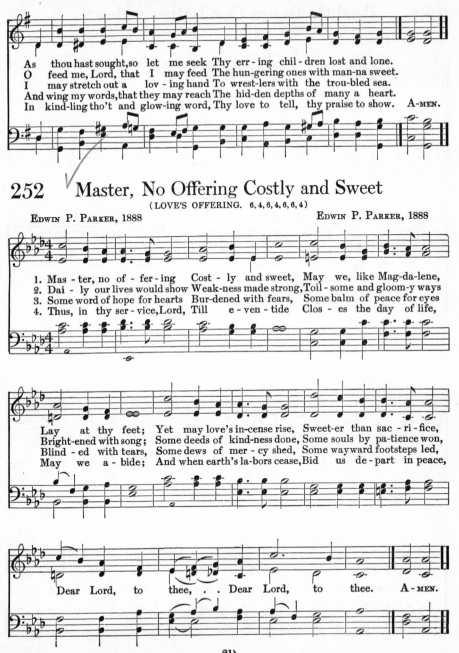

As thou hast sought, so let me seek Thy err-ing chil-dren lost and lone.
O feed me, Lord, that I may feed The hun-ger-ing ones with man-na sweet.
I may stretch out a lov-ing hand To wrest-lers with the trou-bled sea.
And wing my words, that they may reach The hid-den depths of many a heart.
In kind-ling tho't and glow-ing word, Thy love to tell, thy praise to show. A-MEN.

252 Master, No Offering Costly and Sweet

(LOVE'S OFFERING. 6, 4, 6, 4, 6, 6, 4)

EDWIN P. PARKER, 1888   EDWIN P. PARKER, 1888

1. Mas-ter, no of-fer-ing Cost-ly and sweet, May we, like Mag-da-lene,
2. Dai-ly our lives would show Weak-ness made strong, Toil-some and gloom-y ways
3. Some word of hope for hearts Bur-dened with fears, Some balm of peace for eyes
4. Thus, in thy ser-vice, Lord, Till e-ven-tide Clos-es the day of life,

Lay at thy feet; Yet may love's in-cense rise, Sweet-er than sac-ri-fice,
Bright-ened with song; Some deeds of kind-ness done, Some souls by pa-tience won,
Blind-ed with tears, Some dews of mer-cy shed, Some wayward footsteps led,
May we a-bide; And when earth's la-bors cease, Bid us de-part in peace,

Dear Lord, to thee, . . Dear Lord, to thee. A-MEN.

253 Brightly Beams Our Father's Mercy

(LOWER LIGHTS. 8, 7, 8, 7. With Refrain)

PHILIP P. BLISS, 1877

PHILIP P. BLISS, 1877

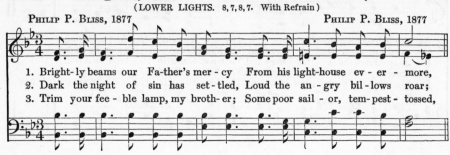

1. Bright-ly beams our Fa-ther's mer-cy From his light-house ev - er - more,
2. Dark the night of sin has set - tled, Loud the an - gry bil-lows roar;
3. Trim your fee - ble lamp, my broth - er; Some poor sail - or, tem-pest - tossed,

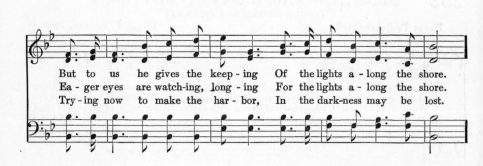

But to us he gives the keep - ing Of the lights a - long the shore.
Ea - ger eyes are watch-ing, long - ing For the lights a - long the shore.
Try - ing now to make the har - bor, In the dark-ness may be lost.

REFRAIN

Let the low - er lights be burn-ing! Send a gleam a -cross the wave!

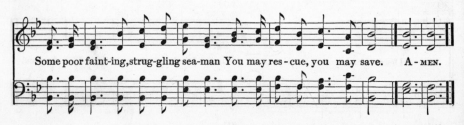

Some poor faint-ing, strug-gling sea-man You may res - cue, you may save.   A - MEN.

254 Rise Up, O Men of God
(ST. THOMAS. S. M.)

WILLIAM PIERSON MERRILL, 1911　　　　AARON WILLIAMS, 1763

1. Rise up, O men of God, Have done with less-er things,
2. Rise up, O men of God, His king-dom tar-ries long;
3. Rise up, O men of God, The church for you doth wait,
4. Lift high the cross of Christ, Tread where his feet have trod;

Give heart and soul and mind and strength To serve the King of kings.
Bring in the day of broth-er-hood And end the night of wrong.
Her strength un-e-qual to her task; Rise up, and make her great.
As broth-ers of the Son of man, Rise up, O men of God! A-MEN.

Words copyright by William P. Merrill

255 God Send Us Men Whose Aim 'Twill Be
(MELROSE. L. M.)

FREDERICK J. GILLMAN, altered　　　　FREDERICK C. MAKER, 1844–1927

1. God send us men whose aim 'twill be, Not to de-fend some an-cient creed,
2. God send us men a-lert and quick His loft-y pre-cepts to trans-late,
3. God send us men of stead-fast will, Pa-tient, cou-ra-geous, strong and true;
4. God send us men with hearts a-blaze, All truth to love, all wrong to hate;

But to live out the laws of Christ In eve-ry tho't and word and deed.
Un-til the laws of Christ be-come The laws and hab-its of the state.
With vi-sion clear and mind e-quipped, His will to learn, his work to do.
These are the pa-triots na-tions need, These are the bulwarks of the state. A-MEN.

213

256 Faith of Our Fathers, Living Still
(ST. CATHERINE. L.M. With Refrain)

FREDERICK W. FABER, 1849   HENRI F. HEMY and JAMES G. WALTON, 1874

1. Faith of our fa - thers, liv - ing still In spite of dun-geon, fire and sword,
2. Our fa-thers,chained in pris - ons dark, Were still in heart and conscience free,
3. Faith of our fa - thers, we will strive To win all na - tions un - to thee;
4. Faith of our fa - thers, we will love Both friend and foe in all our strife,

O how our hearts beat high with joy When-e'er we hear that glo- rious word!
And blest would be their chil-dren's fate, If they,like them,should die for thee:
And thro' the truth that comes from God Man-kind shall then in - deed be free:
And preach thee,too, as love knows how, By kind - ly words and vir -tuous life:

REFRAIN

Faith of our fa-thers, ho - ly faith, We will be true to thee till death. A -MEN.

257 Thou Lord of Light, Across the Years
(DEVENTER. L.M.)

FRANK MASON NORTH, 1917   BERTHOLD TOURS, 1872

1. Thou Lord of light, a - cross the years Thy shin-ing path of love we see;
2. We thank thee for these years of power,For stal-wart souls, for gen - tle life,
3. For men who gird the world with flame, Who count for thee all things but loss,
4. Yet, beat-ing thro' our grat - i - tude, We feel the pulse of com - ing days;
5. High cour - age grant, the out-look broad,The strength of joy, the zest for right,

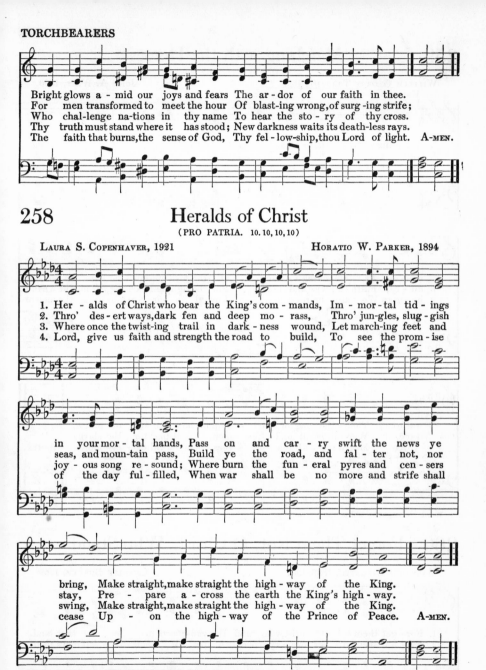

Bright glows a - mid our joys and fears The ar - dor of our faith in thee.
For men transformed to meet the hour Of blast-ing wrong, of surg -ing strife;
Who chal-lenge na-tions in thy name To hear the sto - ry of thy cross.
Thy truth must stand where it has stood; New darkness waits its death-less rays.
The faith that burns, the sense of God, Thy fel - low-ship, thou Lord of light. A-MEN.

258

Heralds of Christ

(PRO PATRIA. 10. 10, 10, 10)

LAURA S. COPENHAVER, 1921   HORATIO W. PARKER, 1894

1. Her - alds of Christ who bear the King's com - mands, Im - mor - tal tid - ings
2. Thro' des - ert ways, dark fen and deep mo - rass, Thro' jun-gles, slug - gish
3. Where once the twist-ing trail in dark - ness wound, Let march-ing feet and
4. Lord, give us faith and strength the road to build, To see the prom - ise

in your mor - tal hands, Pass on and car - ry swift the news ye
seas, and moun-tain pass, Build ye the road, and fal - ter not, nor
joy - ous song re - sound; Where burn the fun - eral pyres and cen - sers
of the day ful - filled, When war shall be no more and strife shall

bring, Make straight, make straight the high - way of the King.
stay, Pre - pare a - cross the earth the King's high - way.
swing, Make straight, make straight the high - way of the King.
cease Up - on the high - way of the Prince of Peace. A-MEN.

Music copyright by Mrs. Horatio Parker

Alternative tune, Ancient of Days, No. 247

259 Marching with the Heroes

(GODFREY. 6, 5, 6, 5, D,)

WILLIAM GEORGE TARRANT, 1890   JOHN A. WEST, 1900

UNISON

1. March-ing with the he - roes, Com-rades of the strong, Lift we hearts and
2. Glo - ry to the he - roes, Who, in days of old, Trod the path of
3. So we sing the sto - ry Of the brave and true, Till a - mong the

voic-es As we march a - long; O the joy-ful mu - sic All in cho-rus
du - ty, Faith-ful, wise and bold; For the right unflinch-ing, Strong the weak to
he - roes We are he-roes, too; Loy-al to our Cap-tain Like the men of

raise! Theirs the song of tri - umph, Ours the song of praise.
save, War - riors all and free - men, Fight-ing for the slave.
yore, March-ing with the he - roes On - ward, ev - er - more. A-MEN.

Words copyright by William G. Tarrant

260 Forget Them Not, O Christ, Who Stand

(TRURO. L. M.)

MARGARET SANGSTER, 1838–1907   CHARLES BURNEY, 1769

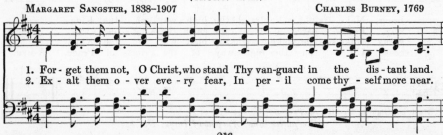

1. For - get them not, O Christ, who stand Thy van-guard in the dis - tant land.
2. Ex - alt them o - ver eve - ry fear, In per - il come thy - self more near.

In flood, in flame, in dark, in dread, Sustain, we pray, each lift-ed head.
Be with thine own, thy loved, who stand, Christ's van-guard, in the storm-swept land. A-MEN.

261   # Who Goes There, in the Night
(ASE'S DEATH. S. M.)

THOMAS CURTIS CLARK, 1917

EDWARD GRIEG, 1844–1907
Arranged by H. A. S., 1928

UNISON

1. Who goes there, in the night, A - cross the storm - swept plain?

We are the ghosts of a val-iant war— A mil - lion mur-dered men!

2. Who goes there, at the dawn, A - cross the sun - swept plain?

We are the hosts of those who swear: It shall not be a-gain! A-MEN.

Words copyright by Thomas Curtis Clark   217

262 The Son of God Goes Forth to War

(ALL SAINTS NEW. C.M.D.)

REGINALD HEBER, 1827

HENRY S. CUTLER, 1872

1. The Son of God goes forth to war, A king-ly crown to gain;
2. The mar-tyr first, whose ea-gle eye Could pierce be-yond the grave,
3. A glo-rious band, the cho-sen few On whom the Spir-it came,
4. A no-ble ar-my, men and boys, The ma-tron and the maid,

His blood-red ban-ner streams a-far; Who fol-lows in his train?
Who saw his Mas-ter in the sky, And called on him to save;
Twelve val-iant saints, their hope they knew, And mocked the cross and flame;
A-round the Sav-iour's throne re-joice, In robes of light ar-rayed:

Who best can drink his cup of woe Tri-umph-ant o-ver pain,
Like him, with par-don on his tongue, In midst of mor-tal pain,
They met the ty-rant's brand-ished steel, The li-on's go-ry mane;
They climbed the steep as-cent of heaven Through per-il, toil and pain:

Who pa-tient bears his cross be-low, He fol-lows in his train.
He prayed for them that did the wrong: Who fol-lows in his train?
They bowed their necks the stroke to feel: Who fol-lows in their train?
O God, to us may grace be given To fol-low in their train. A-MEN.

263
Forward Through the Ages

(ONWARD. 6, 5, 6, 5, D. With Refrain)

FREDERICK L. HOSMER, 1908

J. W. BARRINGTON

1. For-ward thro' the a - ges In un-bro-ken line, Move the faith-ful spir - its,
2. Wid - er grows the king-dom, Reign of love and light; For it we must la - bor
3. Not a - lone we con - quer, Not a-lone we fall; In each loss or tri-umph

At the call di - vine; Gifts in dif-fering meas - ure, Hearts of one ac - cord,
Till our faith is sight; Proph-ets have pro-claimed it, Mar-tyrs tes - ti - fied,
Lose or tri-umph all. Bound by God's far pur - pose In one liv - ing whole,

REFRAIN

Man - i-fold the serv-ice, One the sure re - ward. For-ward thro' the a - ges
Po - ets sung its glo - ry, He-roes for it died.
Move we on to-geth - er To the shin - ing goal.

In un-bro-ken line, Move the faithful spir - its At the call di-vine. A - MEN.

Words copyright by Mrs. Edward Lanning

219

264 Hail the Glorious Golden City

(AUSTRIAN HYMN. 8, 7, 8, 7, D.)

FELIX ADLER, 1878

FRANZ JOSEPH HAYDN, 1797
Descant by E. H. INGRAM, 1925

Descant with 2nd and 3rd stanzas

1. Hail   the glo - rious gold-en   cit - y,   Pic-tured by   the seers   of old!
2. We   are build-ers of that   cit - y,   All our joys and all   our groans
3. And   the work that we have   build-ed,   Oft with bleed-ing hands   and tears,

Ev -   er-last-ing light shines   o'er it,   Won-drous tales of   it   are told:
Help   to rear its   shin-ing   ram-parts; All our lives are build-ing stones:
Oft   in er - ror, oft in   an-guish, Will not per - ish with   our years:

On - ly   righteous men and   wom-en   Dwell with-in   its gleam - ing wall!
Wheth-er   hum-ble   or ex - alt - ed,   All   are called   to task   di-vine;
It   will   live and shine trans-fig - ured In   the fi - nal reign   of right;

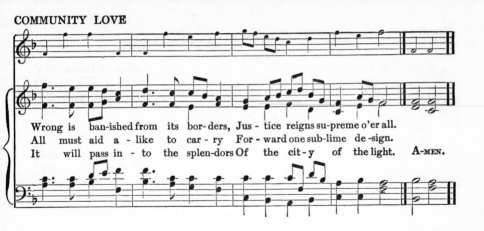

Wrong is ban-ished from its bor-ders, Jus-tice reigns su-preme o'er all.
All must aid a-like to car-ry For-ward one sub-lime de-sign.
It will pass in-to the splen-dors Of the cit-y of the light. A-MEN.

265 Where Cross the Crowded Ways of Life

(GERMANY. L. M.)

FRANK MASON NORTH, 1903   WILLIAM GARDINER's Sacred Melodies, 1815

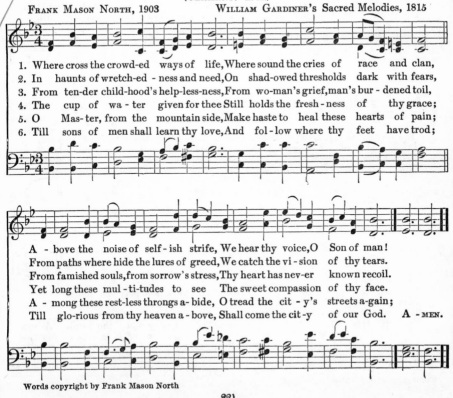

1. Where cross the crowd-ed ways of life, Where sound the cries of race and clan,
2. In haunts of wretch-ed-ness and need, On shad-owed thresholds dark with fears,
3. From ten-der child-hood's help-less-ness, From wo-man's grief, man's bur-dened toil,
4. The cup of wa-ter given for thee Still holds the fresh-ness of thy grace;
5. O Mas-ter, from the mountain side, Make haste to heal these hearts of pain;
6. Till sons of men shall learn thy love, And fol-low where thy feet have trod;

A-bove the noise of self-ish strife, We hear thy voice, O Son of man!
From paths where hide the lures of greed, We catch the vi-sion of thy tears.
From famished souls, from sorrow's stress, Thy heart has nev-er known recoil.
Yet long these mul-ti-tudes to see The sweet compassion of thy face.
A-mong these rest-less throngs a-bide, O tread the cit-y's streets a-gain;
Till glo-rious from thy heaven a-bove, Shall come the cit-y of our God. A-MEN.

Words copyright by Frank Mason North

266 The Fathers Built This City

(ALFORD. 7, 6, 8, 6, D.)

WILLIAM G. TARRANT, 1905

JOHN B. DYKES, 1875

1. The fa - thers built this cit - y How man - y years a - go!
2. Yet still the cit - y stand - eth, A hive of toil - ing men,
3. Let all the peo - ple praise thee, Give all thy sav - ing health,
4. A com - mon-weal of broth - ers, U - nit - ed, great and small,

And bus - y in its bus - y streets, They hur - ried to and fro;
And moth - er's love makes hap - py home For chil - dren now as then;
Or vain the la - borer's strong right arm And vain the mer-chant's wealth.
Up - on our ban - ner blaz - oned be The char - ter, 'Each for all.'

The chil - dren played a - round them And sang the songs of yore,
O God of a - ges, help us Such cit - i - zens to be
Send forth thy light to ban - ish The shad - ows and the shame,
Nor let us cease from bat - tle, Nor wea - ry sheathe the sword,

Till one by one, they fell a - sleep, To work and play no more.
That chil-dren's chil-dren here may sing The songs of lib - er - ty.
Till all the civ - ic vir - tues shine A - round our cit - y's name.
Un - til this cit - y is be - come The cit - y of the Lord. A- MEN.

Words copyright by William G. Tarrant

267 City of God, How Broad and Far

(NOX PRAECESSIT. C. M.)

SAMUEL JOHNSON, 1864

J. BAPTISTE CALKIN, 1875

1. Cit - y of God, how broad and far Out - spread thy walls sub - lime!
2. One ho - ly Church, one ar - my strong, One stead - fast, high in - tent,
3. How pure - ly hath thy speech come down From man's prim - e - val youth!
4. How gleam thy watch-fires thro' the night With nev - er - faint - ing ray!

The true thy char - tered free - men are, Of eve - ry age and clime.
One work - ing band, one har - vest - song, One King om - nip - o - tent!
How grand - ly hath thine em - pire grown Of free - dom, love and truth!
How rise thy towers, se - rene and bright, To meet the dawn - ing day! A-MEN.

268 Send Down Thy Truth, O God

(GARDEN CITY. S. M.)

EDWARD ROWLAND SILL, 1867

HORATIO W. PARKER, 1890

1. Send down thy truth, O God; Too long the shad - ows frown,
2. Send down thy spir - it free, Till wil - der - ness and town
3. Send down thy love, thy life, Our less - er lives to crown,
4. Send down thy peace, O Lord, Earth's bit - ter voic - es drown

Too long the dark-ened way we've trod, Thy truth, O Lord, send down.
One tem - ple for thy wor-ship be, Thy spir - it, O send down.
And cleanse them of their hate and strife, Thy liv - ing love send down.
In one deep o - cean of ac - cord, Thy peace, O God, send down. A - MEN.

269 And Did Those Feet in Ancient Time

(JERUSALEM. L.M.D.)

Arranged from WILLIAM BLAKE, 1757–1827   C. HUBERT H. PARRY, 1848–1918

1. And did those feet in an - cient time Walk up-on Zi-on's mountains green? And was the ho - ly Lamb of God In Zi - on's pleasant pas-tures seen? And could that
2. Bring me my bow of burn-ing gold! Bring me my ar-rows of de - sire! Bring me my spear! O clouds, un-fold! Bring me my char-i - ot of fire! I will not

coun - te-nance di-vine Shine forth upon our clouded hills? And could Jerusa-lem a -
cease from men-tal fight, Nor shall my sword sleep in my hand, Till we have built Je-ru - sa -

1st ending   *2nd ending*

rise A-mong these dark satan-ic mills?
lem, In   eve-ry green and pleasant (*Omit.*)   land.

270   O God, Beneath Thy Guiding Hand

Duke Street, No. 278

1 O God, beneath thy guiding hand
   Our exiled fathers crossed the sea;
And when they trod the wintry strand,
   With prayer and psalm they worshipped
   thee.

2 Thou heard'st, well pleased, the song, the
      prayer:
   Thy blessing came; and still its power
Shall onward, through all ages, bear
   The memory of that holy hour.

3 Laws, freedom, truth and faith in God
   Came with those exiles o'er the waves;
And, where their pilgrim feet have trod,
   The God they trusted guards their graves.

4 And here thy name, O God of love,
   Their children's children shall adore,
Till these eternal hills remove,
   And spring adorns the earth no more.

LEONARD BACON, 1833

271 O Beautiful for Spacious Skies

(MATERNA. C. M. D.)

KATHARINE LEE BATES, 1893, 1904   SAMUEL A. WARD, 1882

1. O beau - ti - ful for spa - cious skies, For am - ber waves of grain,
2. O beau - ti - ful for pil - grim feet, Whose stern, im - pas-sioned stress
3. O beau - ti - ful for he - roes proved In lib - er - at - ing strife,
4. O beau - ti - ful for pa - triot dream That sees be - yond the years

For pur - ple moun - tain maj - es - ties A - bove the fruit - ed plain!
A thor - ough - fare for free - dom beat A - cross the wil - der - ness!
Who more than self their coun - try loved, And mer - cy more than life!
Thine al - a - bas - ter cit - ies gleam, Un - dimmed by hu - man tears!

A - mer - i - ca! A - mer - i - ca! God shed his grace on thee,
A - mer - i - ca! A - mer - i - ca! God mend thine eve - ry flaw,
A - mer - i - ca! A - mer - i - ca! May God thy gold re - fine,
A - mer - i - ca! A - mer - i - ca! God shed his grace on thee,

And crown thy good with broth - er - hood From sea to shin - ing sea.
Con - firm thy soul in self - con - trol, Thy lib - er - ty in law.
Till all suc - cess be no - ble - ness, And eve - ry gain di - vine.
And crown thy good with broth - er - hood From sea to shin - ing sea. A-MEN.

FATHERLAND

272 O Lord, Our God, Thy Mighty Hand

(REPUBLIC. C. M. D.)

HENRY VAN DYKE, 1912   WILLIAM PIERSON MERRILL, 1912

1. O   Lord, our God, thy might-y hand Hath made our coun-try free;
2. The strength of eve-ry state in-crease In   un-ion's gold-en chain;
3. O   suf-fer not her feet to stray; But guide her un-taught might,
4. Thro' all   the wait-ing land pro-claim Thy gos-pel of good-will;

From all   her broad and hap-py land May wor-ship rise to   thee.
Her   thou-sand cit-ies   fill with peace, Her mil-lion fields with grain.
That she may walk in peace-ful day, And lead the world in   light.
And may the joy of Je-sus' name In eve-ry bo-som thrill.

Ful - fill the prom-ise of her youth, Her lib-er-ty de-fend;
The   vir-tues of her min-gled blood In one new peo-ple blend;
Bring down the proud, lift up   the poor, Un-e-qual ways a-mend;
O'er hill and vale, from sea to   sea, Thy ho-ly reign ex-tend;

By law and or-der, love and truth, A-mer-i-ca,   A-mer-i-ca, be-friend!
By u-ni-ty and broth-er-hood, A-mer-i-ca,   A-mer-i-ca, be-friend!
By jus-tice, na-tion-wide and sure, A-mer-i-ca,   A-mer-i-ca, be-friend!
By faith and hope and char-i-ty, A-mer-i-ca,   A-mer-i-ca, be-friend! A-MEN.

273 God of Our Fathers, Whose Almighty Hand

(NATIONAL HYMN. 10, 10, 10, 10)

DANIEL C. ROBERTS, 1876

GEORGE W. WARREN, 1892

Trumpets before each stanza

1. God of our fa - thers, whose al - might - y hand
2. Thy love di - vine hath led us in the
3. From war's a - larms, from dead - ly pes - ti -
4. Re - fresh thy peo - ple on their toil - some

hand Leads forth in beau - ty all the star - ry band
past, In this free land by thee our lot is cast;
lence, Be thy strong arm our ev - er sure de - fense;
way, Lead us from night to nev - er - end - ing day;

Of shin - ing worlds in splen - dor through the skies,
Be thou our rul - er, guard - ian, guide and stay,
Thy true re - lig - ion in our hearts in - crease,
Fill all our lives with love and grace di - vine,

Our grate - ful songs be - fore thy throne a - rise.
Thy word our law, thy paths our cho - sen way.
Thy boun - teous good - ness nour - ish us in peace.
And glo - ry, laud and praise be ev - er thine. A-MEN.

274 God of the Nations, Who from Dawn

(SUMMERFORD. 10, 10, 10, 10)

W. RUSSELL BOWIE, 1913

JOHN T. GRIMLEY, 1887

1. God of the na - tions, who, from dawn of days,
2. Thine an - cient might re - buked the Phar - aoh's boast,
3. Thy hand has led a - cross the hun - gry sea
4. Then, for thy grace to grow in broth - er - hood

Hast led thy peo - ple in their widen - ing ways,
Thou wast the shield for Is - rael's march - ing host,
The ea - ger peo - ples flock - ing to be free,
For hearts a - flame to serve thy des - tined good,

Through whose deep pur - pose stran - ger thou - sands stand
And, all the a - ges through, past crumb - ling throne
And, from the breeds of earth, thy si - lent sway
For faith and will to win what faith shall see,

Here in the bor - ders of our prom-ised land.
And bro - ken fet - ter, thou hast brought thine own.
Fash - ions the na - tion of the broaden-ing day.
God of thy peo - ple, hear us cry to thee. A-MEN.

275 O Beautiful, My Country

(SALVE DOMINE. 7, 6, 7, 6, D.)

FREDERICK L. HOSMER, 1884   LAWRENCE W. WATSON, 1909

1. O beau - ti - ful, my coun - try! Be thine a no - bler care
2. For thee our fa - thers suf - fered, For thee they toiled and prayed;
3. O beau - ti - ful, our coun - try! Round thee in love we draw;

Than all thy wealth of com - merce, Thy har - vests wav - ing fair;
Up - on thy ho - ly al - tar Their will - ing lives they laid:
Thine is the grace of free - dom, The ma - jes - ty of law:

Be it thy pride to lift up The man - hood of the poor;
Thou hast no com - mon birth - right, Grand mem - ories on thee shine;
Be right - eous - ness thy scep - tre, Jus - tice thy di - a - dem;

Be thou to the op - press - ed Fair free - dom's o - pen door.
The blood of pil - grim na - tions Com - min - gled flows in thine.
And on thy shin - ing fore - head Be peace the crown - ing gem. A - MEN.

Words copyright by Mrs. Edward Lanning
Music copyright by G. Russell Watson

276 The Land We Love Is Calling

(ALL HALLOWS. 7, 6, 7, 6, D.)

SARAH JOSSELYN WILSON, 1922   GEORGE CLEMENT MARTIN, 1892

UNISON

1. The land we love is call - ing, From plain and moun - tain height,
2. The soul - starved moun-tain high- lands, The need of coun - try - si de,
3. O her - alds of the morn - ing, Stand in your ra - diant might,

Her val - iant sons and daugh - ters To lift her bea - con light;
The cit - y's creep - ing dark - ness, Where sin and fear a - bide,
Splen-did with faith tri - umph - ant, Touched by the liv - ing light;

From coast to coast the an - swer Comes ring - ing loud and free,
Shall see the march - ing thou -sands That come from far and near:
For faith - ful, lov - ing ser - vice Thy coun - try calls to thee,

HARMONY

'A - mer - i - ca, A - mer - i - ca, We bring our lives to thee.'
'A - mer - i - ca, A - mer - i - ca, Thy plead - ing call we hear!'
Till God's redeemed A - mer - i - ca Thy shin - ing crown shall be. A-MEN.

277 Judge Eternal, Throned in Splendor

(PICARDY. 8, 7, 8, 7, 8, 7)

HENRY SCOTT HOLLAND, 1902

French Folk Song

UNISON

1. Judge e - ter - nal, throned in splen - dor, Lord of lords and King of kings,
2. Still the wea - ry folk are pin - ing For the hour that brings re - lease,
3. Crown, O God, thine own en - deav - or; Cleave our darkness with thy sword;

With thy liv - ing fire of judg - ment Purge this land of bit - ter things;
And the cit - y's crowd - ed clang - or Cries a - loud for sin to cease;
Feed the faint and hun - gry peo - ple With the rich - ness of thy word;

So - lace all its wide do - min - ion With the heal - ing of thy wings.
And the home-stead and the wood - land Plead in si - lence for their peace.
Cleanse the bod - y of this na - tion Thro' the glo - ry of the Lord. AMEN.

Words from 'The English Hymnal,' copyright by Oxford University Press

278 Wild Roars the Blast

(DUKE STREET. L. M.)

ALLEN EASTMAN CROSS, 1920

JOHN HATTON, –1793

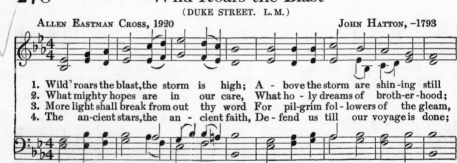

1. Wild roars the blast, the storm is high; A - bove the storm are shin - ing still
2. What mighty hopes are in our care, What ho - ly dreams of broth - er - hood;
3. More light shall break from out thy word For pil - grim fol - lowers of the gleam,
4. The an - cient stars, the an - cient faith, De - fend us till our voyage is done;

Words copyright by Allen Eastman Cross

232

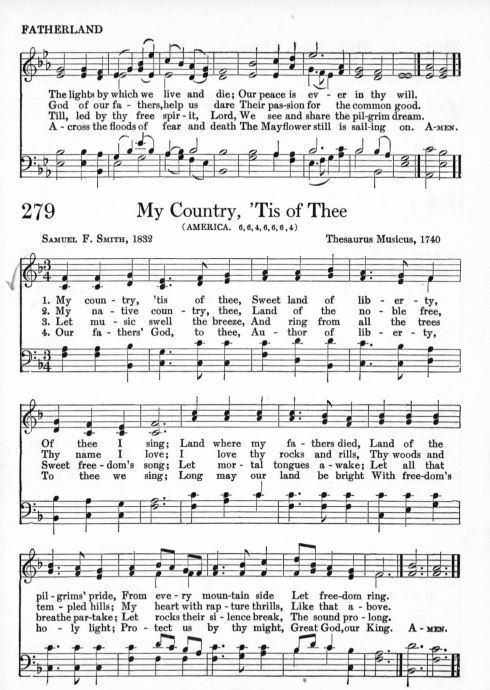

The lights by which we live and die; Our peace is ev - er in thy will.
God of our fa - thers, help us dare Their pas-sion for the common good.
Till, led by thy free spir - it, Lord, We see and share the pil-grim dream.
A - cross the floods of fear and death The Mayflower still is sail-ing on. A-MEN.

279   My Country, 'Tis of Thee

(AMERICA. 6, 6, 4, 6, 6, 6, 4)

SAMUEL F. SMITH, 1832   Thesaurus Musicus, 1740

1. My coun - try, 'tis of thee, Sweet land of lib - er - ty,
2. My na - tive coun - try, thee, Land of the no - ble free,
3. Let mu - sic swell the breeze, And ring from all the trees
4. Our fa - thers' God, to thee, Au - thor of lib - er - ty,

Of thee I sing; Land where my fa - thers died, Land of the
Thy name I love; I love thy rocks and rills, Thy woods and
Sweet free - dom's song; Let mor - tal tongues a - wake; Let all that
To thee we sing; Long may our land be bright With free - dom's

pil - grims' pride, From eve - ry moun-tain side Let free-dom ring.
tem - pled hills; My heart with rap - ture thrills, Like that a - bove.
breathe par-take; Let rocks their si - lence break, The sound pro - long.
ho - ly light; Pro - tect us by thy might, Great God, our King. A - MEN.

280 Mine Eyes Have Seen the Glory

(BATTLE HYMN OF THE REPUBLIC. 15,15,15,6. With Refrain)

JULIA WARD HOWE, 1861   WILLIAM STEFFE, 1852

1. Mine eyes have seen the glo-ry of the com-ing of the Lord;
2. I have seen him in the watch-fires of a hun-dred cir-cling camps;
3. He has sound-ed forth the trum-pet that shall nev-er sound re-treat;
4. In the beau-ty of the lil-ies Christ was born a-cross the sea,

He is tramp-ling out the vin-tage where the grapes of wrath are stored;
They have build-ed him an al-tar in the eve-ning dews and damps;
He is sift-ing out the hearts of men be-fore his judg-ment seat;
With a glo-ry in his bos-om that trans-fig-ures you and me;

He hath loosed the fate-ful light-ning of his ter-ri-ble swift sword;
I can read his right-eous sen-tence by the dim and flar-ing lamps,
O be swift, my soul, to an-swer him; be ju-bi-lant, my feet!
As he died to make men ho-ly, let us die to make men free!

REFRAIN

His truth is march-ing on. Glo-ry! glo-ry! Hal-le-lu-jah!
His day is march-ing on.
Our God is march-ing on.
While God is march-ing on.

234

281 **O Native Land, How Fair You Seem**

(HAGERUP. L. M.)

MYRTLE K. CHERRYMAN, 1919   EDWARD H. GRIEG, 1843-1907

1. O Na-tive Land, how fair you seem, With lakes as love-ly as a dream, And,
2. Thy gracious farms, with fields un-furled, With wealth to feed a hun-gry world; How
3. O God of na-tions, help us grow In kind-ness, as in power; to know The

stretch-ing far from sea to sea, Great moun-tains, high in maj - es - ty.
fair thy mis-sion, how di-vine, To give thy aid, dear land of mine.
free - dom of true brotherhood And wealth of love the high - est good. A-MEN.

Words copyright by Hall and McCreary. From ' The Gray Book of Favorite Songs.'
235

282 God of Our Fathers, Known of Old

(LEST WE FORGET. 8, 8, 8, 8, 8, 8)

RUDYARD KIPLING, 1897

GEORGE F. BLANCHARD, 1898

1. God of our fa-thers, known of old, Lord of our far-flung bat-tle line,
2. The tu-mult and the shout-ing dies; The cap-tains and the kings de-part;
3. Far-called our na-vies melt a-way, On dune and head-land sinks the fire;
4. If drunk with sight of power, we loose Wild tongues that have not thee in awe,
5. For heath-en heart that puts her trust In reek-ing tube and i-ron shard,

Be-neath whose aw-ful hand we hold Do-min-ion o-ver palm and pine:
Still stands thine an-cient sac-ri-fice, An hum-ble and a con-trite heart:
Lo, all the pomp of yes-ter-day Is one with Nin-e-veh and Tyre!
Such boast-ing as the Gen-tiles use Or less-er breeds with-out the law:
All val-iant dust that builds on dust, And, guard-ing, calls not thee to guard;

Lord God of hosts, be with us yet, Lest we for-get, lest we for-get.
Lord God of hosts, be with us yet, Lest we for-get, lest we for-get.
Judge of the na-tions, spare us yet, Lest we for-get, lest we for-get.
Lord God of hosts, be with us yet, Lest we for-get, lest we for-get.
For fran-tic boast and fool-ish word, Thy mer-cy on thy peo-ple, Lord! A-MEN.

283 God Bless Our Native Land

(DORT. 6, 6, 4, 6, 6, 6, 4)

SIEGFRIED A. MAHLMANN, 1815
Tr. by C. T. BROOKS, 1833, and J. S. DWIGHT, 1844

LOWELL MASON, 1832

1. God bless our native land, Firm may she ev-er stand Thro' storm and night; When the wild
2. For her our prayers shall rise To God a-bove the skies, On him we wait; Thou who art

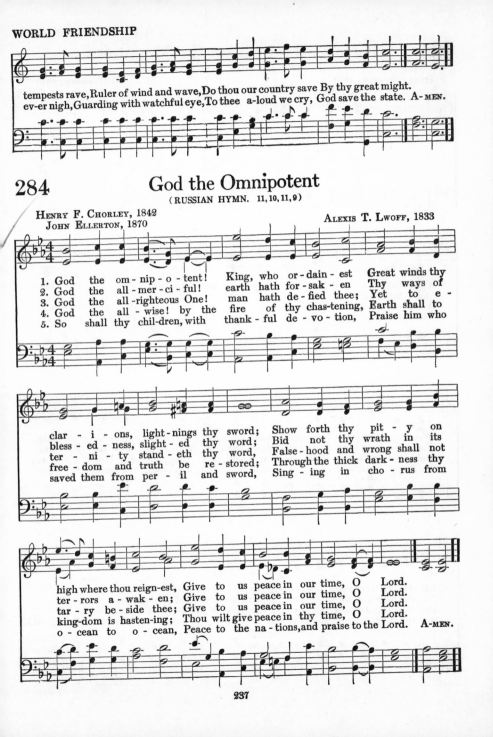

tempests rave, Ruler of wind and wave, Do thou our country save By thy great might.
ev-er nigh, Guarding with watchful eye, To thee a-loud we cry, God save the state. A-MEN.

284 God the Omnipotent

(RUSSIAN HYMN. 11, 10, 11, 9)

HENRY F. CHORLEY, 1842
JOHN ELLERTON, 1870

ALEXIS T. LWOFF, 1833

1. God the om-nip-o-tent! King, who or-dain-est Great winds thy
2. God the all-mer-ci-ful! earth hath for-sak-en Thy ways of
3. God the all-righteous One! man hath de-fied thee; Yet to e-
4. God the all-wise! by the fire of thy chas-tening, Earth shall to
5. So shall thy chil-dren, with thank-ful de-vo-tion, Praise him who

clar-i-ons, light-nings thy sword; Show forth thy pit-y on
bless-ed-ness, slight-ed thy word; Bid not thy wrath in its
ter-ni-ty stand-eth thy word; False-hood and wrong shall not
free-dom and truth be re-stored; Through the thick dark-ness thy
saved them from per-il and sword, Sing-ing in cho-rus from

high where thou reign-est, Give to us peace in our time, O Lord.
ter-rors a-wak-en; Give to us peace in our time, O Lord.
tar-ry be-side thee; Give to us peace in our time, O Lord.
king-dom is hasten-ing; Thou wilt give peace in thy time, O Lord.
o-cean to o-cean, Peace to the na-tions, and praise to the Lord. A-MEN.

237

285 There's a Light upon the Mountains

(MT. HOLYOKE. 15, 15, 15, 15)

Henry Burton, 1910

M. L. Wostenholm, 1910

1. There's a light up-on the moun-tains, and the day is at the spring,
2. In the fad-ing of the star-light we may see the com-ing morn;
3. He is break-ing down the bar-riers, he is cast-ing up the way;
4. Hark! we hear a dis-tant mu-sic, and it comes with full-er swell:

When our eyes shall see the beau-ty and the glo-ry of the King:
And the lights of men are pal-ing in the splen-dors of the dawn;
He is call-ing for his an-gels to build up the gates of day;
'Tis the tri-umph-song of Je-sus, of our King, Em-man-u-el!

Wea-ry was our heart with wait-ing, and the night-watch seemed so long,
For the east-ern skies are glow-ing as with light of hid-den fire,
But his an-gels here are hu-man, not the shin-ing hosts a-bove;
Go ye forth with joy to meet him! and, my soul, be swift to bring

But his tri-umph-day is break-ing, and we hail it with a song.
And the hearts of men are stir-ring with the throbs of deep de-sire.
For the drum-beats of his ar-my are the heart-beats of our love.
All thy sweet-est and thy dear-est for the tri-umph of our King! A-men.

286 At Length There Dawns the Glorious Day

(ALL SAINTS NEW. C. M. D.)

OZORA S. DAVIS, 1909

HENRY S. CUTLER, 1872

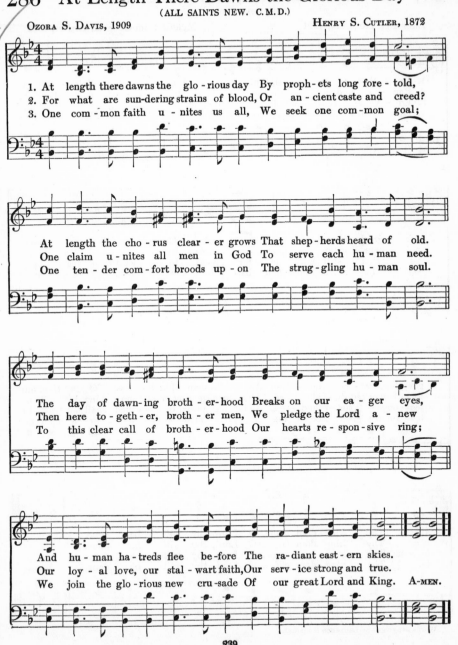

1. At length there dawns the glo-rious day By proph-ets long fore-told,
2. For what are sun-dering strains of blood, Or an-cient caste and creed?
3. One com-mon faith u-nites us all, We seek one com-mon goal;

At length the cho-rus clear-er grows That shep-herds heard of old.
One claim u-nites all men in God To serve each hu-man need.
One ten-der com-fort broods up-on The strug-gling hu-man soul.

The day of dawn-ing broth-er-hood Breaks on our ea-ger eyes,
Then here to-geth-er, broth-er men, We pledge the Lord a-new
To this clear call of broth-er-hood Our hearts re-spon-sive ring;

And hu-man ha-treds flee be-fore The ra-diant east-ern skies.
Our loy-al love, our stal-wart faith, Our serv-ice strong and true.
We join the glo-rious new cru-sade Of our great Lord and King. A-MEN.

239

287 Father Eternal, Ruler of Creation

(OLD 124TH. 11, 10, 11, 10, 10)

LAURENCE HOUSMAN, 1921   Melody from Genevan Psalter, 1551

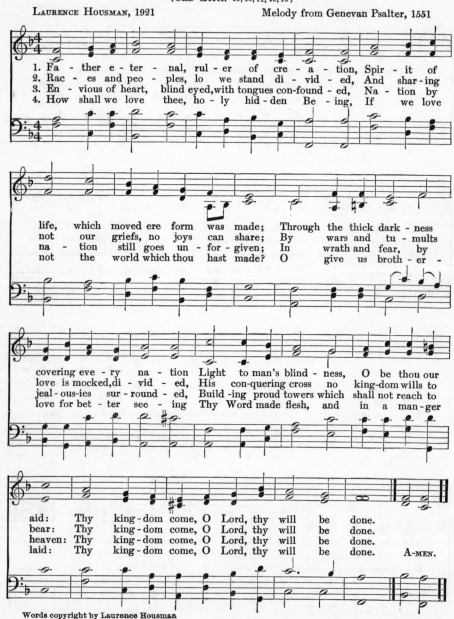

1. Fa - ther e - ter - nal, rul - er of cre - a - tion, Spir - it of
2. Rac - es and peo - ples, lo we stand di - vid - ed, And shar-ing
3. En - vious of heart, blind eyed, with tongues con-found - ed, Na - tion by
4. How shall we love thee, ho - ly hid - den Be - ing, If we love

life, which moved ere form was made; Through the thick dark - ness
not our griefs, no joys can share; By wars and tu - mults
na - tion still goes un - for - given; In wrath and fear, by
not the world which thou hast made? O give us broth - er -

covering eve - ry na - tion Light to man's blind - ness, O be thou our
love is mocked, di - vid - ed, His con-quering cross no king-dom wills to
jeal - ous-ies sur - round - ed, Build-ing proud towers which shall not reach to
love for bet - ter see - ing Thy Word made flesh, and in a man-ger

aid: Thy king-dom come, O Lord, thy will be done.
bear: Thy king-dom come, O Lord, thy will be done.
heaven: Thy king-dom come, O Lord, thy will be done.
laid: Thy king-dom come, O Lord, thy will be done. A-MEN.

Words copyright by Laurence Housman

288 When Wilt Thou Save the People

(COMMONWEALTH. 7, 6, 7, 6, 8, 8, 8, 5)

EBENEZER ELLIOTT, 1850   JOSIAH BOOTH, 1888

1. When wilt thou save the peo - ple? O God of mer - cy, when?
2. Shall crime bring crime for - ev - er, Strength aid - ing still the strong?
3. When wilt thou save the peo - ple? O God of mer - cy, when?

Not kings and lords, but na - tions, Not thrones and crowns, but men.
Is it thy will, O Fa - ther, That man shall toil for wrong?
The peo - ple, Lord, the peo - ple, Not thrones and crowns, but men.

Flowers of thy heart, O God, are they; Let them not pass, like weeds, a - way;
'No,' say thy moun - tains, 'No,' thy skies; Man's cloud - ed sun shall bright - ly rise,
God save thy peo - ple; thine they are, Thy chil - dren, as thine an - gels fair;

Their her - it - age a sun - less day: God save the peo - ple!
And songs as - cend in - stead of sighs: God save the peo - ple!
From vice, op - pres - sion and de - spair: God save the peo - ple! A - MEN.

Music copyright by Clifford Booth

289 God of the Shining Hosts
(ELLAH. 10, 10, 10, 10)

MAY A. ROWLAND, 1928   LILY RENDLE, 1928

1. God of the shin-ing hosts that range on high, Lord of the ser-aphs
2. Thine are the ar-rows of the storm-cloud's breath, Thine, too, the tem-pest
3. High in the track-less space that paves thy throne, Claim by thy love these

serv-ing day and night, Hear us for these, our squad-rons of the
or the zeph-yr still; Take in thy keep-ing those, who fac-ing
souls in dan-ger's thrall; Be thou their pi-lot through the great un-

sky, And give to them the shel-ter of thy might.
death, Brave-ly go forth to do a na-tion's will.
known, Then shall they mount as ea-gles and not fall. A-MEN.

290 Lord, Guard and Guide the Men Who Fly
(LEIPZIG. L. M.)

MARY C. D. HAMILTON, 1915   FELIX MENDELSSOHN-BARTHOLDY, 1809–1847

1. Lord, guard and guide the men who fly Through the great
2. Thou who dost keep with ten-der might The bal-anced
3. Con-trol their minds with in-stinct fit What time, ad-
4. A-loft in sol-i-tudes of space, Up-hold them

spa - ces of the sky; Be with them tra - vers -
birds in all their flight, Thou of the tem - pered
ven - tur - ing, they quit The firm se - cur - i -
with thy sav - ing grace. O God, pro - tect the

ing the air In dark-ening storms or sun - shine fair.
winds, be near, That, hav - ing thee, they know no fear.
ty of land; Grant stead-fast eye and skil - ful hand.
men who fly Thro' lone - ly ways be - neath the sky. A-MEN.

291 Let There Be Light, Lord God of Hosts
(PENTECOST. L. M.)

WILLIAM MERRILL VORIES, 1908

WILLIAM BOYD, 1868

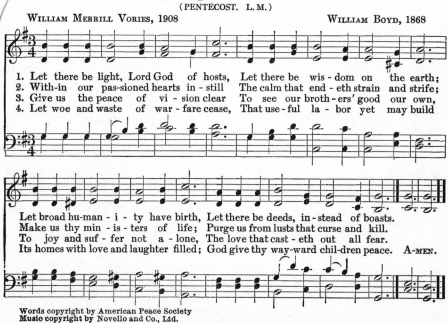

1. Let there be light, Lord God of hosts, Let there be wis - dom on the earth;
2. With - in our pas-sioned hearts in - still The calm that end - eth strain and strife;
3. Give us the peace of vi - sion clear To see our broth-ers' good our own,
4. Let woe and waste of war - fare cease, That use - ful la - bor yet may build

Let broad hu-man - i - ty have birth, Let there be deeds, in - stead of boasts.
Make us thy min - is - ter of life; Purge us from lusts that curse and kill.
To joy and suf - fer not a - lone, The love that cast - eth out all fear.
Its homes with love and laughter filled; God give thy way-ward chil-dren peace. A-MEN.

292 Down the Dark Future

(SPRINGFIELD. 11, 10, 11, 10)

HENRY W. LONGFELLOW, 1807–1882

EDWARD H. GRIEG, 1844–1907

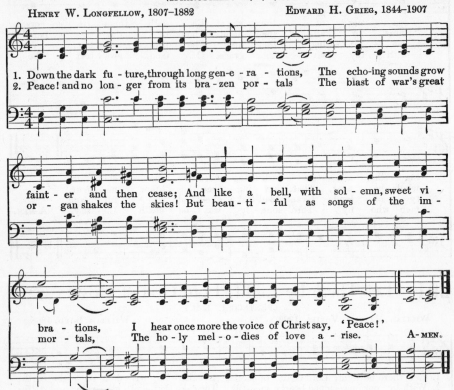

1. Down the dark fu - ture, through long gen-e - ra - tions, The echo-ing sounds grow
2. Peace! and no lon - ger from its bra - zen por - tals The blast of war's great

faint - er and then cease; And like a bell, with sol - emn, sweet vi -
or - gan shakes the skies! But beau - ti - ful as songs of the im -

bra - tions, I hear once more the voice of Christ say, 'Peace!'
mor - tals, The ho - ly mel - o - dies of love a - rise.   A - MEN.

293 These Things Shall Be—a Loftier Race

(MENDON. L. M.)

German Melody
Arranged by SAMUEL DYER, 1828

JOHN ADDINGTON SYMONDS, 1880

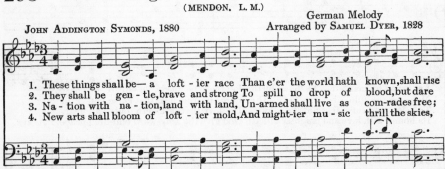

1. These things shall be— a loft - ier race Than e'er the world hath known, shall rise
2. They shall be gen - tle, brave and strong To spill no drop of blood, but dare
3. Na - tion with na - tion, land with land, Un-armed shall live as com-rades free;
4. New arts shall bloom of loft - ier mold, And might-ier mu - sic thrill the skies,

Alternative tune, Truro, No. 295

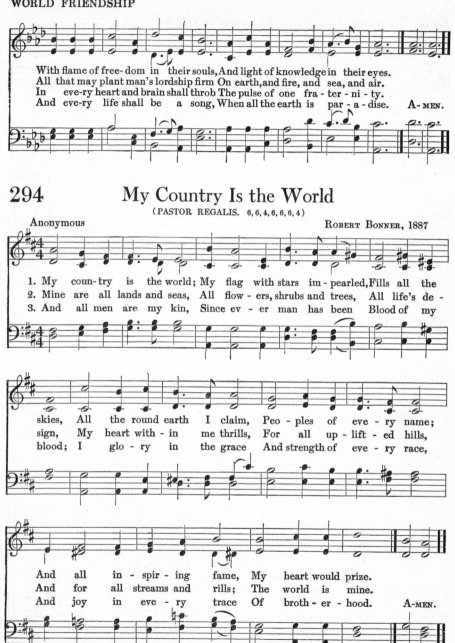

With flame of free-dom in their souls, And light of knowledge in their eyes.
All that may plant man's lordship firm On earth, and fire, and sea, and air.
In eve-ry heart and brain shall throb The pulse of one fra-ter-ni-ty.
And eve-ry life shall be a song, When all the earth is par-a-dise. A-MEN.

294 My Country Is the World

(PASTOR REGALIS. 6, 6, 4, 6, 6, 6, 4)

Anonymous

ROBERT BONNER, 1887

1. My coun-try is the world; My flag with stars im-pearled, Fills all the
2. Mine are all lands and seas, All flow-ers, shrubs and trees, All life's de-
3. And all men are my kin, Since ev-er man has been Blood of my

skies, All the round earth I claim, Peo-ples of eve-ry name;
sign, My heart with-in me thrills, For all up-lift-ed hills,
blood; I glo-ry in the grace And strength of eve-ry race,

And all in-spir-ing fame, My heart would prize.
And for all streams and rills; The world is mine.
And joy in eve-ry trace Of broth-er-hood. A-MEN.

295 Lift Up Our Hearts, O King of Kings

(TRURO. L.M.)

JOHN HOWARD MASTERMAN, 1867–

CHARLES BURNEY, 1769

1. Lift up our hearts, O King of kings, To bright-er hopes and kindlier things,
2. Thy world is wea-ry of its pain, Of self-ish greed and fruitless gain,
3. Al-might-y Fa-ther, who dost give The gift of life to all who live,

To vis-ions of a larg-er good, And ho-lier dreams of broth-er-hood.
Of tar-nished hon-or, false-ly strong, And all its an-cient deeds of wrong.
Look down on all earth's sin and strife, And lift us to a no-bler life. A-MEN.

296 God of the Nations, Near and Far

(SAWLEY. C.M.)

JOHN HAYNES HOLMES, 1911

JAMES WALCH, 1860

1. God of the na-tions, near and far, Rul-er of all man-kind,
2. The clash of arms still shakes the sky, King bat-tles still with king;
3. But clear-er far the friend-ly speech Of sci-en-tists and seers,
4. And strong-er far the clasp-ed hands Of la-bor's teem-ing throngs,

Bless thou thy peo-ple as they strive The paths of peace to find.
Wild thro' the frighted air of night The blood-y toc-sins ring.
The wise de-bate of statesmen and The shouts of pi-o-neers.
Who in a hun-dred tongues re-peat The common creeds and songs. A-MEN.

5 From shore to shore the peoples call
   In loud and sweet acclaim,
The gloom of land and sea is lit
   With Pentecostal flame.

6 O Father, from the curse of war
   We pray thee give release,
And speed, O speed the blessed day
   Of justice, love, and peace.

297　Not in Vain the Distance Beacons

(MT. HOLYOKE. 15, 15, 15, 15)

ALFRED TENNYSON, 1842　　　　　　　　M. L. WOSTENHOLM, 1910

1. Not in vain the dis-tance bea-cons—For-ward, for-ward let us range,
2. O, we see the cres-cent prom-ise of man's spir-it has not set;
3. Yea, we dip in-to the fu-ture, far as hu-man eye can see,

Let the great world spin for-ev-er down the ring-ing grooves of change;
An-cient founts of in-spi-ra-tion well through all his fan-cy yet;
See the vi-sion of the world, and all the won-der that shall be,

Through the shad-ow of the globe we sweep a-head to heights sub-lime,
And we doubt not through the a-ges one in-creas-ing pur-pose runs,
Hear the war drum throb no lon-ger, see the bat-tle flags all furled,

We, the heirs of all the a-ges in the fore-most files of time.
And the thoughts of men are wid-ened with the pro-cess of the suns.
In the Par-lia-ment of man, the Fed-er-a-tion of the world.

298 Watchman, Tell Us of the Night

(ABERYSTWYTH. 7, 7, 7, 7, D.)

John Bowring, 1825

Joseph Parry, 1879

1. Watch-man, tell us of the night, What its signs of prom-ise are:
2. Watch-man, tell us of the night, High-er yet that star as-cends;
3. Watch-man, tell us of the night, For the morn-ing seems to dawn:

Trav-eler, o'er yon moun-tain's height, See that glo-ry-beam-ing star.
Trav-eler, bless-ed-ness and light, Peace and truth its course por-tends.
Trav-eler, dark-ness takes its flight, Doubt and ter-ror are with-drawn.

Watch-man, does its beau-teous ray Aught of joy or hope fore-tell?
Watch-man, will its beams a-lone Gild the spot that gave them birth?
Watch-man, let thy wan-derings cease; Hie thee to thy qui-et home:

Trav-eler, yes; it brings the day, Prom-ised day of Is-ra-el.
Trav-eler, a-ges are its own; See, it bursts o'er all the earth.
Trav-eler, lo, the Prince of Peace, Lo, the Son of God is come. A-men.

Music copyright by H. Hughes and Son

Watchman, Tell Us of the Night

(WATCHMAN. 7,7,7,7,D.) *Second Tune*

JOHN BOWRING, 1825

LOWELL MASON, 1830

Watchman, tell us of the night, What its signs of prom-ise are: Traveler, o'er yon mountain's height,

See that glo - ry-beam-ing star. Watchman, does its beau-teous ray Aught of joy or

hope foretell? Trav-eler, yes; it brings the day, Promised day of Is - ra - el. A-MEN.

299 In Christ There Is No East Or West

(ST. PETER. C. M.)

JOHN OXENHAM, 1908

ALEXANDER R. REINAGLE, 1836

1. In Christ there is no East or West, In him no South or North; But
2. In him shall true hearts eve - ry-where Their high com - mun - ion find; His
3. Join hands then, broth-ers of the faith, What-e'er your race may be; Who
4. In Christ now meet both East and West, In him meet South and North; All

one great fel - low - ship of love Through-out the whole wide earth.
ser - vice is the gold - en cord Close - bind - ing all man - kind.
serves my Fa - ther as a son Is sure - ly kin to me.
Christ - ly souls are one in him Through-out the whole wide earth. A-MEN.

300 Gather Us In, Thou Love, That Fillest All

(PENITENTIA. 10, 10, 10, 10)

GEORGE MATHESON, 1890

EDWARD DEARLE, 1874

1. Gath - er us in, thou love, that fill - est all;
2. Gath - er us in: we wor - ship on - ly thee;
3. Thine is the mys - tic life great In - dia craves;
4. Thine is the Ro - man's strength with-out his pride;
5. Some seek a Fa - ther in the heavens a - bove;

Gath - er our ri - val faiths with - in thy fold;
In va - ried names we stretch a com - mon hand;
Thine is the Par - see's sin - de - stroy - ing beam;
Thine is the Greek's glad world with - out its graves;
Some ask a hu - man im - age to a - dore;

Rend each man's tem - ple - veil, and bid it fall,
In di - verse forms a com - mon soul we see;
Thine is the Bud - dhist's rest from toss - ing waves;
Thine is Ju - de - a's law with love be - side,
Some crave a spir - it vast as life and love;

That we may know that thou hast been of old.
In man - y ships we seek one spir - it - land.
Thine is the em - pire of vast Chi - na's dream.
The truth that cen - sures and the grace that saves.
With - in thy man - sions we have all and more. A - MEN.

301 Hail to the Lord's Anointed

(WEBB. 7, 6, 7, 6, D.)

JAMES MONTGOMERY, 1821

GEORGE J. WEBB, 1837

1. Hail to the Lord's A-noint-ed, Great Da-vid's great-er Son!
2. He comes with suc-cor speed-y To those who suf-fer wrong;
3. He shall come down like show-ers Up-on the fruit-ful earth,
4. O'er eve-ry foe vic-to-rious, He on his throne shall rest;

Hail, in the time ap-point-ed, His reign on earth be-gun!
To help the poor and need-y, And bid the weak be strong;
Love, joy and hope, like flow-ers, Spring in his path to birth:
From age to age more) glo-rious, All-bless-ing, and all-blest;

He comes to break op-pres-sion, To set the cap-tive free,
To give them songs for sigh-ing, Their dark-ness turn to light,
Be-fore him on the moun-tains Shall peace, the her-ald, go;
The tide of time shall nev-er His cov-e-nant re-move;

To take a-way trans-gres-sion, And rule in e-qui-ty.
Whose souls condemned and dy-ing, Were pre-cious in his sight.
And right-eous-ness in foun-tains From hill to val-ley flow.
His name shall stand for-ev-er, His change-less name of Love. A-MEN.

302 We've a Story to Tell to the Nations

(MESSAGE. 10, 8, 8, 7, 7. With Refrain)

COLIN STERNE, 1896

Adapted from H. ERNEST NICHOL, 1896

1. We've a sto - ry to tell to the na - tions That shall
2. We've a song to be sung to the na - tions, That shall
3. We've a mes - sage to give to the na - tions, That the
4. We've a Sav - iour to show to the na - tions, Who the

turn their hearts to the right, A sto - ry of truth and mer - cy,
lift their hearts to the Lord; A song that shall con - quer e - vil
Lord who reign - eth a - bove Hath sent us his Son to save us,
path of sor - row has trod, That all of the world's great peo - ples

A sto - ry of peace and light, A sto - ry of peace and light.
And shat - ter the spear and sword, And shat - ter the spear and sword.
And show us that God is love, And show us that God is love.
Might come to the truth of God, Might come to the truth of God.

REFRAIN

For the dark-ness shall turn to dawn - ing, And the dawn-ing to noon-day bright,

Words and music copyright by Representatives of the late H. Ernest Nichol

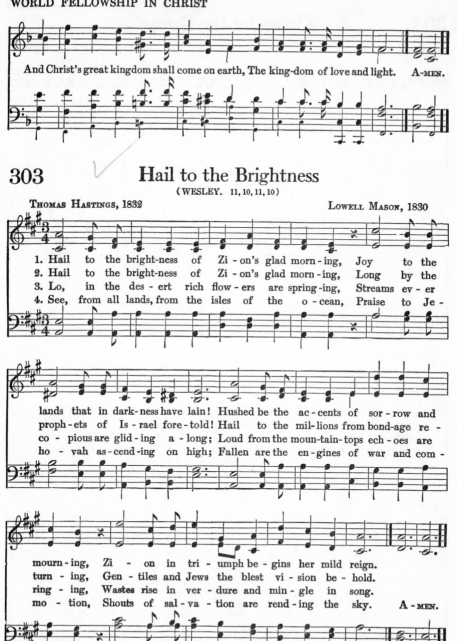

And Christ's great kingdom shall come on earth, The king-dom of love and light. A-men.

303   Hail to the Brightness
(WESLEY. 11, 10, 11, 10)

Thomas Hastings, 1832   Lowell Mason, 1830

1. Hail to the bright-ness of Zi-on's glad morn-ing, Joy to the
2. Hail to the bright-ness of Zi-on's glad morn-ing, Long by the
3. Lo, in the des-ert rich flow-ers are spring-ing, Streams ev-er
4. See, from all lands, from the isles of the o-cean, Praise to Je-

lands that in dark-ness have lain! Hushed be the ac-cents of sor-row and
proph-ets of Is-rael fore-told! Hail to the mil-lions from bond-age re-
co-pious are glid-ing a-long; Loud from the moun-tain-tops ech-oes are
ho-vah as-cend-ing on high; Fallen are the en-gines of war and com-

mourn-ing, Zi-on in tri-umph be-gins her mild reign.
turn-ing, Gen-tiles and Jews the blest vi-sion be-hold.
ring-ing, Wastes rise in ver-dure and min-gle in song.
mo-tion, Shouts of sal-va-tion are rend-ing the sky. A-men.

253

304 Fling Out the Banner

(WALTHAM. L. M.)

GEORGE W. DOANE, 1848   J. BAPTISTE CALKIN, 1872

1. Fling out the ban-ner! let it float Sky-ward and sea-ward, high and wide:
2. Fling out the ban-ner! an-gels bend In anx-ious si-lence o'er the sign,
3. Fling out the ban-ner! dis-tant lands Shall see from far the glo-rious sight,
4. Fling out the ban-ner! sin-sick souls That sink and per-ish in the strife,
5. Fling out the ban-ner! wide and high, Sky-ward and sea-ward, let it shine:

The sun that lights its shin-ing folds, The cross on which the Sav-iour died.
And vain-ly seek to com-pre-hend The won-der of the love di-vine.
And na-tions, crowding to be born, Bap-tize their spir-its in its light.
Shall touch in faith its ra-diant hem, And spring im-mor-tal in-to life.
Nor skill, nor might, nor mer-it ours; We con-quer on-ly in that sign. A-MEN.

Music copyright by Novello and Co., Ltd.

305 Jesus Shall Reign Where'er the Sun

(DUKE STREET. L. M.)

ISAAC WATTS, 1719   JOHN HATTON, −1793

1. Je-sus shall reign wher-e'er the sun Does his suc-ces-sive jour-neys run;
2. For him shall end-less prayer be made, And prais-es throng to crown his head;
3. Peo-ple and realms of eve-ry tongue Dwell on his love with sweet-est song,
4. Bless-ings a-bound wher-e'er he reigns; The pris-oner leaps to loose his chains;

His kingdom stretch from shore to shore, Till moons shall wax and wane no more.
His name, like sweet per-fume, shall rise With eve-ry morn-ing sac-ri-fice;
And in-fant voic-es shall pro-claim Their ear-ly bless-ings on his name.
The wea-ry find e-ter-nal rest, And all the sons of want are blest. A-MEN.

306 O Zion, Haste, Thy Mission High Fulfilling

(TIDINGS. 11, 10, 11, 10. With Refrain)

MARY ANN THOMSON, 1870

JAMES WALCH, 1875

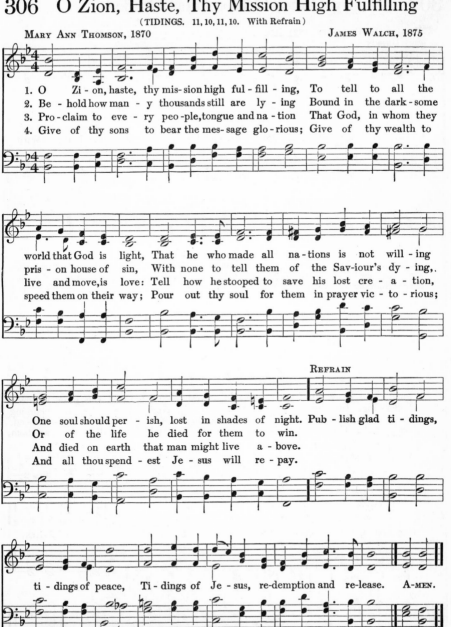

1. O Zi-on, haste, thy mis-sion high ful-fill-ing, To tell to all the world that God is light, That he who made all na-tions is not will-ing One soul should per-ish, lost in shades of night.

2. Be-hold how man-y thousands still are ly-ing Bound in the dark-some pris-on house of sin, With none to tell them of the Sav-iour's dy-ing, Or of the life he died for them to win.

3. Pro-claim to eve-ry peo-ple, tongue and na-tion That God, in whom they live and move, is love: Tell how he stooped to save his lost cre-a-tion, And died on earth that man might live a-bove.

4. Give of thy sons to bear the mes-sage glo-rious; Give of thy wealth to speed them on their way; Pour out thy soul for them in prayer vic-to-rious; And all thou spend-est Je-sus will re-pay.

REFRAIN

Pub-lish glad ti-dings, ti-dings of peace, Ti-dings of Je-sus, re-demption and re-lease. A-MEN.

307 Thy Hand, O God, Has Guided

(THORNBURY. 7, 6, 7, 6, D.)

EDWARD H. PLUMPTRE, 1821–1891   BASIL HARWOOD, 1859–

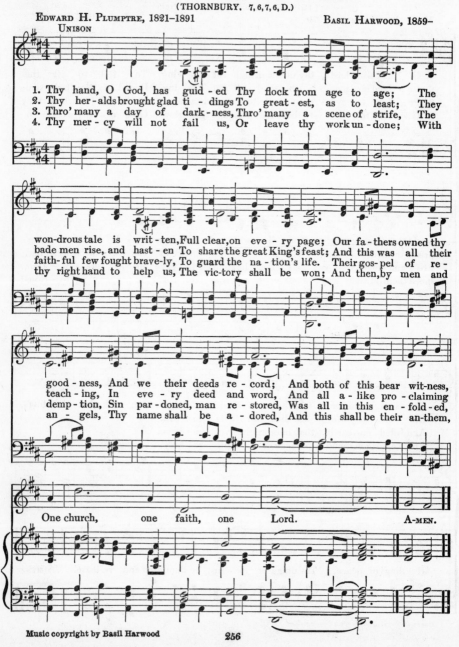

1. Thy hand, O God, has guid-ed Thy flock from age to age; The
2. Thy her-alds brought glad ti-dings To great-est, as to least; They
3. Thro' many a day of dark-ness, Thro' many a scene of strife, The
4. Thy mer-cy will not fail us, Or leave thy work un-done; With

won-drous tale is writ-ten, Full clear, on eve-ry page; Our fa-thers owned thy
bade men rise, and hast-en To share the great King's feast; And this was all their
faith-ful few fought brave-ly, To guard the na-tion's life. Their gos-pel of re-
thy right hand to help us, The vic-tory shall be won; And then, by men and

good-ness, And we their deeds re-cord; And both of this bear wit-ness,
teach-ing, In eve-ry deed and word, And all a-like pro-claiming
demp-tion, Sin par-doned, man re-stored, Was all in this en-fold-ed,
an-gels, Thy name shall be a-dored, And this shall be their an-them,

One church, one faith, one Lord. A-MEN.

Music copyright by Basil Harwood   256

308 The Church's One Foundation

(AURELIA. 7, 6, 7, 6, D.)

SAMUEL S. WESLEY, 1864

SAMUEL J. STONE, 1866

Descant by WILLIAM LESTER BATES, 1930

Descant

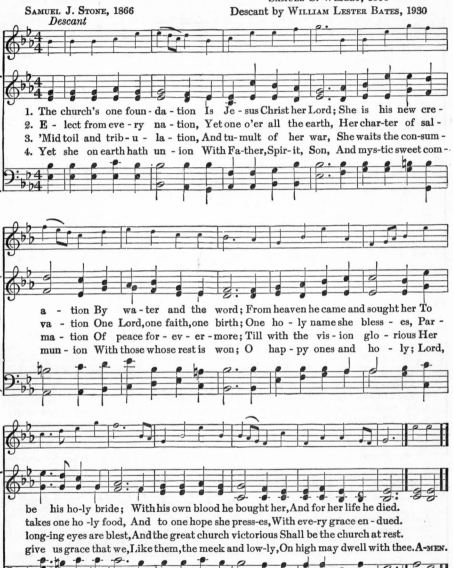

1. The church's one foun-da-tion Is Je-sus Christ her Lord; She is his new cre-a-tion By wa-ter and the word; From heaven he came and sought her To be his ho-ly bride; With his own blood he bought her, And for her life he died.

2. E-lect from eve-ry na-tion, Yet one o'er all the earth, Her char-ter of sal-va-tion One Lord, one faith, one birth; One ho-ly name she bless-es, Par-takes one ho-ly food, And to one hope she press-es, With eve-ry grace en-dued.

3. 'Mid toil and trib-u-la-tion, And tu-mult of her war, She waits the con-sum-ma-tion Of peace for-ev-er-more; Till with the vis-ion glo-rious Her long-ing eyes are blest, And the great church victorious Shall be the church at rest.

4. Yet she on earth hath un-ion With Fa-ther, Spir-it, Son, And mys-tic sweet com-mun-ion With those whose rest is won; O hap-py ones and ho-ly; Lord, give us grace that we, Like them, the meek and low-ly, On high may dwell with thee. A-MEN.

309 O Thou, Whose Glory Shone Like Fire

(CANONBURY. L. M.)

GEORGE A. WARBURTON

ROBERT SCHUMANN, 1839

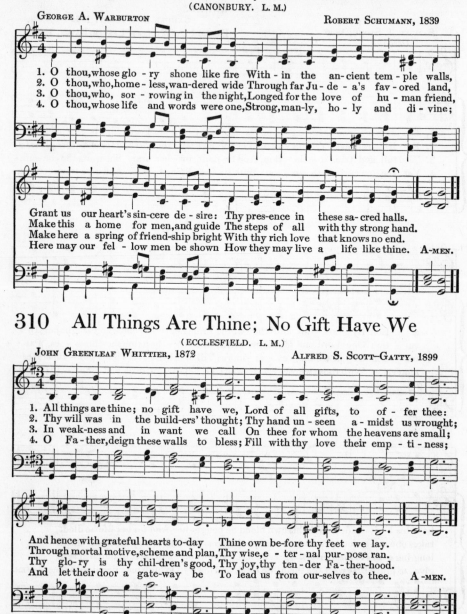

1. O thou, whose glo - ry shone like fire With - in the an-cient tem - ple walls,
2. O thou, who, home - less, wan-dered wide Through far Ju - de - a's fav - ored land,
3. O thou, who, sor - rowing in the night, Longed for the love of hu - man friend,
4. O thou, whose life and words were one, Strong, man-ly, ho - ly and di - vine,

Grant us our heart's sin-cere de - sire: Thy pres-ence in these sa-cred halls.
Make this a home for men, and guide The steps of all with thy strong hand.
Make here a spring of friend-ship bright With thy rich love that knows no end.
Here may our fel - low men be shown How they may live a life like thine. A-MEN.

310 All Things Are Thine; No Gift Have We

(ECCLESFIELD. L. M.)

JOHN GREENLEAF WHITTIER, 1872

ALFRED S. SCOTT–GATTY, 1899

1. All things are thine; no gift have we, Lord of all gifts, to of - fer thee:
2. Thy will was in the build-ers' thought; Thy hand un - seen a - midst us wrought;
3. In weak-ness and in want we call On thee for whom the heavens are small;
4. O Fa - ther, deign these walls to bless; Fill with thy love their emp - ti - ness;

And hence with grateful hearts to-day Thine own be-fore thy feet we lay.
Through mortal motive, scheme and plan, Thy wise, e - ter - nal pur-pose ran.
Thy glo - ry is thy chil-dren's good, Thy joy, thy ten - der Fa - ther-hood.
And let their door a gate-way be To lead us from our-selves to thee. A - MEN.

311   I Love Thy Kingdom, Lord

(ST. THOMAS. S.M.)

TIMOTHY DWIGHT, 1800

AARON WILLIAMS, 1763

1. I love thy king - dom, Lord, The house of thine a - bode,
2. I love thy church, O God; Her walls be - fore thee stand,
3. Sure as thy truth shall last, To Zi - on shall be given

The church our blest Re - deem - er saved With his own pre - cious blood.
Dear as the ap - ple of thine eye, And grav - en on thy hand.
The bright-est glo - ries earth can yield, And bright - er bliss of heaven. A - MEN.

312   Blest Be the Tie That Binds

(BOYLSTON. S.M.)

JOHN FAWCETT, 1782, altered

LOWELL MASON, 1832

1. Blest be the tie that binds Our hearts in Chris - tian love:
2. Be - fore our Fa - ther's throne We pour our ar - dent prayers;
3. We share each oth - er's woes, Each oth - er's bur - dens bear;
4. When we are called to part It gives us in - ward pain;

The fel - low - ship of kin - dred minds Is like to that a - bove.
Our fears, our hopes, our aims are one, Our com - forts and our cares.
And oft - en for each oth - er flows The sym - pa - thiz - ing tear.
But we shall still be joined in heart, And hope to meet a - gain. A - MEN.

313 O Happy Home, Where Thou Art Loved

(VESALIUS. 11, 10, 11, 10)

CARL J. P. SPITTA, 1833
Translated by SARAH L. FINDLATER, 1858

E. COOPER PERRY, 1895

1. O hap-py home, where thou art loved the dear-est, Thou lov-ing
2. O hap-py home, where each one serves thee, low-ly, What-ev-er
3. O hap-py home, where thou art not for-got-ten When joy is

Friend and Sav-iour of our race, And where a-mong the guests there nev-er
his ap-point-ed work may be, Till eve-ry com-mon task seems great and
o-ver-flow-ing, full and free; O hap-py home,where eve-ry wound-ed

com-eth One who can hold such high and hon-ored place.
ho-ly, When it is done, O Lord, as un-to thee.
spir-it Is brought, Phy-si-cian, Com-fort-er, to thee. A-MEN.

Music copyright by E. Cooper Perry

314 O Thou Whose Gracious Presence Blest

(WHITTIER. 8, 6, 8, 8, 6)

LOUIS F. BENSON, 1925

FREDERICK C. MAKER, 1887

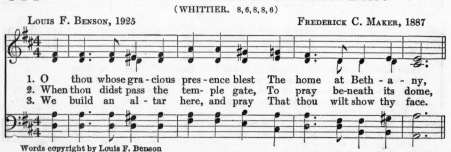

1. O thou whose gra-cious pres-ence blest The home at Beth-a-ny,
2. When thou didst pass the tem-ple gate, To pray be-neath its dome,
3. We build an al-tar here, and pray That thou wilt show thy face.

Words copyright by Louis F. Benson

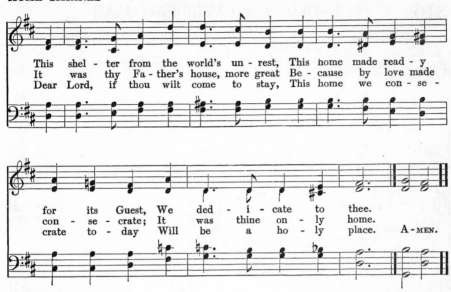

This shel - ter from the world's un - rest, This home made read - y
It was thy Fa - ther's house, more great Be - cause by love made
Dear Lord, if thou wilt come to stay, This home we con - se -

for its Guest, We ded - i - cate to thee.
con - se - crate; It was thine on - ly home.
crate to - day Will be a ho - ly place. A - MEN.

315　　From Homes of Quiet Peace

(CARLISLE. S. M.)

WILLIAM HENRY DRAPER, 1855-　　　　CHARLES LOCKHART, 1745-1815

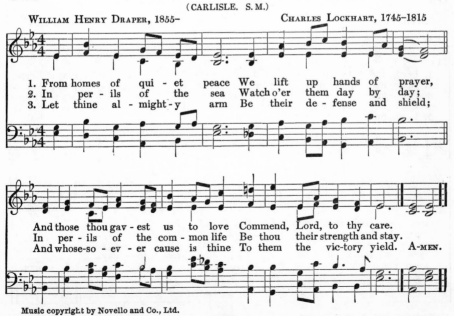

1. From homes of qui - et peace We lift up hands of prayer,
2. In per - ils of the sea Watch o'er them day by day;
3. Let thine al - might - y arm Be their de - fense and shield;

And those thou gav - est us to love Commend, Lord, to thy care.
In per - ils of the com - mon life Be thou their strength and stay.
And whose-so - ev - er cause is thine To them the vic-tory yield. A - MEN.

Music copyright by Novello and Co., Ltd.

316 O Father, Thou Who Givest All

(BELOIT. L. M.)

JOHN HAYNES HOLMES, 1908   CARL G. REISSIGER, 1798–1859

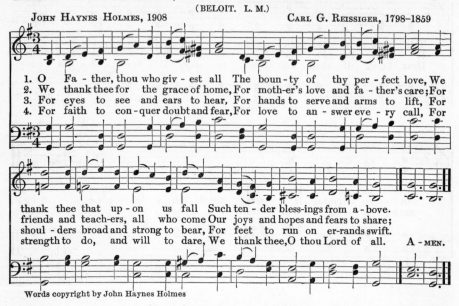

1. O Fa-ther, thou who giv-est all The boun-ty of thy per-fect love, We
2. We thank thee for the grace of home, For moth-er's love and fa-ther's care; For
3. For eyes to see and ears to hear, For hands to serve and arms to lift, For
4. For faith to con-quer doubt and fear, For love to an-swer eve-ry call, For

thank thee that up-on us fall Such ten-der bless-ings from a-bove.
friends and teach-ers, all who come Our joys and hopes and fears to share;
shoul-ders broad and strong to bear, For feet to run on er-rands swift.
strength to do, and will to dare, We thank thee, O thou Lord of all. A-MEN.

Words copyright by John Haynes Holmes

317 Lord, for Tomorrow and Its Needs

(BELLEVILLE. 8,4,8,4)

SYBIL F. PARTRIDGE, 1876   JAMES EDMUND JONES, 1906

1. Lord, for to-mor-row and its needs I do not pray; Keep
2. Let me both dil-i-gent-ly work And du-ly pray; Let
3. Let me be slow to do my will, Prompt to o-bey; Help
4. Let me no wrong nor i-dle word Un-think-ing say; Set
5. Lord, for to-mor-row and its needs, I do not pray; But

me, my God, from stain of sin, Just for to-day.
me be kind in word and deed, Just for to-day.
me to sac-ri-fice my-self, Just for to-day.
thou a seal up-on my lips, Just for to-day.
keep me, guide me, love me, Lord, Just for to-day. A-MEN.

Music copyright by James E. Jones

318 O Blessed Day of Motherhood!

(MATER. C. M. D.)

ERNEST F. McGREGOR, 1925   ARTHUR DEPEW, 1925

1. O bless - ed day of moth - er-hood! We lift our hearts in praise,
2. O sa - cred day of moth - er-hood! Our faith, by thee in - creased,
3. O pre - cious day of moth - er-hood! Teach us in thee to find
4. O won - drous day of moth - er-hood! Thy love to all a - bound;

To thank thee, Source of eve-ry good, Thy joy crowns all our days. O
Hath each al - lur - ing foe with-stood; Our souls thou hast re - leased. O
The great - er gifts of broth-er - hood; Bring peace to all man - kind. O
Be - side the cross once Ma - ry stood; A - gain let love be crowned. O

God, our Fa - ther, bless this day, En - rich its gold - en store

Of bless - ed moth - er love, and may Thy chil-dren thee a - dore.
Of sa - cred moth - er love, and may Thy chil-dren thee a - dore.
Of pre-cious moth - er love, and may Thy chil-dren thee a - dore.
Of wondrous moth - er love, and may Thy chil-dren thee a - dore. A-MEN.

319 The Spring Again Is Here

(TERRA BEATA. S.M.D.)

ARTHUR C. BENSON, 1862–1925

Traditional English Melody
Harmonized by EDWARD SHIPPEN BARNES, 1926

1. The spring a-gain is here; Life wakes from win-ter's gloom;
2. The morn is fresh and bright, The slow, dark hours de-part;

In field and for-est far and near Sweet open-ing flower-ets bloom.
Let days un-stained and pure de-light Bring sun-shine to the heart.

O mys-tery strange and sweet! That life so dumb-ly bound Should
Lord, touch our care-less eyes; New life, new ar-dors bring, That

rise, our thank-ful gaze to greet, And break from un-der ground.
we may read thy mys-ter-ies, The won-der of thy spring! A-MEN.

320 With Happy Voices Singing

(BERTHOLD. 7, 6, 7, 6, D.)

WILLIAM G. TARRANT, 1888

BERTHOLD TOURS, 1872

1. With hap - py voic - es sing - ing, Thy chil - dren, Lord, ap - pear;
2. For though no eye be - holds thee, No hand thy touch may feel,
3. And shall we not a - dore thee, With more than joy - ous song,

Their joy - ous prais - es bring - ing In an - thems full and clear;
Thy u - ni - verse un - folds thee, Thy star - ry heavens re - veal;
And live in truth be - fore thee, All beau - ti - ful and strong?

For skies of gold - en splen - dor, For az - ure roll - ing sea,
The earth and all its glo - ry, Our homes and all we love,
Lord, bless our souls' en - deav - or Thy ser - vants true to be,

For blos - soms sweet and ten - der, O Lord, we wor - ship thee.
Tell forth the won - drous sto - ry Of One who reigns a - bove.
And through all life, for - ev - er, To live our praise to thee. A-MEN.

265

321 The Summer Days Are Come Again

(LAND OF REST. C. M. D.)

SAMUEL LONGFELLOW, 1859

RICHARD S. NEWMAN, 1879

1. The sum-mer days are come a-gain; Once more the glad earth yields
2. The sum-mer days are come a-gain; The birds are on the wing;

Her gold-en wealth of rip-ening grain, And breath of clo-ver fields,
God's prais-es, in their lov-ing strain, Un-con-scious-ly they sing:

And deep-ening shade of sum-mer woods, And glow of sum-mer air,
We know who giv-eth all the good That doth our cup o'er-brim,

And wing-ing thoughts, and hap-py moods Of love and joy and prayer.
For sum-mer joy in field and wood We lift our song to him. A-MEN.

322 Come, Ye Thankful People, Come

(ST. GEORGE'S, WINDSOR. 7, 7, 7, 7, D.)

HENRY ALFORD, 1844
HUGH HARTSHORNE, 1915

GEORGE J. ELVEY, 1858
Descant by CHARLES REPPER, 1930

1. Come, ye thank-ful peo-ple, come, Raise the song of har-vest home;
2. All the bless-ings of the field, All the stores the gar-dens yield;
3. These to thee, our God, we owe, Source whence all our bless-ings flow;

All is safe-ly gath-ered in, Ere the win-ter storms be-gin;
All the fruits in full sup-ply, Rip-ened 'neath the sum-mer sky;
And for these our souls shall raise Grate-ful vows and sol-emn praise.

(Descant with 1st and 3rd stanzas only)

1. Our Mak-er doth pro-vide Our wants to be sup-plied;
3. Come, thank-ful peo-ple, come, With song of har-vest-home;

God, our Mak-er, doth pro-vide For our wants to be sup-plied;
All that spring with boun-teous hand Scat-ters o'er the smil-ing land;
Come, then, thank-ful peo-ple, come, Raise the song of har-vest-home;

1,3. Come to God's own tem-ple, come, Raise the song of har-vest home. AMEN.

Come to God's own tem-ple, come, Raise the song of har-vest home.
All that lib-eral au-tumn pours From her rich o'er-flow-ing stores;
Come to God's own tem-ple, come, Raise the song of har-vest home. AMEN.

323 We Plough the Fields and Scatter

(DRESDEN. 7, 6, 7, 6, D. With Refrain)

MATTHIAS CLAUDIUS, 1782
Translated by JANE M. CAMPBELL, 1861

JOHANN A. P. SCHULZ, 1800

1. We plough the fields, and scat - ter The good seed on the land,
2. He on - ly is the Mak - er Of all things near and far;
3. We thank thee, then, O Fa - ther, For all things bright and good,

But it is fed and wa - tered By God's al - might - y hand;
He paints the way - side flow - er, He lights the eve - ning star;
The seed - time and the har - vest, Our life, our health, our food;

He sends the snow in win - ter, The warmth to swell the grain,
The winds and waves o - bey him, By him the birds are fed;
The gifts that we would of - fer, For all thy love im - parts,

The breez - es and the sun - shine, And soft re - fresh - ing rain.
Much more to us, his chil - dren, He gives our dai - ly bread.
Are those thou most de - sir - est, Our hum - ble, thank - ful hearts.

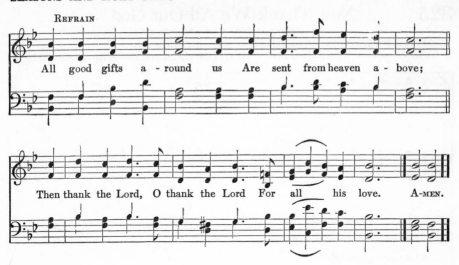

REFRAIN

All good gifts a - round us Are sent from heaven a - bove;

Then thank the Lord, O thank the Lord For all his love. A-MEN.

324 Once More the Liberal Year Laughs Out
(WALTHAM. L. M.)

JOHN GREENLEAF WHITTIER, 1859   J. BAPTISTE CALKIN, 1872

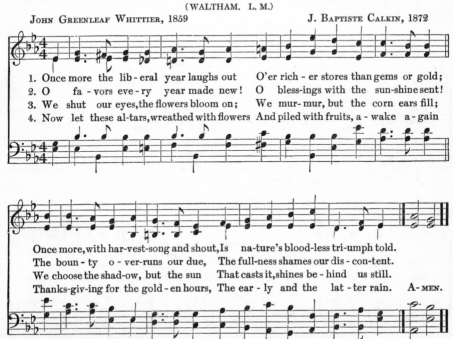

1. Once more the lib - eral year laughs out   O'er rich - er stores than gems or gold;
2. O fa - vors eve - ry year made new!   O bless-ings with the sun-shine sent!
3. We shut our eyes, the flowers bloom on;   We mur- mur, but the corn ears fill;
4. Now let these al-tars, wreathed with flowers And piled with fruits, a - wake a-gain

Once more, with har-vest-song and shout, Is na-ture's blood-less tri-umph told.
The boun - ty o - ver-runs our due, The full-ness shames our dis - con-tent.
We choose the shad-ow, but the sun That casts it, shines be - hind us still.
Thanks-giv-ing for the gold - en hours, The ear - ly and the lat - ter rain. A- MEN.

325 Now Thank We All Our God

(NUN DANKET. 6, 7, 6, 7, 6, 6, 6, 6)

MARTIN RINKART, 1636. Translated
by CATHERINE WINKWORTH, 1858

JOHANN CRUGER, 1647. Harmonized by
FELIX MENDELSSOHN-BARTHOLDY, 1809–1847

1. Now thank we all our God With heart and hands and voic - es,
2. O may this boun - teous God Thro' all our life be near us,

Who won-drous things hath done, In whom his world re - joic - es;
With ev - er joy - ful hearts And bless - ed peace to cheer us;

Who from our moth - ers' arms Hath blessed us on our way
And keep us in his grace, And guide us when per - plexed,

With count - less gifts of love, And still is ours to - day.
And free us from all ills In this world and the next. A-MEN.

326   All Beautiful the March of Days

(SHACKELFORD. C. M. D.)

FRANCES W. WILE, 1912   FREDERICK H. CHEESWRIGHT, 1880

1. All beau - ti - ful the march of days, As sea - sons come and go;
2. O'er white ex - pan - ses spark - ling pure The ra - diant morns un - fold;
3. O thou from whose un - fath - omed law The year in beau - ty flows,

The hand that shaped the rose hath wrought The crys - tal of the snow;
The sol - emn splen - dors of the night Burn bright - er through the cold;
Thy - self the vi - sion pass - ing by In crys - tal and in rose,

Hath sent the hoa - ry frost of heaven, The flow - ing wa - ters sealed,
Life mounts in eve - ry throb - bing vein, Love deep - ens round the hearth,
Day un - to day doth ut - ter speech, And night to night pro - claim,

And laid a si - lent love - li - ness On hill and wood and field.
And clear - er sounds the an - gel - hymn, 'Good - will to men on earth.'
In ev - er - chang - ing words of light, The won - der of thy name. A-MEN.

327 **Ring Out, Wild Bells**

(MOZART. L. M.)

ALFRED TENNYSON, 1849   School of Mozart, 18th Century

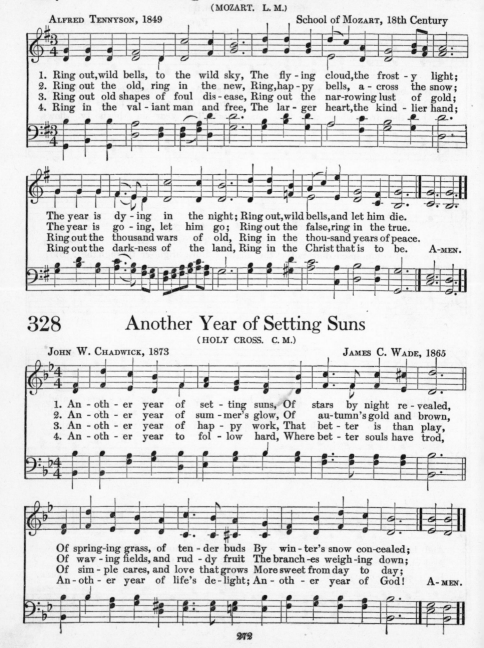

1. Ring out, wild bells, to the wild sky, The fly-ing cloud, the frost-y light;
2. Ring out the old, ring in the new, Ring, hap-py bells, a-cross the snow;
3. Ring out old shapes of foul dis-ease, Ring out the nar-rowing lust of gold;
4. Ring in the val-iant man and free, The lar-ger heart, the kind-lier hand;

The year is dy-ing in the night; Ring out, wild bells, and let him die.
The year is go-ing, let him go; Ring out the false, ring in the true.
Ring out the thousand wars of old, Ring in the thou-sand years of peace.
Ring out the dark-ness of the land, Ring in the Christ that is to be. A-MEN.

328 **Another Year of Setting Suns**

(HOLY CROSS. C. M.)

JOHN W. CHADWICK, 1873   JAMES C. WADE, 1865

1. An-oth-er year of set-ting suns, Of stars by night re-vealed,
2. An-oth-er year of sum-mer's glow, Of au-tumn's gold and brown,
3. An-oth-er year of hap-py work, That bet-ter is than play,
4. An-oth-er year to fol-low hard, Where bet-ter souls have trod,

Of spring-ing grass, of ten-der buds By win-ter's snow con-cealed;
Of wav-ing fields, and rud-dy fruit The branch-es weigh-ing down;
Of sim-ple cares, and love that grows More sweet from day to day;
An-oth-er year of life's de-light; An-oth-er year of God! A-MEN.

329 Hark, Hark, My Soul!

(PILGRIMS. 11, 10, 11, 10. With Refrain)

FREDERICK W. FABER, 1854   HENRY SMART, 1868

1. Hark, hark, my soul! an - gel - ic songs are swell-ing O'er earth's green fields and
2. On - ward we go, for still we hear them sing-ing, 'Come, wea - ry souls, for
3. Far, far a - way, like bells at eve-ning peal-ing, The voice of Je - sus
4. An - gels, sing on, your faith-ful watch-es keep-ing; Sing us sweet frag-ments

o - cean's wave-beat shore; How sweet the truth those bless-ed strains are tell - ing
Je - sus bids you come;' And thro' the dark, its ech-oes sweet-ly ring - ing,
sounds o'er land and sea; And la - den souls, by thousands meek-ly steal-ing,
of the songs a - bove; Till morn-ing's joy shall end the night of weep-ing,

REFRAIN

Of that new life when sin shall be no more. An-gels of Je - sus,
The mu - sic of the gos - pel leads us home.
Kind Shep-herd, turn their wea - ry steps to thee.
And life's long shad-ows break in cloud - less love.

an - gels of light, Sing-ing to wel-come the pil-grims of the night. A-MEN.

273

330 For All the Saints

(SINE NOMINE. 10, 10, 10, 4)

WILLIAM WALSHAM HOW, 1864
Verses 1, 2, 3, and 7, 8

R. VAUGHAN WILLIAMS, 1906

1. For all the saints, who from their la - bors rest, Who thee by faith be -
2. Thou wast their rock, their for - tress and their might; Thou, Lord, their cap - tain
3. O may thy sol - diers, faith -ful, true and bold, Fight as the saints who
7. But lo! there breaks a yet more glo-rious day; The saints tri - um -phant
8. From earth's wide bounds, from o-cean's far-thest coast, Thro' gates of pearl streams

fore the world con-fessed, Thy name, O Je - sus, be for - ev - er blest.
in the well-fought fight; Thou, in the dark - ness drear, their one true light
no - bly fought of old, And win with them the vic -tor's crown of gold.
rise in bright ar - ray; The King of glo - ry pass - es on his way.
in the count-less host, Sing - ing to Fa - ther, Son and Ho - ly Ghost,

Al - le - lu - ia, Al - le - lu - ia! A-MEN.

Verses 4, 5, 6
HARMONY

4. O blest com - mun - ion, fel - low-ship di - vine! We fee - bly
5. And when the strife is fierce, the war - fare long, Steals on the
6. The gold - en eve - ning bright - ens in the west; Soon, soon to

274

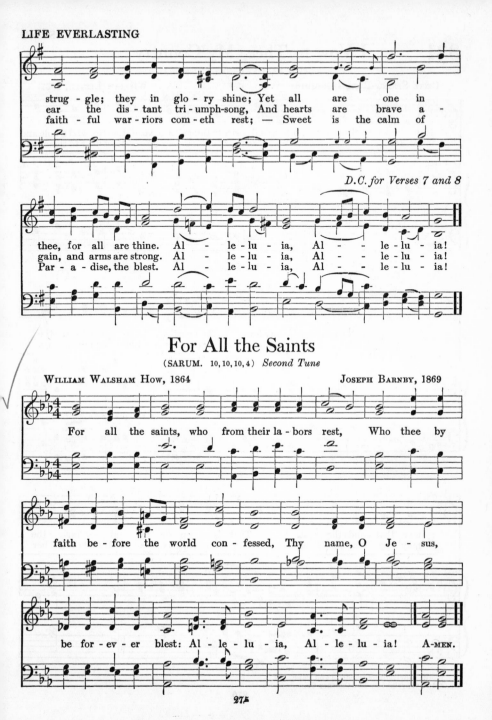

struggle; they in glory shine; Yet all are one in
ear the distant triumph-song, And hearts are brave a-
faithful warriors cometh rest; — Sweet is the calm of

D.C. for Verses 7 and 8

thee, for all are thine. Al - le - lu - ia, Al - - - le - lu - ia!
gain, and arms are strong. Al - le - lu - ia, Al - - - le - lu - ia!
Paradise, the blest. Al - le - lu - ia, Al - - - le - lu - ia!

For All the Saints

(SARUM. 10, 10, 10, 4) *Second Tune*

WILLIAM WALSHAM HOW, 1864   JOSEPH BARNBY, 1869

For all the saints, who from their labors rest, Who thee by

faith before the world confessed, Thy name, O Jesus,

be forever blest: Al - le - lu - ia, Al - le - lu - ia! A-MEN.

275

331 I Vow to Thee, My Country

(TWO FATHERLANDS. Irregular)

CECIL SPRING–RICE, 1859–1918   WILLIAM LESTER, 1927

1. I vow to thee, my coun-try, all earth-ly things a-bove— En-tire and whole and
2. And there's an-oth- er coun-try I've heard of long a - go— Most dear to them that

per - fect, the ser-vice of my love, The love that asks no ques-tions: the
love her, most great to them that know. We may not count her ar-mies: we

love that stands the test, That lays up-on the al - tar the
may not see her King— Her for-tress is a faith-ful heart, her

dear - est and the best: The love that nev-er fal - ters, the love that pays the
pride is suf -fer -ing. And soul by soul and si-lent- ly her shin-ing bounds in-

price, The love that makes un-daunted the fi - nal sac - ri -fice.
crease,—And her ways are ways of gentleness and all her paths are peace. A - MEN.

332 I Know Not What the Future Hath

(WARREN. 8, 6, 8, 6, 6)

JOHN GREENLEAF WHITTIER, 1865   LEROY CAMPBELL, 1930

UNISON

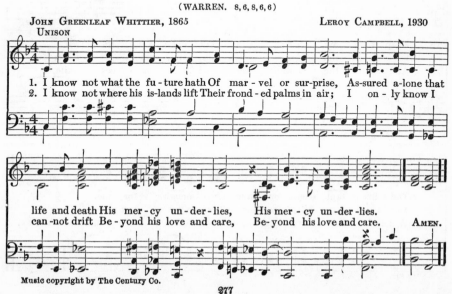

1. I know not what the fu - ture hath Of mar - vel or sur-prise, As-sured a-lone that
2. I know not where his is-lands lift Their frond - ed palms in air; I on - ly know I

life and death His mer - cy un-der -lies, His mer - cy un-der -lies.
can -not drift Be - yond his love and care, Be-yond his love and care. AMEN.

Music copyright by The Century Co.

333 Lead, Kindly Light

(LUX BENIGNA. 10, 4, 10, 4, 10, 10)

JOHN H. NEWMAN, 1833

JOHN B. DYKES, 1867

1. Lead, kind-ly Light, a-mid th'en-cir-cling gloom, Lead thou me on;
2. I was not ev-er thus, nor prayed that thou Shouldst lead me on;
3. So long thy power hath blest me, sure it still Will lead me on,

The night is dark, and I am far from home, Lead thou me on:
I loved to choose and see my path, but now Lead thou me on.
O'er moor and fen, o'er crag and tor-rent, till The night is gone;

Keep thou my feet; I do not ask to see
I loved the gar-ish day, and, spite of fears,
And with the morn those an-gel fa-ces smile,

The dis-tant scene, one step e-nough for me.
Pride ruled my will; re-mem-ber not past years.
Which I have loved long since, and lost a-while. A-MEN.

334 Praise God, from Whom All Blessings Flow

(OLD HUNDREDTH. L. M.)

THOMAS KEN, 1709   LOUIS BOURGEOIS, Genevan Psalter, 1551

Praise God, from whom all bless-ings flow; Praise him all crea-tures here be-low;

Praise him a-bove, ye heavenly host; Praise Fa-ther, Son and Ho-ly Ghost. A-MEN.

335 Glory Be to the Father

(GLORIA PATRI. Irregular)

Greek, 2nd Century   HENRY W. GREATOREX

Glo-ry be to the Fa-ther, and to the Son, and to the Ho-ly Ghost; As it

was in the be-ginning, is now, and ever shall be, world without end. A - men, A - men.

336 Holy, Holy, Holy

(SANCTUS. Irregular)

From 'The Holy City'
ALFRED R. GAUL, 1837-1913

Ho-ly, ho-ly, ho-ly, Lord of hosts: Ho-ly, ho-ly, ho-ly is the Lord of hosts. A-MEN.

337

Glory to the King of Angels

(REGENT SQUARE. 8, 7, 8, 7, 8, 7)

HORATIUS BONAR, 1808–1889

HENRY SMART, 1867

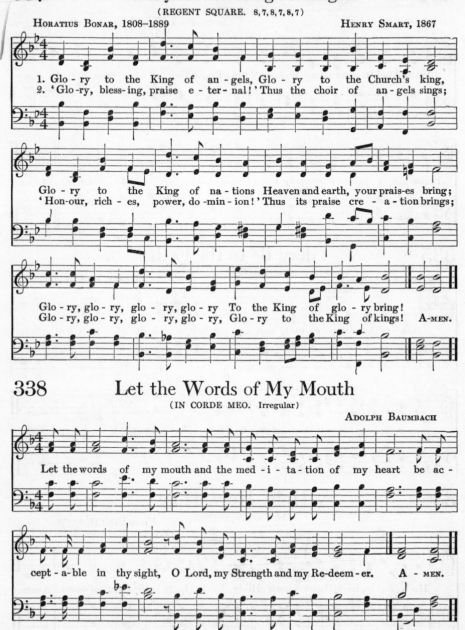

1. Glo - ry to the King of an - gels, Glo - ry to the Church's king,
2. 'Glo - ry, bless - ing, praise e - ter - nal!' Thus the choir of an - gels sings;

Glo - ry to the King of na - tions Heaven and earth, your prais - es bring;
'Hon - our, rich - es, power, do - min - ion!' Thus its praise cre - a - tion brings;

Glo - ry, glo - ry, glo - ry, glo - ry To the King of glo - ry bring!
Glo - ry, glo - ry, glo - ry, glo - ry, Glo - ry to the King of kings! A - MEN.

338

Let the Words of My Mouth

(IN CORDE MEO. Irregular)

ADOLPH BAUMBACH

Let the words of my mouth and the med - i - ta - tion of my heart be ac -

cept - a - ble in thy sight, O Lord, my Strength and my Re - deem - er. A - MEN.

339   ## We Give Thee But Thine Own
(SCHUMANN. S.M.)

WILLIAM WALSHAM HOW, 1858

MASON AND WEBB'S
'Cantica Laudis,' Boston, 1850

1. We give thee but thine own, What-e'er the gift may be: All that we have is thine a-lone, A trust, O Lord, from thee.
2. May we thy boun-ties thus As stew-ards true re-ceive, And glad-ly, as thou bless-est us, To thee our first-fruits give. A-MEN.

340   ## Bless Thou the Gifts
(CANONBURY. L.M.)

SAMUEL LONGFELLOW, 1886

ROBERT SCHUMANN, 1839

Bless thou the gifts our hands have brought: Bless thou the work our hearts have planned;

Ours is the faith, the will, the tho't; The rest, O God, is in thy hand. A-MEN.

341   ## All Things Come of Thee, O Lord
(OFFERTORY. IRREGULAR)

LUDWIG VAN BEETHOVEN, 1770–1827

All things come of thee, O Lord; and of thine own have we giv-en thee. A-MEN.

342 Hear Our Prayer, O Lord

GEORGE WHELPTON, 1897

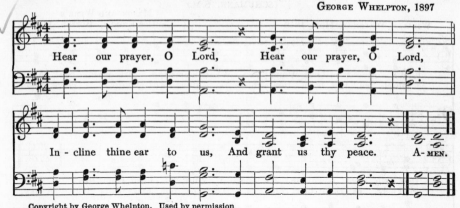

Hear our prayer, O Lord, Hear our prayer, O Lord,

In - cline thine ear to us, And grant us thy peace. A - MEN.

Copyright by George Whelpton. Used by permission

343 O Come, Let Us Worship

Anonymous

O come, let us wor - ship and bow down:

Let us kneel be - fore the Lord our mak - er. A - MEN.

344 Day Is Done, Gone the Sun

(TAPS. Irregular)

Anonymous

Day is done, gone the sun, from the lake, from the hills, from the

sky, Safe - ly rest, all is well, God is nigh.

Worship Section

NUMBERS

AIDS TO WORSHIP 345–355

UNISON READINGS 356–362

RESPONSIVE READINGS 363–381

SCRIPTURE SELECTIONS 382–387

PRAYERS AND HIGH RESOLVES 388–429

DEVOTIONAL POETRY AND PROSE 430–540

SERVICES OF WORSHIP . . . . Pages 341–368

Introduction

The liturgical material which this book provides is prepared with the general aim, — to aid youth in the interpretation and expression of religious experience. To accomplish this the following objectives are in view:

(1) To present a limited number of services of worship, arranged according to vital and inspirational themes, such as will serve as representative of the types of services which young people themselves may build.

(2) To provide within these services of worship those elements which may contribute to a complete experience of worship.

(3) To provide a wealth of source material which will be of inspiration and value in itself, and which will enable young people to readily build services of worship according to individual and group initiative.

(4) To provide beauty in rhythm, sound and word which will minister to the aesthetic needs of youth.

(5) To provide spiritual content for self-expression such as will enrich the spiritual life of youth.

This book will be of value as a text book for the Week Day School of Religion where special courses in worship may be taught; it will be the worship manual for young people's societies and departments of the Church School; it will serve as guide to teachers and leaders of youth in the leadership of worship for every occasion.

If youth may be led to a greater reality of spiritual values, and to a deeper, richer experience in the expression of personal feeling, then the object of this compilation of material will have been realized.

THE EDITOR

Index to Worship Section
Including Author's Index and Copyrights

No.
AIDS TO WORSHIP
345 The Call to Worship
346 Spirit, Light, Love
    Arranged by Albert W. Palmer
347 Let us Praise God
    From the Gray Book, Oxford University Press
348 Beatitudes of Light and Life and Love
    John Hunter, From "Hunter's Devotional
    Services."
    Copyright by J. M. Dent and Sons
349 Litany of Joy
    William C. Gannett, Beacon Press
350 Litany of Aspiration
351 Litany of Thanksgiving
    Responsive Readings (Sources Ancient and
    Modern), Beacon Press
352 Litany of Adoration
    Arranged by Shepherd Knapp
353 Commandments with Responses
    From Devotional Offices for General Use
    The Century Co. By John W. Suter
354 The Te Deum Laudamus
355 Meditation and Prayer

UNISON READINGS
(King James Version)
356 His Glory at Morn
    Psalm 19: 1-6
357 With Joy and Rejoicing
    Psalm 100
358 The King of Glory
    Psalm 24
359 The Shepherd Divine
    Psalm 23
360 The Keeper Eternal
    Psalm 121
361 The Growing Life
    Psalm 1
362 Nature Appreciation
    Psalm 8

RESPONSIVE READINGS
(American Revised Version)
363 Sing unto the Lord
    Psalm 96
364 How Manifold are thy Works
    Psalm 104: 1-24
365 Among all Nations
    Psalm 67
366 The Prince of Peace
    Isaiah 9: 2-7; Micah 4: 2-4; Isaiah 11: 9
367 The Way of Wisdom
    Selections from Proverbs 1, 2, 3, 4, 9
368 The Loyalty of Love
    Ruth 1: 8-11, 14-18
369 Secrets of the Happy Life
    (The Beatitudes), Matt. 5: 3-12
370 The Master's Friendship
    John 15: 8-17
371 My Place in Life
    Luke 4: 16-21
372 Likeness unto Him
    John 13: 12-17
373 The Good Shepherd
    John 10: 11, 14, 16; Luke 15: 4-6; Matt. 9, 10

No.
374 Marks of the Master
    Matthew 11: 1-6
375 In Love's Devotion
    Luke 10: 38-42
376 Unto the Least of These
    Matthew 25
377 True Greatness
    Mark 10: 42-45
378 The Love that Abides
    I Corinthians 13
379 The Well-armed Warrior
    Ephesians 6: 10-17
380 Glory in the Highest
    Luke 2: 8-20
381 The Easter Story
    John 20: 1-18

SCRIPTURE SELECTIONS
(Moffat Translation)
382 New Life in the Valley
    Isaiah 41: 17-20
383 This is the Way: Walk Here
    Isaiah 30: 18-21
384 In Brotherly Love
    Galatians 6: 3-9
385 Tongues of Fire
    James 3: 2-6
386 A Call to Wisdom
    Proverbs 3: 1-9
387 Meditation
    Psalm 139: 1-12, 23-24

PRAYERS AND HIGH RESOLVES
388 For Knowledge of God
    Galasian Sacramentary
389 For Abundant Life
390 That we may Hear Thee
391 That we may Learn
392 For Myself
    W. H. Aitken
393 For all Gifts: Thanks
    Hugh Elmer Brown
394 For the Kingdom of God
    Laura Armstrong
395 The Temple of Health
    Marshall Dawson, from "Prayer that Prevails"
396 For Those who Care for Us
    Girl's Everyday Book, The Woman's Press
397 For Vigor of Life
    Girl's Everyday Book, The Woman's Press
398 Prayer of a Camper
399 Out Door Prayer
    Dartmouth Outing Club
400 For Cleanness of Life
    Book of Prayers for Students
401 For Right Conduct
    William DeWitt Hyde
402 For Consecration to Our Work
    Dr. Arnold of Rugby
403 Day unto Day
    Joseph Fort Newton
404 Purposeful Life
    Tompkins, Prayers for the Quiet Life
405 For the Good Life
    Joseph Fort Newton, from
    "Altar Stairs," Macmillan Co.

No.

406 Beauty and Joy

407 The Quest

408 For the Pioneer Spirit
Harry Kimball

409 Friendship
Bishop Thirkield; Services and Prayers for
Church and Home, The Abingdon Press

410 The Sabbath
Margaret Slattery, from Girl's Book of Prayers
The Pilgrim Press

411 Flames of Fire

412 The Book of Books
Joseph Fort Newton, from
" Altar Stairs," Macmillan Co.

413 Prayer for all Workers
From the "Gray Book," Oxford University Press

414 For Our City

415 For True Patriotism

416 A Bethany Home

417 For Our Home

418 Mother's Day
Henry Van Dyke

419 Christmas
Edmund H. Reeman

420 Transcending all Differences
Joseph Fort Newton

421 The Morning
Robert Bartlett, The Pilgrim Press

422 Every Day
Joseph Fort Newton, from
" Altar Stairs," Macmillan Co.

423 Motherhood
Songs of Work and Worship

424 Christmas
Joseph Fort Newton, from
" Altar Stairs," Macmillan Co.

425 For Friendship
Robert Barlett, The Pilgrim Press

426 For a Worthy Career
Robert Bartlett

427 For Respect for Law
Robert Bartlett

428 For New Americans
Robert Bartlett

429 Youth's Desire
Psalm 119: 33-40. Moffat Translation

DEVOTIONAL POETRY AND PROSE

430 Some Gay Adventurous Thing
Grace Noll Crowell, from Good Housekeeping

431 God's World
Robert Browning

432 Purpose for this Day
John H. Vincent

433 The Stainless White Radiance
Rabindranath Tagore

434 God
Catherine Cate Coblentz

435 Voices of God
Samuel Coleridge

436 Learn about God
Alfred Tennyson

437 God's Trees
Joyce Kilmer

438 The One Thousandth Psalm
Edward Everett Hale

439 The One Thousandth Psalm
Edward Everett Hale

No.

440 Canticle to the Sun
Francis of Assisi, Translated by John Ruskin

441 Life as Lovely as Nature

442 Wind in the Pines
Lew Sarett, from " The Box of God "
Henry Holt and Co.

443 I Shall Arrive
Robert Browning

444 A Psalm of Faith
Winfred L. Bryning

445 Care for My Needs
Margaret Sangster

446 Beholding God
Walt Whitman, from
Leaves of Grass, David C. McKay Co.

447 The Soul of Jesus is Restless
Cyrus R. Mitchell

448 The Universal Book
Walt Whitman

449 God's Word
John Greenleaf Whittier

450 A New Light
Winfred Ernest Garrison

451 The Spirit of the Christ Child
Girl's Everyday Book, Woman's Press

452 Christmas Everywhere
Phillips Brooks

453 Far Trumpets Blowing
Louis F. Benson

454 Room for the Christ Child

455 Christ, Straight and Wise
Carl Sandberg

456 Judean Hills are Holy
William I. Stidger

457 Joses, the Brother of Jesus
Harry Kemp, from
"Chants and Ballads," Brentanos, Publishers.

458 Jesus Saith
Katharine Lee Bates

459 Who are You, Jesus?
Girl's Everyday Book, Woman's Press

460 The Song of a Heathen
Richard Watson Gilder

461 A Fisherman Speaks
Scharmel Iris

462 Napoleon Speaks for Christ
Napoleon Bonaparte

463 Fling Wide the Gates

464 Palm Sunday
John T. MacFarland

465 He Still Lives
Edward Thompson

466 Nature's Victorious Life

467 I Know a Name

468 The Everlasting Mercy
John Masefield, Macmillan Co.

469 My Body
Elmer Fehlhaber

470 Life of my Life
Rabindranath Tagore

471 Self-Mastery
William C. Gannett, The Beacon Press

472 Gifts of the Spirit
Henry Van Dyke, from " God of the Open Air,"
Charles Scribner's Sons

473 Lord of the Mountain
Navajo Prayer

474 Temptation
Robert Browning

Index to Worship Section

No.
475 For Loyalty
Edward Horton
476 The Voice, the Power, and the Angel
Florence Buck
477 For Strength
Rabindranath Tagore
478 Fight On
479 Right and True
The "Southern Agriculturist," from
A Calendar of Country Song
480 Youth Builds
Mary Carolyn Davies
481 Building Forever
John Ruskin
482 The Gift of Labor
Katharine Atherton Grimes
483 We Shall Build On
Studdert Kennedy
484 The Spirit of Reality
S. Hoyland, W. Heffer and Sons, Ltd.
485 Four Things
Henry Van Dyke
486 There is No Unbelief
Elizabeth York Case
487 Great is Truth
1st Esdras 4
488 The Things of the Spirit
Douglas Malloch; used by permission
489 The Sky-Born Music
490 Vision
Katharine Lee Bates
491 The Inspirations of Beauty
Composite from John Keats, Robert Browning,
Persian Proverb, Mrs. Browning, Studdert
Kennedy
492 O Beautiful Human Life
Richard Jefferies, from
"The Story of My Heart"
493 The Inspiration of Nature
Henry David Thoreau, from
"Early Spring in Massachusetts."
494 Thanks
Olive Schreiner, from "From Man
to Man"
495 To Strive, to Seek, to Find
Alfred Tennyson, from "Ulysses"
496 Life's Victors
William W. Story
497 Faithful Souls
Edward Everett Hale
498 Build Thee More Stately Mansions
Oliver Wendell Holmes, from
"The Chambered Nautilus"
499 Greatheart
John Oxenham
500 Unselfish Giving
James Russell Lowell, from
"The Vision of Sir Launfal"
501 Friendship Fire
Girl's Everyday Book,
Woman's Press
502 The Upward Road
Mary S. Edgar
503 The Arrow and the Song
Henry Wadsworth Longfellow
504 Cooperation
Marcus Aurelius
505 Pass on the Torch
George Bernard Shaw

No.
506 The Surgeon's Hands
Ida Norton Munson
507 Evidence of Faith in Modern Achievement
Laura Armstrong and
Melrose High School Students
508 Livingstone
David Livingstone, John Oxenham
509 The Spirit of Amundson
Thomas Curtis Clark
510 On! Sail On!
Joaquin Miller
511 Latimer's Light
512 What Makes a City Great
513 The Higher Citizenship
Socrates
514 Lincoln's Speech at Gettysburg
Abraham Lincoln
515 America's Making
Rabbi Abba Hillel Silver
516 The American Flag
Franklin K. Lane
517 Dost Thou Prosper, Dearest Land
Henry Van Dyke
518 O Thrilling Age
Angela Morgan. Copyright by Dodd, Mead
519 Let the People Love   [and Co.
520 In the Dawn
Odell Shepard, from "In the Dawn"
521 Make Way for Brotherhood
Edwin Markham
522 Vision
Alfred Tennyson
523 In Christ there is no East or West
John Oxenham
524 The Christian Church
Theodore Parker
525 The Church of God
William Cullen Bryant
526 Church of the Living God
From "World Call"
527 House Blessing
Arthur Guiterman
528 Beatitudes for the Home
John Oxenham
529 The Family Altar
John Martin and Others. Copyright by Har-
530 The House Beautiful   [per and Brothers
Louis Untermeyer
531 Outward Bound
W. W. W. Argow
532 A Blessing for the Loaf
Maltbie Babcock
533 Autumn
William Herbert Carruth
534 All Hail, All Hail to the New
Mary Ann Lathbury
535 Building Eternity
Edwin Markham
536 Crossing the Bar
Alfred Tennyson
537 Some Late Lark Singing
William Ernest Henley. Copyright by Charles
538 My Life Dynamic   [Scribner's Sons
Rudolph C. Stoll
539 My Future
Girl's Everyday Book, Woman's Press
540 Immortality
Girl's Everyday Book, Woman's Press
Used by permission

Services of Worship

I. Mountains of Vision

A Service, using Unison and Responsive Readings from the King James, American Revised, and Goodspeed Translations of the Bible.

FOR THE NEW YEAR, RALLY DAY AND ANNIVERSARY OCCASIONS.

II. Broad Stripes and Bright Stars

A Service, with Pledges of Loyalty and Salutes to the Flag.

FOR PATRIOT'S BIRTHDAYS, FLAG DAY, FOURTH OF JULY AND HOME MISSIONS.

III. Following the Master

A Picture Service.

FOR THE LENTEN SEASON, DECISION DAYS AND YOUTH CONFERENCES AND CAMPS.

IV. The Singing World

A Hymn Service, featuring Chant and Doxology, the Reading and Singing of Hymns and Antiphonal and Dramatic Hymns.

FOR EASTER, SPRINGTIME, CHILDREN'S DAY, GENERAL PRAISE.

V. Friendship

A Brief Service for General use.

VI. The Temple of the Out-of-Doors

A Service of Prayers and High Resolves with Special Music.

FOR ALL SEASONS OF THE YEAR.

VII. Be Still, and Know that I am God

A Service of Silences.

FOR VESPERS, SUMMER CAMP AND GENERAL WORSHIP.

VIII. The Light

An Outline Service of Symbols.

FOR CHRISTMAS, BIBLE SUNDAY AND THE QUEST OF YOUTH.

IX. Commemoration

A Service using Litanies and the Offertory as the Climax.

FOR COLUMBUS DAY, WASHINGTON'S AND LINCOLN'S BIRTHDAYS, DECORATION AND ARMISTICE DAYS.

X. The Human Race

A Ceremonial of Maps.

FOR ARMISTICE DAY, CHRISTMAS, MISSIONARY AND PEACE SUNDAYS.

288

Aids to Worship*

345. The Call to Worship

O come, let us worship and bow down,
Let us kneel before the Lord, our Maker:
For he is our God,
And we are the people of his pasture, and the sheep of his hand.

Lift up your hearts.
We lift them up unto the Lord.
O Lord, open thou our lips;
And our mouth shall show forth thy praise.
Praise ye the Lord.
The Lord's name be praised.

Who shall ascend into the hill of the Lord?
And who shall stand in his holy place?
He that hath clean hands, and a pure heart;
Who hath not lifted up his soul unto vanity,
And hath not sworn deceitfully.

The hour cometh, and now is, when the true worshippers shall worship the Father in spirit and in truth; for the Father seeketh such to worship him. God is a spirit, and they that worship him must worship him in spirit and in truth.

Know ye not that ye are the temple of God, and that the spirit of God dwelleth in you?
For as many as are led by the spirit of God, they are children of God.

Lord of life! Open wide the window of our spirits, and fill us full of light; open wide the door of our hearts, that we may receive and entertain thee with all our powers of adoration and love. Amen.

346. Spirit, Light, Love

God is a spirit, and they that worship him must worship him in spirit and in truth.

O come let us worship and bow down, let us kneel before the Lord our maker.

God is light, and the Father of lights in whom is no variableness neither shadow that is cast by turning.

O Lord, send out thy light and thy truth, let them lead us to thy holy hill.

God is love, and he that dwelleth in love dwelleth in God and God in him.

O thou who makest the outgoings of the morning and evening to rejoice, keep us in thy love this day and forevermore.

347. Let Us Praise God

Let us praise God
For the Day, for the glory and warmth of the sun, for the stir of life, and for honest toil that wins food and rest.
God be praised for the Day.
For the gift of Children; may he help us to train them to be reverent

and truthful, that they may gladden our hearts and bring joy to the world.

God be praised for Children.

For good Friends to rejoice with us in our joys, to cheer us in trouble and to lighten our tasks; may he help us to repay them in fellowship and service.

God be praised for our Friends.

Let us praise God for Life.

All praise be to God.

348. Beatitudes of Light and Life and Love

Blessed are they that dwell in thy house, O Lord; they will still be praising thee.

Shine on us, O thou Light and Life and Love Divine.

Blessed is the man that feareth the Lord, that delightest greatly in his commandments.

Let thy truth within us shine.

Blessed is the man that walketh not in the counsel of the ungodly, nor standeth in the way of sinners, nor sitteth in the seat of the scornful; but his delight is in the law of the Lord, and in his law doth he meditate day and night.

O send out thy light and thy truth, let them lead me.

Blessed are they that keep the testimonies of the Lord, that seek him with the whole heart.

Lord, have mercy upon us, and incline our hearts to keep thy law.

Blessed is he that considereth the poor, the Lord will deliver him in time of trouble.

Lord, have mercy upon us, and fill our hearts with the love of Christ.

Blessed are the people who know the joyful sound; they walk, O Lord, in the light of thy countenance.

O Lord, open thou our lips, and our mouth shall show forth thy praise.

349. Litany of Joy

For the gift of life in this wonderful world; for days of health, and for nights of quiet sleep,

We thank thee, our Father.

For the beautiful face of the year; for the glory of the seasons and the sure and bountiful harvests,

We thank thee, our Father.

For our homes and our friends, for the humble, the faithful and the loving people of the world,

We thank thee, our Father.

For the faith that makes us faithful, for thy gifts to every child of earth, for the privilege of sharing and helping others to obtain their share of thy bounty,

We thank thee, our Father.

For the good at the heart of our world, for the faith in the eternal Goodness, for all the gladness of life and for the heart's assurance of Life Eternal in thee,

We bless thee, and thank thee, O God of our joy.

350. Litany of Aspiration

For all thy protection and care this day,

We thank thee, our Father.

For the gift of life, and the ability to enjoy it,

We give thee thanks, our heavenly Father.

For friends and all that their companionship means to us,

We thank thee, Lord.

For the fact that we can share in thy work,

We give thee our thanks.

For the desire thou dost give us to work for great causes,

Accept our thanks, O Lord.

For the power to think great thoughts,

Dear Lord, we praise thee.

For the freedom of our land, and the challenge which that freedom brings,

We thank thee, our Heavenly Father.

For the opportunity to come apart and worship thee, and for rest that we may be prepared for the duties of the morrow,

For all these things, Lord, we give thee thanks.

351. Litany of Thanksgiving

For the poetry of spring, for the pageantry of summer, for the soft intonations of autumn, for the austere majesty of winter,

We lift up thankful hearts.

For all the unknown toilers in mine and field, in factory and office, whose strength has redeemed us from want, whose blood has purchased our welfare, the fruit of whose labor is our rich inheritance,

We lift up thankful hearts.

For the unsung dreamers in every land and age, whose undying faith has woven a fadeless tapestry of hope wherein we behold the pattern of a better world to be,

We lift up thankful hearts.

For the sustaining strength of those near and dear, whose understanding love brings serenity and peace to our restless souls, and assures us that our lives have value for others,

We lift our thankful hearts.

For the enchantment of wonder, the allurement of mystery, the appeal of beauty, the challenge of goodness, the sacrificial strength of love,

We lift our thankful hearts.

For the sacrament of work, through which we have fellowship with an unending creation that maketh all things new,

We lift up thankful hearts.

For the unbought privilege of life in a world wherein human souls may attain an eternal worth, and where great dreams come true,

We lift up thankful hearts.

352. Litany of Adoration

Holy, holy, holy, is the Lord God, the Almighty, who was, and who is, and who is to come.

All glory be to thee, O Lord most High.

Great and marvellous are thy works, O Lord God, the Almighty; righteous and true are thy ways, thou King of the Ages. Who shall not worship thee, O Lord, and glorify thy Name? For thou only art holy.

All glory be to thee, O Lord most High.

Oh, the depth of the riches, both of the wisdom and the knowledge of God! How unsearchable are his judgments, and his ways past finding out. For of him, and through him, and unto him are all things.

All glory be to thee, O Lord most High.

Now unto the King, eternal, immortal, invisible, the only God, be honor and glory forever.

All glory be to thee, O Lord most High.

Aids to Worship

353. Commandments with Responses

I am the Lord thy God; thou shalt have none other gods but me.

We cannot serve God and mammon. Let us worship the Lord our God, and him only let us serve.

Thou shalt not make to thyself any graven image, nor the likeness of any thing that is in heaven above, or in the earth beneath, or in the water under the earth; thou shalt not bow down to them, nor worship them.

God is a spirit; and we who worship him must worship him in spirit and in truth.

Thou shalt not take the name of the Lord thy God in vain.

Let us swear not at all; neither by heaven, for it is God's throne; nor by the earth, for it is his footstool.

Remember that thou keep holy the Sabbath-day.

The Sabbath was made for man. Let us follow him who said, Come ye yourselves apart, and rest awhile.

Honor thy father and thy mother.

Let us be kindly affectioned one to another with brotherly love: in honor preferring one another.

Thou shalt do no murder.

Let us not be angry with our brothers. Let us love our enemies, and do good to them that hate us; that we may be the children of our Father which is in heaven.

Thou shalt not commit adultery.

Let us be pure in heart. that we may see God.

Thou shalt not steal.

If we have stolen, let us steal no more, but rather labor with our hands for the thing which is good, that we may have to give to him that needeth.

Thou shalt not bear false witness against thy neighbor.

Putting away lying, let us speak every man truth with his neighbor for we are members one of another.

Thou shalt not covet.

Let us lay up for ourselves treasures in heaven; for where our treasure is, there will our hearts be also.

O Almighty Lord, and everlasting God, vouchsafe, we beseech thee, to direct, sanctify, and govern, both our hearts and bodies, in the ways of thy laws, and in the works of thy commandments; that, through thy most mighty protection, both here and ever, we may be preserved in body and soul; through our Lord and Saviour, Jesus Christ. Amen.

354. Te Deum Laudamus

We praise thee, O God; we acknowledge thee to be the Lord.

All the earth doth worship thee, the Father everlasting.

To thee all angels cry aloud;

The heavens, and all the powers therein;

To thee cherubim and seraphim continually do cry, — Holy, holy, holy, Lord God of Sabaoth;

Heaven and earth are full of the majesty of thy glory.

The glorious company of the apostles praise thee.

The goodly fellowship of the prophets praise thee.

The noble army of martyrs praise thee.

The holy Church throughout all the world doth acknowledge thee,

The Father of an infinite majesty;

Thine adorable, true and only Son;

Also the Holy Ghost, the Comforter.

Thou art the King of Glory, O Christ; thou art the everlasting Son of the Father.

When thou tookest upon thee to deliver man, thou didst humble thyself to be born of a virgin.

When thou hadst overcome the sharpness of death thou didst open the kingdom of heaven to all believers.

Thou sittest at the right hand of God, in the glory of the Father.

We believe that thou shalt come to be our Judge.

We therefore pray thee, help thy servants, whom thou hast redeemed with thy precious blood.

Make them to be numbered with thy saints, in glory everlasting.

O Lord, save thy people, and bless thine heritage.

Govern them, and lift them up for ever.

Day by day we magnify thee;

And we worship thy name ever, world without end.

Vouchsafe, O Lord, to keep us this day without sin.

O Lord, have mercy upon us, have mercy upon us.

O Lord, let thy mercy be upon us, as our trust is in thee.

O Lord, in thee have I trusted; let me never be confounded.

355. Meditation and Prayer

Let us remember Jesus: Who, though he was rich, yet for our sakes became poor and dwelt among us. Who was content to be subject to his parents, the child of a poor man's home. Who lived for thirty years the common life, earning his living with his own hands and declining no humble tasks. Whom the common people heard gladly, for he understood their ways.

(MOMENT OF MEDITATION)

Let us remember Jesus: Who was mighty in deed, healing the sick and the disordered, using for others the powers he would not invoke for himself. Who refused to force men's allegiance. Who was master and Lord to his disciples, yet was among them as their companion and as one who served.

(MEDITATION)

Let us remember Jesus: Who loved men, yet retired from them to pray, rose a great while before day, watched through a night, stayed in the wilderness, went up into a mountain, sought a garden. Who, when he would help a tempted disciple, prayed for him, and for the perfecting of those who received him.

(MEDITATION)

Let us remember Jesus: Who believed in men to the last and never despaired of them. Who through all disappointment never lost heart. Who disregarded his own comfort and convenience and thought first of others' needs, and though he suffered long was always kind. Who, when he was reviled, reviled not again, and when he suffered, threatened not. Who humbled himself and carried obedience to the point of death, even death on the cross, and endured faithfully to the end.

(UNISON PRAYER)

O Christ, our only Saviour, so come to dwell in us that we may go forth with the light of thy hope in our eyes, and thy faith and love in our hearts. Amen.

Unison Readings

(King James Version)

356. His Glory at Morn

The heavens declare the glory of God; and the firmament sheweth his handiwork.

Day unto day uttereth speech, and night unto night sheweth knowledge.

There is no speech nor language, where their voice is not heard.

Their line is gone out through all the earth, and their words to the end of the world. In them hath he set a tabernacle for the sun,

Which is as a bridegroom coming out of his chamber, and rejoiceth as a strong man to run a race.

His going forth is from the end of the heaven, and his circuit unto the ends of it: and there is nothing hid from the heat thereof.
Psalm 19: 1-6

357. With Joy and Rejoicing

Make a joyful noise unto the Lord, all ye lands.

Serve the Lord with gladness: come before his presence with singing.

Know ye that the Lord he is God: it is he that hath made us, and not we ourselves; we are his people, and the sheep of his pasture.

Enter into his gates with thanksgiving, and into his courts with praise: be thankful unto him, and bless his name.

For the Lord is good; his mercy is everlasting; and his truth endureth to all generations.
Psalm 100

358. The King of Glory

The earth is the Lord's, and the fulness thereof; the world, and they that dwell therein.

For he hath founded it upon the seas, and established it upon the floods.

Who shall ascend into the hill of the Lord? or who shall stand in his holy place?

He that hath clean hands, and a pure heart; who hath not lifted up his soul unto vanity, nor sworn deceitfully.

He shall receive the blessing from the Lord, and righteousness from the God of his salvation.

This is the generation of them that seek him, that seek thy face, O Jacob.

Lift up your heads, O ye gates; and be ye lifted up, ye everlasting doors; and the King of glory shall come in.

Who is this King of glory? The Lord strong and mighty, the Lord mighty in battle.

Lift up your heads, O ye gates; even lift them up, ye everlasting doors; and the King of glory shall come in.

Who is this King of glory? The Lord of hosts, he is the King of glory.
Psalm 24

359. The Shepherd Divine

The Lord is my shepherd; I shall not want.

He maketh me to lie down in green pastures: he leadeth me beside the still waters.

294

Unison Readings

He restoreth my soul: he leadeth me in the paths of righteousness for his name's sake.

Yea, though I walk through the valley of the shadow of death, I will fear no evil: for thou art with me; thy rod and thy staff they comfort me.

Thou preparest a table before me in the presence of mine enemies: thou anointest my head with oil; my cup runneth over.

Surely goodness and mercy shall follow me all the days of my life: and I will dwell in the house of the Lord for ever.

Psalm 23

360. The Keeper Eternal

I will lift up mine eyes unto the hills, from whence cometh my help.

My help cometh from the Lord, which made heaven and earth.

He will not suffer thy foot to be moved: he that keepeth thee will not slumber.

Behold, he that keepeth Israel shall neither slumber nor sleep.

The Lord is thy keeper: the Lord is thy shade upon thy right hand.

The sun shall not smite thee by day, nor the moon by night.

The Lord shall preserve thee from all evil: he shall preserve thy soul.

The Lord shall preserve thy going out and thy coming in from this time forth, and even for evermore.

Psalm 121

361. The Growing Life

Blessed is the man that walketh not in the counsel of the ungodly, nor standeth in the way of sinners, nor sitteth in the seat of the scornful.

But his delight is in the law of the Lord; and in his law doth he meditate day and night.

And he shall be like a tree planted by the rivers of water, that bringeth forth his fruit in his season; his leaf also shall not wither; and whatsoever he doeth shall prosper.

The ungodly are not so: but are like the chaff which the wind driveth away.

Therefore the ungodly shall not stand in the judgment, nor sinners in the congregation of the righteous.

For the Lord knoweth the way of the righteous: but the way of the ungodly shall perish.

Psalm 1

362. Nature Appreciation

O Lord our Lord, how excellent is thy name in all the earth! who hast set thy glory above the heavens.

Out of the mouth of babes and sucklings hast thou ordained strength because of thine enemies, that thou mightest still the enemy and the avenger.

When I consider thy heavens, the work of thy fingers, the moon and the stars, which thou hast ordained;

What is man, that thou art mindful of him? and the son of man, that thou visitest him?

For thou hast made him a little lower than the angels, and hast crowned him with glory and honor.

Thou madest him to have dominion over the works of thy hands; thou hast put all things under his feet:

All sheep and oxen, yea, and the beasts of the field;

The fowl of the air, and the fish of the sea, and whatsoever passeth through the paths of the seas.

O Lord our Lord, how excellent is thy name in all the earth!

Psalm 8

Responsive Readings
(American Revised Version)*

363. Sing Unto the Lord

O sing unto the Lord a new song: Sing unto the Lord, all the earth.

Sing unto the Lord, bless his name; Shew forth his salvation from day to day.

Declare his glory among the nations, His marvellous works among all the peoples.

Honor and majesty are before him: Strength and beauty are in his sanctuary.

Give unto the Lord, ye kindreds of the peoples, Give unto the Lord glory and strength.

Give unto the Lord the glory due unto his name.

Bring an offering, and come into his courts.

O worship the Lord in the beauty of holiness: Fear before him, all the earth.

Let the heavens rejoice, and let the earth be glad;

Let the sea roar, and the fulness thereof;

Let the field be joyful, and all that is therein; Then shall all the trees of the wood sing for joy: before the Lord, for he cometh; for he cometh to judge the earth:

He shall judge the world with righteousness, And the peoples with his truth.   Psalm 96

364. How Manifold Are Thy Works

Bless the Lord, O my soul. O Lord my God, thou art very great; thou art clothed with honor and majesty: who coverest thyself with light as with a garment: who stretchest out the heavens like a curtain: who maketh the clouds his chariot: who walketh upon the wings of the wind:

Who maketh his angels spirits; his ministers a flaming fire:

Who laid the foundations of the earth, that it should not be removed for ever. Thou coveredst it with the deep as with a garment: the waters stood above the mountains. At thy rebuke they fled; at the voice of thy thunder they hasted away. They go up by the mountains; they go down by the valleys unto the place which thou hast founded for them.

Thou hast set a bound that they may not pass over; that they turn not again to cover the earth.

He sendeth the springs into the valleys, which run among the hills. They give drink to every beast of the field: the wild asses quench their thirst.

By them shall the fowls of the heaven have their habitation, which sing among the branches.

He causeth the grass to grow for the cattle, and herb for the service of man: that he may bring forth food out of the earth; and bread which strengtheneth man's heart. The trees of the

Lord are full of sap; the cedars of Lebanon, which he hath planted; where the birds make their nests: as for the stork, the fir trees are her house. The high hills are a refuge for the wild goats; and the rocks for the conies.

He appointed the moon for seasons: the sun knoweth his going down.

Thou makest darkness, and it is night: wherein all the beasts of the forest do creep forth. The sun ariseth, they gather themselves together, and lay them down in their dens. Man goeth forth unto his work and to his labor until the evening.

O Lord, how manifold are thy works! in wisdom hast thou made them all: the earth is full of thy riches.

Psalm 104

365. Among All Nations

God be merciful unto us, and bless us, and cause his face to shine upon us; that thy way may be known upon earth, thy salvation among all nations.

Let the peoples praise thee, O God; let all the peoples praise thee.

Oh let the nations be glad and sing for joy; for thou wilt judge the peoples with equity, and govern the nations upon earth.

Let the peoples praise thee, O God; let all the peoples praise thee.

The earth hath yielded its increase: God, even our own God, will bless us.

God will bless us; and all the ends of the earth shall fear him.

Psalm 67

366. The Prince of Peace

The people that walked in darkness have seen a great light: they that dwell in the land of the shadow of death, upon them hath the light shined.

For all the armor of the armed man in the tumult, and the garments rolled in blood, shall be for burning, for fuel of fire.

For unto us a child is born, unto us a son is given; and the government shall be upon his shoulder; and his name shall be called, Wonderful Counsellor, Mighty God, Everlasting Father, Prince of Peace.

Of the increase of his government and of peace there shall be no end, ... to uphold it with justice and with righteousness from henceforth even forever.

Isaiah 9: 2-7

And many nations shall go and say, Come ye, let us go up to the mountain of the Lord and to the house of the God of Jacob; and he will teach us his ways, and we will walk in his paths.

And he will judge between many peoples, and will decide concerning strong nations afar off.

And they shall beat their swords into plowshares, and their spears into pruning-hooks;

Nation shall not lift up sword against nation, neither shall they learn war any more.

But they shall sit every man under his vine and under his fig-tree; and none shall make them afraid.

Micah 4: 2-4

They shall not hurt nor destroy in all my holy mountain; for the earth shall be full of the knowledge of the Lord, as the waters cover the sea.

Isaiah 11: 9

367. The Way of Wisdom

The fear of the Lord is the beginning of wisdom; and the knowledge of the Holy One is understanding.

Proverbs 9: 10

Happy is the man that findeth wisdom, and the man that getteth understanding.

For the gaining of it is better than the gaining of silver, and the profit thereof than fine gold.

She is more precious than rubies; and none of the things thou canst desire are to be compared unto her.

Proverbs 3: 13-15

My son, hear the instruction of thy father, and forsake not the teaching of thy mother;

For they shall be a chaplet of grace unto thy head, and chains about thy neck. *Proverbs 1: 8-9*

Then shalt thou understand righteousness and justice, and equity, yea, every good path;

For wisdom shall enter into thy heart, and knowledge shall be pleasant to thy soul.

Discretion shall watch over thee, understanding shall keep thee;

To deliver thee from the way of evil, from the men that speak perverse things. *Proverbs 2: 9-12*

When thou goest, thy steps shall not be straitened, and if thou runnest, thou shalt not stumble.

Enter not into the path of the wicked, and walk not in the way of evil men;

For they eat the bread of wickedness and drink the wine of violence.

But the path of the righteous is as a dawning light, that shineth more and more unto the perfect day.

Proverbs 4: 12, 14, 17, 18

368. The Loyalty of Love

And Naomi said unto her two daughters-in-law,

Go, return each of you to her mother's house:

The Lord deal kindly with you as he hath dealt with the dead and with me.

The Lord grant you that ye may find rest,

Each of you in the house of her husband.

Then she kissed them, and they lifted up their voice and wept.

And they said unto her, Nay,

But we will return with thee unto thy people.

And Naomi said, Turn again, my daughters:

Why will ye go with me?

And they lifted up their voice and wept again:

And Orpah kissed her mother-in-law;

But Ruth clave unto her.

And she said, Behold, thy sister-in-law has gone back

Unto her people, and unto her God:

Return thou after thy sister-in-law.

And Ruth said, Entreat me not to leave thee,

And to return from following after thee;

For whither thou goest, I will go;

And where thou lodgest, I will lodge;

Thy people shall be my people, and thy God my God;

Where thou diest, will I die,

And there will I be buried:

The Lord do so to me, and more also,

If aught but death part thee and me.

Ruth 1: 8-11, 14-18

369. Secrets of the Happy Life
(Beatitudes)

Blessed are the poor in spirit:

For theirs is the kingdom of heaven.

Blessed are they that mourn:

For they shall be comforted.

Blessed are the meek:

For they shall inherit the earth

Blessed are they that hunger and thirst after righteousness:
For they shall be filled.
Blessed are the merciful:
For they shall obtain mercy.
Blessed are the pure in heart:
For they shall see God.
Blessed are the peacemakers:
For they shall be called sons of God.
Blessed are they that have been persecuted for righteousness' sake:
For theirs is the kingdom of heaven.
Blessed are ye when men shall reproach you, and persecute you,
And say all manner of evil against you falsely,
For my sake.
Rejoice, and be exceeding glad:
For great is your reward in heaven:
For so persecuted they the prophets that were before you.

Matt. 5: 3-12

370. The Master's Friendship

Herein is my Father glorified,
That ye bear much fruit;
And so shall ye be my disciples.
Even as the Father hath loved me,
I also have loved you:
Abide ye in my love.
If ye keep my commandments, ye shall abide in my love;
Even as I have kept my Father's commandments, and abide in his love.
These things have I spoken unto you; that my joy may be in you,
And that your joy may be made full.
This is my commandment,
That ye love one another, even as I have loved you.
Greater love hath no man than this,
That a man lay down his life for his friends.
Ye are my friends,

If ye do the things which I command you.
No longer do I call you servants;
For the servant knoweth not what his Lord doeth:
But I have called you friends;
For all the things that I heard from my Father
I have made known unto you.
Ye did not choose me, but I chose you and appointed you,
That ye should go and bear fruit, and that your fruit should abide:
That whatsoever ye shall ask of the Father in my name,
He may give it you.
These things I command you,
That ye may love one another.

John 15: 8-17

371. My Place in Life

And he came to Nazareth, where he had been brought up:
And he entered, as his custom was,
Into the synagogue on the sabbath day,
And stood up to read.
And there was delivered unto him the book of the prophet Isaiah.
And he opened the book, and found the place where it was written,
The spirit of the Lord is upon me,
Because he hath anointed me to preach good tidings to the poor:
He hath sent me to proclaim release to the captives,
And recovering of sight to the blind,
To set at liberty them that are bruised,
To proclaim the acceptable year of the Lord.
And he closed the book,
And gave it back to the attendant, and sat down:

And the eyes of all in the synagogue were fastened on him.

And he began to say unto them,
Today hath this scripture been fulfilled in your ears. Luke 4: 16-21

372. Likeness Unto Him

So when he had washed their feet, and taken his garments,
And sat down again, he said unto them,
Know ye what I have done to you?
Ye call me, Teacher, and Lord:
And ye say well; for so I am.
If I then, the Lord and the Teacher, have washed your feet,
Ye also ought to wash one another's feet.
For I have given you an example,
That ye also should do as I have done to you.
Verily, verily, I say unto you,
A servant is not greater than his lord;
Neither is one that is sent
Greater than he that sent him.
If ye know these things,
Blessed are ye if ye do them.
John 13: 12-17

373. The Good Shepherd

Jesus saith unto them: I am the good shepherd. The good shepherd layeth down his life for the sheep.

I came that they might have life and have it abundantly.

I am the good shepherd and I know mine own and mine own know me.

And other sheep have I, which are not of this fold; them also must I bring, and they shall hear my voice; and they shall become one flock, one shepherd. John 10: 16

What man of you, having a hundred sheep, and having lost one of them, doth not leave the ninety and nine in the wilderness and go out after that which is lost, until he find it?

And when he hath found it he layeth it on his shoulder, rejoicing.

And when he cometh home he calleth together his friends and neighbors, saying unto them,

Rejoice with me for I have found my sheep which was lost. Luke 15: 4-6

When Jesus saw the multitude he was moved with compassion for them, because they were distressed and scattered, as sheep not having a shepherd.

And he called unto him his twelve disciples . . . saying, Go to the lost sheep of the house of Israel. And as ye go, preach, saying, The kingdom of heaven is at hand.
Matthew 9: 36; 10: 1, 7

374. Marks of the Master

And it came to pass when Jesus had finished
Commanding his twelve disciples,
He departed thence to teach and preach in their cities.
Now when John heard in the prison the works of the Christ,
He sent by his disciples
And said unto him,
Art thou he that cometh, or look we for another?
And Jesus answered and said unto them,
Go and tell John the things which ye hear and see:
The blind receive their sight, and the lame walk,
The lepers are cleansed, and the deaf hear,
And the dead are raised up,
And the poor have good tidings preached to them.

And blessed is he,
Whosoever shall find no occasion of stumbling in me. Matt. 11: 1-6

375. In Love's Devotion

Now as they went on their way,
He entered into a certain village:
And a certain woman named Martha
Received him into her house.
And she had a sister called Mary,
Who also sat at the Lord's feet,
And heard his word.
But Martha was cumbered about much serving;
And she came up to him, and said,
Lord, dost thou not care
That my sister did leave me to serve alone?
Bid her therefore that she help me.
But the Lord answered and said unto her,
Martha, Martha, thou art anxious and troubled about many things:
But one thing is needful:
For Mary hath chosen the good part,
Which shall not be taken away from her. Luke 10: 38-42

376. Unto the Least of These

Then shall the King say unto them on his right hand, Come, ye blessed of my Father, inherit the kingdom prepared for you from the foundation of the world:
For I was an hungred, and ye gave me meat: I was thirsty, and ye gave me drink: I was a stranger, and ye took me in:
Naked, and ye clothed me: I was sick and ye visited me: I was in prison, and ye came unto me.
Then shall the righteous answer him, saying, Lord, when saw we thee an hungred, and fed thee? or thirsty, and gave thee drink?

When saw we thee a stranger, and took thee in? or naked, and clothed thee?
Or when saw we thee sick, or in prison, and came unto thee?
And the King shall answer and say unto them, Verily I say unto you, Inasmuch as ye have done it unto one of the least of these my brethren, ye have done it unto me. Matthew 25: 34-40

377. True Greatness

To sit on my right hand and on my left hand
Is not mine to give;
It shall be given to them for whom it is prepared.
And when the ten heard it
They began to be much displeased with James and John.
But Jesus called them to him,
And said unto them,
Ye know that they which are accounted to rule over the Gentiles
Exercise lordship over them;
And their great ones exercise authority upon them.
But so shall it not be among you;
But whosoever shall be great among you
Shall be your minister.
And whosoever of you shall be the chiefest,
Shall be servant of all.
For even the Son of Man
Came not to be ministered unto
But to minister,
And to give his life
A ransom for many. Mark 10: 42-45

378. The Love That Abides

If I speak with the tongues of men and of angels, but have not love,
I am become sounding brass, or a clanging cymbal.

Responsive Readings

And if I have the gift of prophecy,
And know all mysteries and all knowledge;
And if I have all faith, so as to remove mountains,
But have not love, I am nothing.

And if I bestow all my goods to feed the poor,
And if I give my body to be burned, but have not love,
It profiteth me nothing.

Love suffereth long, and is kind;
Love envieth not;
Love vaunteth not itself, is not puffed up,

Doth not behave itself unseemly,
Seeketh not its own, is not provoked,
Taketh not account of evil;

Rejoiceth not in unrighteousness,
But rejoiceth with the truth;

Beareth all things, believeth all things,
Hopeth all things, endureth all things.

Love never faileth:
But whether there be prophecies, they shall be done away;
Whether there be tongues, they shall cease;
Whether there be knowledge, it shall be done away.

For we know in part, and we prophesy in part;

But when that which is perfect is come,
That which is in part shall be done away.

When I was a child, I spake as a child,
I felt as a child, I thought as a child:
Now that I am become a man, I have put away childish things.

For now we see in a mirror, darkly; but then face to face:

Now I know in part;
But then shall I know fully even as also I was fully known.

But now abideth faith, hope, love, these three;
And the greatest of these is love.

I Cor. 13

379. The Well-Armed Warrior

Finally, be strong in the Lord,
And in the strength of his might.

Put on the whole armor of God,
That ye may be able to stand against the wiles of the devil.

For our wrestling is not against flesh and blood,
But against the principalities, against the powers,
Against the world-rulers of this darkness,
Against the spiritual hosts of wickedness in the heavenly places.

Wherefore take up the whole armor of God,
That ye may be able to withstand in the evil day,
And having done all, to stand.

Stand therefore, having girded your loins with truth,
And having put on the breastplate of righteousness,

And having shod your feet with the preparation
Of the gospel of peace;

Withal taking up the shield of faith,
Wherewith ye shall be able to quench
All the fiery darts of the evil one.

And take the helmet of salvation, and the sword of the Spirit,
Which is the word of God.

Ephesians 6: 10–17

Responsive Readings

380. Glory in the Highest

And there were shepherds in the same country
Abiding in the field,
And keeping watch by night over their flock.

And an angel of the Lord stood by them,
And the glory of the Lord shone round about them:
And they were sore afraid.

And the angel said unto them, Be not afraid;
For behold, I bring you good tidings of great joy
Which shall be to all the people:

For there is born to you this day in the city of David
A Saviour, who is Christ the Lord.

And this is the sign unto you:
Ye shall find a babe wrapped in swaddling clothes,
And lying in a manger.

And suddenly there was with the angel
A multitude of the heavenly host praising God, and saying,

Glory to God in the highest,
And on earth peace among men
In whom he is well pleased.

And it came to pass, when the angels went away from them into heaven,
The shepherds said one to another,
Let us now go even unto Bethlehem,
And see this thing that is come to pass,
Which the Lord hath made known unto us.

And they came with haste, and found both Mary and Joseph,
And the babe lying in the manger.

And when they saw it, they made known concerning the saying

Which was spoken to them about this child.
And all that heard it wondered at the things
Which were spoken unto them by the shepherds.

But Mary kept all these sayings,
Pondering them in her heart.

And the shepherds returned, glorifying and praising God
For all the things that they had heard and seen,
Even as it was spoken unto them.
Luke 2: 8-20

381. The Easter Story

The first day of the week cometh Mary Magdalene early
When it was yet dark, unto the sepulchre
And seeth the stone taken away from the sepulchre.

Then she runneth, and cometh to Simon Peter, and the other disciple whom Jesus loved,
And said unto them,

They have taken away the Lord out of the sepulchre,
And we know not where they have laid him.

Peter therefore went, and that other disciple,
And came unto the sepulchre.

So they ran both together, and that other disciple did outrun Peter
And came first to the sepulchre.

And he, stooping down, and looking in, saw the linen clothes lying,
Yet went he not in;

Then cometh Simon Peter following him,
And went into the sepulchre and seeth the clothes lie.

And the napkin that was about his head.

Not lying with the linen clothes, but wrapped together in a place by itself.

Then went in also that other disciple, which came first to the sepulchre. And he saw and believed.

For as yet they knew not the scripture, That he must arise again from the dead.

Then the disciples went away again unto their own home.

But Mary stood without at the sepulchre weeping;

And as she wept, she stooped down, and looked into the sepulchre,

And seeth two angels in white sitting,

One at the head, and one at the feet, where the body of Jesus had lain.

And they said unto her, Woman, Why weepest thou?

She said unto them, Because they have taken away my Lord

And I know not where they have laid him.

And when she had thus said she turned herself back,

And saw Jesus standing, and knew not that it was Jesus.

Jesus said unto her, Woman, why weepest thou? Whom seekest thou?

She, supposing him to be the gardener, said unto him,

Tell me where thou hast laid him and I will take him away.

Jesus said unto her, Mary.

She turned herself and said unto him,

Rabboni, which is to say, Master.

Jesus said unto her, Touch me not; For I am not yet ascended to my Father;

But go to my brethern and say unto them,

I ascend to my Father and your Father;

And to my God and your God;

Mary Magdalene came and told the disciples that she had seen the Master

And that he had spoken these words unto her.

John 20; 1-18

Scripture Selections

Moffatt Translation*

382. New Life in the Valley

When poor, forlorn folk vainly seek
for water,
With tongues that are parched by
thirst,
I the Eternal will answer them,
I Israel's God will not forsake them;
On the bare heights I will open rivers,
And in the valleys fountains,
I will make deserts into lakes,
And dry land into springs of water;
I will plant cedars in the desert,
Acacias, myrtles, olive-trees;
I will put fir-trees in the wilderness,
And planes and cypresses;
That men may see and understand,
Consider and agree
That the Eternal's hand has done it,
That Israel's Majesty has made it all.
Isaiah 41: 17-20

383. This is the Way: Walk Here

So the Eternal longs to favor you,
And moves to show you pity;
For the Eternal is a loyal God;
Happy are all who long for him!
No more tears for you,
O folk of Sion in Jerusalem!
For he will show you favor when you
sigh,
And answer you, soon as he hears
your cry.
Though scant and scarce may be
Your bread and water from the Lord,
Yet he your Teacher never leaves
you now;
You see your Teacher for yourselves,
And when you swerve to right or left,

You hear a Voice behind you whis-
pering,
"This is the way, walk here."
Isaiah 30: 18-21

384. In Brotherly Love

Let your love be a real thing, with a
loathing for evil and a bent for what is
good. Put affection into your love
for the brotherhood; be forward to
honor one another; never let your
zeal flag; maintain the spiritual glow;
serve the Lord; let your hope be a
joy to you; be steadfast in trouble,
attend to prayer, contribute to needy
saints, make a practice of hospitality.
Bless those who make a practice of
persecuting you; bless them instead of
cursing them. Rejoice with those who
rejoice, and weep with those who weep.
Keep in harmony with one another;
instead of being ambitious, associate
with humble folk; never be self-con-
ceited. Never pay back evil for evil
to anyone; aim to be above reproach
in the eyes of all; be at peace with all
men, if possible, so far as that depends
on you. Never revenge yourselves,
beloved, but let the Wrath of God
have its way; for it is written, Ven-
gence is mine, I will exact a requital —
the Lord has said it. No, if your
enemy is hungry, feed him; if he is
thirsty, give him drink; For in this
way you will make him feel a burning
sense of shame. Do not let evil get
the better of you; get the better of evil
by doing good. Romans 12: 9-21

* From *The Holy Bible: a New Translation* by Professor James Moffatt, Litt.D., copyright, 1926, by Richard R. Smith, Inc.; and used by permission.

385. Tongues of Fire

We all make many a slip, but whoever avoids slips of the speech is a perfect man; he can bridle the whole of the body as well as the tongue. We put bridles into the mouths of horses to make them obey us, and so, you see, we can move the whole of their bodies. Look at ships too; for all their size and speed under stiff winds, they are turned by a tiny rudder wherever the mind of the steersman chooses. So the tongue is a small member of the body, but it can boast of great exploits. What a forest is set ablaze by a little spark of fire! And the tongue is a fire, the tongue proves a very world of mischief among our members, staining the whole of the body and setting fire to the round circle of existence with a flame fed by hell.　James 3: 2-6

386. A Call to Wisdom

My son, if you take to heart what I say, and set store by my commands, bending your ear to wisdom and applying your mind to knowledge; if you cry to intelligence and call for knowledge, seeking her out as silver and searching for her like treasure; then you shall see what is reverence for the Eternal, and find what the knowledge of God means (for it is the Eternal who supplies wisdom, from him come insight and knowledge, he has help ready for the upright, he is a shield for those who live honestly, a safeguard for the straight life, a protection for the pious); then you shall understand duty and goodness, and keep to every honest course, living the life of honest men and keeping to the good man's road.　Proverbs 3: 1-9

387. Meditation

Thou searchest me, Eternal One, thou knowest me, thou knowest me sitting or rising, my very thoughts thou readest from afar; walking or resting, I am scanned by thee, and all my life to thee lies open; ere ever a word comes to my tongue, O thou Eternal, 'tis well known to thee; thou art on every side, behind me and before, laying thy hand on me. . . . Where could I go from thy Spirit, where could I flee from thy face? I climb to heaven? — but thou art there; I nestle in the nether-world? — and there thou art! If I darted swift to the dawn, to the verge of the ocean afar, thy hand even there would fall on me, thy right hand would reach me. . . . Search me, O God, and know my heart, test me and try my thoughts; see if I am taking any course of wrong, and lead me on the lines of life eternal.　Psalm 139: 1-12, 23-24

Prayers and High Resolves *

388. For Knowledge of God

O God, who art the light of the minds that know thee, the life of the souls that love thee, and the strength of the thoughts that seek thee, help us to know thee that we may truly love thee, so to know thee that we may fully serve thee, whose service is perfect freedom; through Jesus Christ our Lord. Amen.

389. For Abundant Life

O Blessed One, spirit of light and love, of truth and beauty, of freedom and joy; behold us a company of seekers for the abundant life. Amen.

390. That We May Hear Thee

O God, we hear thy call in the voice of nature, from the pages of history, from the lips of men, stirring in our own thoughts, crying from our own hearts. Amen.

391. That We May Learn

May we be quick to learn,
And eager to be taught,
And may thy Spirit lead us into all truth. Amen.

392. For Myself

Lord, take my lips, and speak through them;
Take my mind, and think through it;
Take my heart, and set it on fire. Amen.

393. For All Gifts: Thanks!

Infinite Father,
We thank thee for the privilege of breath and the glory of living;
For the happy shelter of our homes and the inner circle of our friendships;
For the joy of the Lord and the genuine laughter thou hast put into our lives;
For health which makes hard work a pleasure and for sickness which ripens the soul;
For the fathers in whose love we found suggestions of thee,
For the mothers, because of whom all women have become sacred for us;
For all gentle souls and for the stimulus of all saintly lives;
For the great names of history, and for the forgotten toilers who have made our civilization possible;
For the temptations to do good and for the inward compulsions of conscience;
For the convictions which are anchors to faith and for doubts which blow away the unessential;
For the steady advance of man, since time began, and for the spreading Kingdom of human kindness;
For the Church of God, Mother of us all, and for Jesus Christ, Master of us all, to whom be praise forever and ever. Amen.

394. For the Kingdom of God

Almighty God, our heavenly Father; we praise and glorify thy holy name, for thou art the maker and the giver

* For authors and copyrights see pages 285-6-7

of all that makes life joyous and rich in human happiness.

We praise thee for life and the power of all living things which are to be found in thy world. We rejoice that thou hast made us for thyself, and we would learn to find rest and contentment in thee.

For the many times that we have failed to acknowledge thy goodness, forgive us, Lord. Help us to find thee in every sign of divine goodness which is in our everyday life. As we feel within us the dynamic of life and the creative power of personality, may we live thy praise in deeds of love and mercy that thy kingdom may come and thy will be done on earth as it is in heaven. Amen.

395. The Temple of Health*

We thank thee, Lord, that thou hast yielded into our hands the keys of health and sickness, of life and death. Give us wisdom to search out, revere and obey thy laws of life. Give us grace to despise no instrument of health; whether material or physical or spiritual, it is from thy hand. O may we not limit thy power through holding that thou canst work through but ,one channel!

How many are the ways through which thou seekest us and wouldst woo us to health and strength! We thank thee for the healing balm of thy fresh air, and the antiseptic rays of the kindly sun! We bless thee for pure water!

Accept, O God, our thanks for thy humble servants, the scientists, whose microscope and test-tube have revealed to us the unseen helpers and foes of human life. We thank thee for consecrated physicians and nurses who

have watched by bed-sides of pain, risking life and health in plague-camp or in homes. We praise thee for all good teachers who have strengthened our faith in the power of truth over inner discord and disease.

Recall us from the waywardness which seeks pleasure and ease through the breaking of thy laws. Chasten us with pain and sickness of body when we forsake thy greater good, lest our spirits die and life be spent in vain. Comfort us, heal us, strengthen us, as we hear thy call and obey. So may we find the universe thy Temple of Health to them that rest upon thee. Amen.

396. For Those Who Care for Us

Father, we thank thee for doctors and nurses; for those who provide for food and comfort; for those who keep the ways of communication open for our need and convenience; for mothers and all others who labor unceasingly for us.

We are ashamed to receive so thoughtlessly what costs them life.

We pray thee that the time may soon come when in every week there shall be a Day of Life for every man and woman and little child in thy great world family. Amen.

397. For Vigor of Life

O God, for whose spirit the bodies of men are a temple, forgive us that we are so regardless of them.

Forgive us for the ways in which we mistreat our own great gift of health and destroy the possibilities of mature strength.

Forgive us more for living so comfortably in a world where day by day thousands of beautiful bodies are crushed and broken by undue toil and

* From *Prayer That Prevails* by Marshall Dawson, copyright by The Macmillan Company.

the hazards of what we call industry. Help us to make this world a place in which all thy children may know the overflowing joy of health. Amen.

398. Prayer of a Camper

God of the hills, grant us thy strength to go back into the cities without faltering, strength to do our daily task without tiring and with enthusiasm, strength to help our neighbors who have no hills to remember.

God of the lake, grant us thy peace and thy restfulness, peace to bring into a world of hurry and confusion, restfulness to carry to the tired whom we shall meet every day, content to do small things with a freedom from littleness, self-control for the unexpected emergency and patience for the wearisome task, with deep depths within our souls to bear us through the crowded places. Grant us the hush of the night time when the pine trees are dark against the sky line, the humbleness of the hills who in their mightiness know it not, and the laughter of the sunny waves to brighten the cheerless spots of a long winter.

God of the stars, may we take back the gifts of friendship and of love for all. Fill us with great tenderness for the needy person at every turning. Grant that in all our perplexities and every-day decisions we may keep an open mind.

God of the wilderness, with thy pure winds from the northland blow away our pettiness; with the harsher winds of winter drive away our selfishness and hypocrisy; fill us with the breadth and the depth and the height of thy wilderness. May we live out the truths which thou hast taught us,

in every thought and word and deed. Amen.

399. Out Door Prayer

We thank thee, O Lord, for the things that are out of doors; for the fresh air and the open sky and the growing grass and the tiny flowers and the setting sun and the wooded hill and the brown earth beneath our feet. They are all good and they all speak the truth, and we rest ourselves, and get new strength to go back to the world of restless men. Keep us ever like thy good world, rugged and wholesome and true. Amen.

400. For Cleanness of Life

Most merciful Lord, who hast taught us that the pure in heart shall see God, cleanse our hearts from all impurity. Give us such hatred of all that is evil and such love of all that is beautiful and strong, that we may be delivered from temptation and become a strength to others who are tempted. Amen.

401. For Right Conduct

Give us clean hands, clean words and clean thoughts, O God. Help us to stand for the hard right against the easy wrong. Save us from habits that harm. Teach us to work as hard and play as fair in thy sight alone as if all the world saw. Forgive us when we are unkind, and help us to forgive those who are unkind to us. Keep us ready to help others at some cost to ourselves. Send us chances to do a little good every day, and so to grow more like Christ. Amen.

402. For Consecration to Our Work

Give thy blessing, we pray thee, to this our daily work, that we may do it in faith heartily as to the Lord, and not unto men. All our powers of body and mind are thine, and we would fain devote them to thy service. Sanctify them and the work in which they are engaged; let us not be slothful, but fervent in spirit, and do thou, O Lord, so bless our efforts, that we may bring forth in us the fruits of true wisdom. Amen.

403. Day Unto Day

Our Father, each day is a little life, each night a tiny death; help us to live with faith and hope and love. Lift our duty above drudgery; let not our strength fail, or the vision fade, in the heat and burden of the day. O God, make us patient and pitiful one with another in the fret and jar of life, remembering that each fights a hard fight and walks a lonely way.

Forgive us, O Lord, if we hurt our fellow souls; teach us a gentler tone, a sweeter charity of words, and a more healing touch. Sustain us, O God, when we must face sorrow; give us courage for the day and hope for the morrow. Day unto day may we lay hold of thy hand and look up into thy face, whatever befall, until our work is finished and the day is done. In his name, Amen.

404. Purposeful Life

O thou Christ of Galilee, who didst go into the homes and the hearts of many folk, and kindle there a light which has burned through all the centuries, make us humble sharers of thy glory and goodness, that so, we may find a purpose and meaning in life.

Teach us to speak and act so that we may cheer and help men. Amen

405. For the Good Life*

O God, we bless thee for the joy of life, the wonder of life, the discipline of labor and sorrow, the glory of struggle and adventure.

Life is a capacity for the highest;

Help us to make it a pursuit of the best — a winged and singing life in thee, through Jesus Christ, the Lord of all good life. Amen.

406. Beauty and Joy**

Creator of life and light,

We bless thee for the beauty of the world;

We thank thee for physical joy;

For the ectasy of swift motion; for deep water to swim in;

For the goodly smell of rain on dry ground;

For hills to climb and hard work to do;

For music that lifts our hearts in one breath to heaven;

For all thy sacraments of beauty and joy, we thank thee.

We thank thee, O God, for the poetry of movement;

For a bird on the wing, a hare at the run;

For a train thundering through the night;

For a yacht with spread of sail;

For a man running and a child dancing. Amen.

407. The Quest

In the spirit of those in the past who have gone forth on great quests, we enter into the fellowship of worship.

May the spirit of an eager searcher enter into our hearts, O God.

In memory of all those who have searched unselfishly for the secrets of the world, we worship side by side.

And grant, our Lord, that we too

---

* From *Altar Stairs*, by Joseph Fort Newton, copyright by The Macmillan Company.
** From *Prayer That Prevails* by Marshall Dawson, copyright by The Macmillan Company.

may be willing to pay the price where the quest of our hearts becomes more costly than we now think. Amen.

408. For the Pioneer Spirit

Dear heavenly Father, be with us on the open road of life, be our good comrade in the every day burdens that we must carry on the road.

Help us to be pioneers in finding unknown truths of life.

Help us to discover in our adventures on the road new ways and by-ways of love, beauty, service and truth.

This we ask in the name of the Great Companion of the Way. Amen.

409. Friendship

O Lord, grant to us so to love thee with all our heart, with all our mind, and with all our soul, and our neighbor for thy sake, that the grace of charity and brotherly love may dwell in us, and all envy, harshness and ill will may die in us; and fill our hearts with feelings of love, kindness and compassion, so that, by constantly rejoicing in the happiness and good success of others, by sympathizing with them in their sorrows, and putting away all harsh judgments and envious thought, we may follow thee, who art thyself the pure and perfect love, through Jesus Christ our Lord. Amen.

410. The Sabbath

In thy wisdom and justice, O Father, thou hast given to us this special day in which to rest, to enjoy our beautiful world, to think of thee and all whom thou dost love.

Forgive us, we pray thee, that so often in carelessness and selfishness we forget thee.

On this holy day speak to our hearts and help us to remember the countless blessings thou hast prepared for our good.

May this be a day which we shall spend as Jesus did, worshipping thee in thy holy temple, walking through fields and by the lake, talking of thee, doing good to all who need our help.

Forbid that through our selfishness the day should be hard for others.

Teach us to be considerate, kind and just, doing unto others on this day as on all days, as we would that they should do unto us.

Accept, we pray, the worship of loving hearts and devotion of daily lives in which we remember others and forget ourselves. Amen.

411. Flames of Fire

God of the rushing wind and the flaming tongue, we pray for thy church of many names, so beset with bewilderment in a new and confused time.

Heal it of ancient schism, we pray thee; purge it of pride, and renew the vision grown dim in its heart.

Teach us, O Lord, that it is not by might, nor by power, but by thy spirit, that the Gospel will run and be glorified through us, sending thy light and thy truth into the dark places of the earth.

Spirit of light and power, at whose altar we bow,

Rekindle a heroic and mighty faith in the heart of thy Church;

Let not the gates of Hell prevail against it.

May it be baptized anew with the spirit of unity, the flame of vision, and the sacrificial passion of Christ, that its stammering voice may become a redeeming anthem in a discordant world;

In the name of Jesus Christ, our Lord. Amen.

412. The Book of Books*

Lord, we thank thee for a wise and
deep-hearted book
that tells us that thy goodness is over
all,
like the mercy of the morning,
and tenderness of the evening.
Help us to give our souls to its heavenly
wisdom,
its vision of the unseen,
its passion for righteousness,
its pity for man.
Teach us to read it, love it and live
with it,
until its spirit mingles with our spirit,
making us pure of heart and fruitful
in goodness. Amen.

413. Prayer for all Workers

Guide, protect and inspire, our heav-
enly Father, all those who learn and
labor truly to get their own living:
For men who face peril,
For women who suffer pain,
For those who till the earth,
For those who tend machinery,
For those who strive on the deep wa-
ters,
For those who venture in far countries,
For those who work in offices and
warehouses,
For those who labor at furnaces and in
factories,
For those who toil in mines,
For those who buy and sell,
For those who keep house,
For those who train children,
For all who live by strength of arm,
For all who live by cunning of hand,
For all who control, direct, or employ,
For all who enrich the common life
through art, and science, and learn-
ing,
For all who guide the common thought,
as writers or as teachers,

For all who may serve the common
good as pastors, physicians, lawyers,
merchants, and for all social workers,
leaders, and statesmen, we beseech
thee. Amen.

414. For Our City

O God, we pray thee for this, the
city of our love and pride. We re-
joice in her spacious beauty and her
busy ways of commerce, in her stores
and factories where hand joins hand
in toil, and in her blessed homes where
heart joins heart for rest and love.
Help us to make our city the common
workshop of our people, where every
one will find his place and task, keen
to do his best with hand and mind.
Bind our citizens together, not by the
bond of money and profit alone, but
by the glow of neighborly good-will,
by the thrill of common joys, and the
pride of common possessions. May
we ever remember that our city's true
wealth and greatness consist not in
the abundance of the things we possess,
but in the justice of her institutions
and the brotherly ways of her citizens.
Through Jesus Christ our Lord.
Amen.

415. For True Patriotism

God of the nations, Father of all, we
would worship thee in the spirit of
true patriotism; with reverence to
thy holy name, honor and glory to all
that thy spirit, working in thy world,
has created, and love shown in deeds
of courage and true valor.

We praise thee for brave men and
courageous deeds which have brought
our country to its place of leadership
among the nations. Help us to prize
and guard the noble heritage which is
ours in the heroic achievement of
liberty and law.

* From *Altar Stairs* by Joseph Fort Newton, copyright by The Macmillan Company

Forgive us for any thought or deed which might endanger the freedom wrought for us by our forefathers. Give truth to our words, and courage to our deeds as we make patriotism beautiful with loyalty and devotion. Amen.

416. A Bethany Home

Make this home a Bethany, our Saviour. Sit with us at the table. Draw us from our worldly cares as thou didst draw Martha. Be our life as thou wert the life of Lazarus. Show us, as thou didst Mary, the better part, we ask it in thy name. Amen.

417. For Our Home

Our Father in heaven, we would reverently recognize thee in all that we do, and give thee thanks for all that thou dost make possible in our lives.

We thank thee for all the gentle and healing ministries of life:

For gladness of the morning, for freedom of the wind, for music of the rain, for joy of the sunshine, and the deep calm of the night; for trees and flowers and clouds and skies; for the tender ministries of human love, the unselfishness of parents, the love that binds man and woman, the confidence and affection of little children, and the strength and devotion of friends.

We would dedicate our home to-day to a love and loyalty to thee, and to the service and blessing of our fellow-men, in the name of our Master, who shared the friendship and hospitality of homes, when he was here upon earth. Amen.

418. Mother's Day

Lord Jesus, thou hast known
A mother's love and tender care,
And thou wilt hear while for my own
mother most dear

I make this Sabbath prayer.
Protect her life, I pray,
Who gave the gift of life to me;
And may she know from day to day,
the deepening glow
Of joy that comes from thee.
I cannot pay my debt
For all the love that she has given;
But thou, love's Lord, wilt not forget
her due reward —
Bless her in earth and heaven. Amen.

419. Christmas

All the earth rejoices in the gladness of good will, and, everywhere, men's hungry hearts await the word of peace.

May we be messengers of Christmas joy to the world, our Lord Emmanuel, bearers of its glad tidings, servants of its gracious spirit, and toilers for its lasting good will.

May there be nothing selfish in our Christmas rejoicings, but may we ever seek to bring all mankind the happiness we crave for ourselves, and thus learn how much joy there is in giving. Amen.

420. Transcending All Differences

Almighty Father, we, who are members of different races and faiths, desire together to worship thy holy name in fellowship with each other. Thou art our Father, and we are thy children; show us that our hopes and fears and aspirations are one. Forgive, O God, the envies, suspicions and misunderstandings which have blinded our eyes and thrust us asunder. Purify our hearts, and teach us to walk together in the laws of thy commandments and in the ways of human friendship.

Help us, O God, to give honor where honor is due, regardless of race, color, or creed, following what our inmost

Prayers and High Resolves

heart tells us to be thy will. Deepen our respect for unlikeness and our eagerness to understand one another, that, in a higher unity of the Spirit, we may transcend our differences. Gladly may we share thy best gifts, working together to build thy City upon earth, we ask in thy holy name. Amen.

HIGH RESOLVES

421. The Morning

O Light, which scatters the shadows that have hidden the flowers and darkened the streets, thou art God's messenger to us.

Be the light of our minds, as the sun is the light of the day. Take away every evil thought that leaves its shadows there. Drive out the darkness of anger, selfishness and impurity. Make us centers of thy sunshine, that we may reflect thy Spirit and scatter cheerfulness about us. May we, with the birds and fields, catch the joy of the morning and carry from this prayer the feeling of thy nearness all through the day.

422. Everyday*

O God, whose splendor fills the world, yet who revealest thyself in the song of a bird, in the face of a flower, in a cup of cold water given to a brother man; teaching us thereby that nothing set for us to do is so small that it may not be glorified in thy name, if we bring the highest truth to the humblest toil; mercifully grant that all our purest visions may ever tend to the plainest duty, and our holiest aspirations touch and transfigure the tasks of every day; that we may serve thy holy will, not fitfully, but in constancy and joy.

423. Motherhood

We bless thee for the great and precious ideal of motherhood.

We praise thee for the present joy and the lasting influence of all good mothers.

We think of the noble women all over the world and in all times who have prayed God to bless them with children, and then have prayed him to bless their children.

We thank thee, our heavenly Father, for the mothers who freely offered themselves that we might live.

We think of their love and their loyalty, their gentleness and their strength, their kindness and care, their sacrifice and patience.

Help us, O God, to honor them by our thoughts, by our words, by our actions, by our appreciation and by our gratitude.

Help us so to learn and grow and live that we may become the fulfilling of our mother's desires and prayers for us.

May we be kind to them as they have been kind to us; may we help them as they have helped us.

424. Christmas

Drive back the gray shadows which the years have cast over us, and let us see thy guiding Star and hear a music not of earth. Let not our souls be busy inns that have no room for thee and thine, but homes of prayer and praise, ready for thy welcoming. Make us to know that near us, even in our city, is Christ the Saviour, whom seeking with joy, we shall find. Humbly we offer our Christmas prayer.

425. For Friendship

We thank thee for the gift of friendship, that makes people care for one another, for the power of love that

*From "Altar Stairs," by Joseph Fort Newton, copyright by The Macmillan Company

314

drives out that which is greedy and mean in human hearts.

We thank thee for those who make our lives happy. May we give them comradeship and love in return. Keep us from being fickle, and make us dependable and loyal.

Guide us in our friendships that we may choose high-minded and worthy companions, whose association will make us better men and women, and who will be our life-long friends. Above all, we want thee as our closest companion through life.

426. For a Worthy Career

We pray that high ambitions may guide us, that we may always keep in mind the goal for which we are working. As we study our daily lessons and go about our tasks, help us to keep our big purposes before us, so that we shall not get discouraged or give up through thinking only of the little job at hand. May we be dissatisfied with second-rate ambitions and seek for the highest place that we can fill.

Guide us in our plans. We pray for a vocation of usefulness, a big and challenging life which will draw out the best that is in us, and which will lead us to play our part in making the world better.

427. For Respect for Law

We are grateful for the government of our nation which protects us from danger and makes it possible for us to be free and happy. Help us to uphold its laws. May we never be guilty of destroying public property or making light of regulations about quietness, cleanliness and decency.

Help us when driving a car not to lose our heads for the sake of a mo-mentary thrill and thus endanger the lives of others as well as our own. May we have backbone enough to resist the company of those who flippantly break the law. Help us to make our community what it ought to be by respecting its laws and being a public-spirited citizen.

428. For New Americans

Father of all people everywhere, bless the new Americans who come in year by year from foreign lands. Help them in their loneliness to find friends, to get work and to be happy. May they feel that America is their country.

Help us, as people from all countries, to live together in this great world-nation. May we forget all difference in color and language and work for the future of our land, seeking to make it a home of freedom and brotherhood. Help us to be more considerate of these immigrants, remembering that they may have more to give to America than we have. May we never speak disrespectfully of them, but treat them as our brothers and work with them for a greater America.

429. Youth's Desire

Teach me, Eternal, how thine orders run, and I will follow to the end; instruct me how to carry out thy law, and I will keep it with all my heart; lead me in thine obedience, for it is my joy. Incline my heart to thy behests, and to no love of gain, make me alive to follow thee, and turn mine eyes from cravings vain. Fulfil thy promise to thy servant, to advance thy faith; remove the insults that I dread, and intervene for good; as thou art true, revive me; I am yearning for thy will.

Devotional Poetry and Prose

MORNING AND EVENING WORSHIP

430. Some Gay, Adventurous Thing

The day will bring some lovely thing,
I say it over each new dawn;
"Some gay, adventurous thing to hold
Against my heart, when it is gone."
And so I rise and go to meet
The day with wings upon my feet.

I come upon it unaware —
Some sudden beauty without name;
A snatch of song, a breath of pine,
A poem lit with golden flame;
High tangled bird notes, keenly
  thinned,
Like flying color on the wing.

No day has ever failed me quite —
Before the grayest day is done,
I come upon some misty bloom
Or a late line of crimson sun.
Each night I pause, remembering
Some gay, adventurous, lovely thing.

431. God's World

The year's at the spring;
The day's at the morn;
Morning's at seven;
The hillside's dew-pearled;
The lark's on the wing;
The snail's on the thorn;
God's in his heaven —
All's right with the world.

432. Purpose for This Day

I will this day try to live a simple,
sincere and serene life; repelling
promptly every thought of discontent,
anxiety, discouragement, impurity and
self-seeking; cultivating cheerfulness,
magnanimity, charity and the habit
of holy silence; exercising economy in
expenditure, carefulness in conversa-
tion, diligence in appointed service,
fidelity to every trust and child-like
faith in God.

433. The Stainless White Radiance*

There comes the morning with the
golden basket in her right hand, bearing
the wreath of beauty, silently to crown
the earth. And there comes the
evening over the lonely meadows
deserted by herds, through trackless
paths, carrying cool draughts of peace
in her golden pitcher from the western
ocean of rest. But there where spreads
the infinite sky for the soul to take her
flight in, reigns the stainless white
radiance. There is no day nor night,
nor form nor color, and never, never,
a word.

THE MIGHTY GOD

434. God

God is beauty.
God is love.
God is understanding.
God is quietness and rest.
God is peace.
God is the song of ecstacy, that bursts
  in the springtime.
God is the blue of a calm day in
  summer.
God is the faith that comes where
  there is no reason for faith.
God is the voice of a bell, the peal of a
  trumpet.

* From *Gitanjali* by Tagore, copyright by The Macmillan Company,

God is timeless, speechless.
God is all heights and all depths.
God is beyond all and in all.
God is simplicity, enveloped by us in complexity.
God is perfection among imperfections.
God is a perfect poem.
God is God.

MAKER OF HEAVEN AND EARTH

435. Voices of God

God! Let the torrents, like a shout of nations,
Answer! and let the ice-plains echo, God!
God! Sing the meadow-streams with gladsome voice.
Ye pine-groves, with your soft and soul-like sounds.
And they too have a voice, yon piles of snow,
And in their perilous fall shall thunder, God!
Ye living flowers that skirt the eternal frost,
Ye wild goats sporting round the eagle's nest,
Ye eagles, playmates of the mountain-storm,
Ye lightnings, the dread arrows of the clouds,
Ye signs and wonders of the elements,
Utter forth God, and fill the hills with praise.

436. Learn About God

Flower in the crannied wall,
I pluck you out of the crannies; —
Hold you here, root and all, in my hand,
Little flower — but if I could understand
What you are, root and all, and all in all,
I should know what God and man is.

437. God's Trees*

I think that I shall never see
A poem lovely as a tree.
A tree whose hungry mouth is pressed
Against the earth's sweet flowing breast;
A tree that looks at God all day,
And lifts her leafy arms to pray:
A tree that may in summer wear
A nest of robins in her hair,
Upon whose bosom snow has lain,
Who intimately lives with rain.
Poems are made by fools like me,
But only God can make a tree.

438. The One Thousandth Psalm

O God, we thank thee for everything:
For the glory and beauty and wonder of the world,
For the glory of springtime, the tints of the flowers and their fragrance;
For the glory of the summer flowers, the roses and cardinals and clethra;
For the glory of the autumn, the scarlet and crimson and gold of the forest;
For the glory of winter, the pure snow on the shrubs and trees.
We thank thee that thou hast placed us here
To use thy gifts for the good of all.

439. The One Thousandth Psalm

O God, we thank thee for everything.
For the sea and its waves, blue, green and gray and always wonderful;
For the beach and the breakers and the spray and the white foam on the rocks;
For the blue arch of heaven; for the clouds in the sky, white and gray and purple;
For the green of the grass; for the forests in their spring beauty; for the wheat and corn and rye and barley.

* From *Trees and Other Poems* by Joyce Kilmer, copyright, 1914, by Doubleday, Doran & Company

Devotional Poetry and Prose

We thank thee for all thou hast made
and that thou hast called it good;
For all the glory and beauty and wonder of the world.
We thank thee that thou hast placed
us in the world to subdue all things
to thy glory,
And to use all things for the good of
thy children.

440. Canticle to the Sun

O most high, almighty, good Lord
God, to thee belong praise, glory,
honor, and all blessing!

Praised be my Lord God with all
his creatures, and especially our
brother, the Sun, who brings us the
day and who brings us the light; fair
is he and shines with a very great
splendor; he signifies thee to us,
O Lord.

Praised be my Lord for our sister,
the Moon, and for the Stars, which
he has set clear and lovely in the
heavens.

Praised be my Lord for our brother,
the Wind, and for Air and Cloud,
Calms and all weather, by which thou
upholdest life in all creatures.

Praised be my Lord for our sister,
Water, who is very serviceable unto
us and humble and precious and
clean.

Praised be my Lord for our brother,
Fire, through whom thou givest us
light in darkness; and he is bright
and pleasant and very mighty and
strong.

Praised be my Lord for our mother,
Earth, who doth sustain us and keep
us, and bringeth forth divers fruits and
flowers of many colors and grass.

Praised be my Lord for all those who
pardon one another for his love's
sake, and who endure weakness and
tribulation; blessed are they who
peaceably shall endure, for thou, O
most High, shalt give them a crown.

Praised be my Lord for our sister,
Death, from which no man escapeth.
Blessed are they who are found walking by thy most holy will.

Praise ye and bless the Lord, and
give thanks unto him and serve him
with great humility.

441. Life as Lovely as Nature

Who does not hear an autumn anthem
singing low in his heart!
Help us, O God, to make the life of
man
As lovely as the world in which he
lives;
The brotherliness of humanity
Equal to the beauty of nature.

442. Wind in the Pines*

Oh, I can hear you, God, above the cry
Of the tossing trees —
Rolling your windy tides across the sky
And splashing your silver seas
Over the pine,
To the water-line
Of the moon.

Oh, I can hear you, God,
Above the wail of the lonely loon —
When the pine-tops pitch and nod —
Chanting your melodies
Of ghastly waterfalls and avalanches,
Swishing your wind among the branches,
To make them pure and white.

Wash over me, God, with your piney
breeze,
And your moon's wet-silver pool;
Wash over me, God, with your wind
and night,
And leave me clean and cool.

* From *The Box of God* by Lew Sarett, copyright by Henry Holt and Company

Devotional Poetry and Prose

443. I Shall Arrive

I go to prove my soul,
I see my way as birds their trackless
way,
I shall arrive. — What time, what
circuit first,
I ask not: but unless God send his hail
Of blinding fireballs, sleet, or stifling
snow,
In some time, his good time, I shall
arrive;
He guides me and the bird, in his good
time.

SHEPHERD OF SOULS

444. A Psalm of Faith

Thou art Infinite Love.
Who can approach nigh unto thee?
Whoso findeth thee in the beauty of
blossoms,
In the promise of spring,
In the fulfillment of fall,
Thinketh he hath found all things;
But verily I say:
Thou art even in the grime and sweat
of slums.
I have seen thy loveliness in the brow
of the immigrant,
Who striveth even as I.
Thou vouchsafest thyself to us
In the unceasing miracle of friends.

In the rush and roar of trains, thou art
there;
And in the toiling of cities, thou art
there;
Thou art in the march of the thousands
that throng in the great crusade:
Thou art of the homeless and of the
outcast.
Thou sittest by us in the lonely places,
When we have come face to face with
our sins;
And in the wonder of thine Infinite
Love, thou takest us to thy heart —
Thou who art the pulse and entity of
all our lives!

445. Care for My Needs

Out of my need you come to me, O
Father,
Not as a spirit, gazing from on high,
Not as a wraith, gigantic in its out-
lines,
Waiting against the tumult of the sky!
Father, you come to me in threads of
music,
And in the blessedness of whispered
mirth,
And in fragrance of frail garden flowers
When summer lies across the drowsy
earth!

Out of my need you come to me, O
Father,
When I can scarcely see the path
ahead —
It is your hand that turns the sky, at
evening,
Into a sea of throbbing, pulsing red —
It is your call that sounds across the
marshes,
It is your smile that touches fields of
grain,
Painting them with pale gold; it is
your nearness
That makes me see new beauty, after
pain!

Out of my need you come to me, O
Father —
Not as a presence vast and great and
still,
But as the purple mist that clings, each
morning
To the slim summit of a pine-crowned
hill.
Not as a vague and awful power that
urges,
Urges and prods and hurries me
along —
But as a hand that paints a lovely
picture,
But as a voice that sings a tender song!

Devotional Poetry and Prose

THE ETERNAL SPIRIT

446. Beholding God

Why should I wish to see God better
than this day?
I see something of God each hour of
the twenty-four, and each moment
then;
In the faces of men and women I see
God, and in my own face in the glass;
I find letters from God dropped in the
street, and every one is signed by
God's name;
And I leave them where they are, for
I know that wheresoe'er I go
Others will punctually come for ever
and ever.

447. The Soul of Jesus is Restless

The soul of Jesus is restless today;
Christ is tramping through the spirit-
world,
Compassion in his heart for the faint-
ing millions;
He trudges through China, througn
Poland,
Through Russia, Austria, Germany,
Armenia;
Patiently he pleads with the Church,
tenderly he woos her.

The wounds of his body are bleeding
afresh
For the sorrows of his shepherdless
people.
We besiege him with selfish petitions,
We weary him with our petty ambi-
tions,
From the needy we bury him in piles
of carved stone,
We obscure him in the smoke of stuffy
incense,
We drown his voice with the snarls and
shrieks
Of our disgruntled bickerings,
We build temples to him with hands
that are bloody,

We deny him the needs and sorrows
Of the exploited "least of his brethren."
The soul of Jesus is restless to-day,
but eternally undismayed.

THE LIVING WORD

448. The Universal Book

How many ages and generations
Have brooded and wept and agonized
Over this Book!
What untellable joys and ecstacies,
What support to martyrs at the stake!
To what myriads has it been
The shore and rock of safety —
The refuge from the driving tempest
and wreck.
Translated into all languages,
How it has united this diverse world!
Of its thousands there is not a verse,
Not a word but is thick-studded
With human emotion.

449. God's Word

We search the world for truth. We
cull
The good, the true, the beautiful,
From graven stone and written scroll,
And all the old flower-fields of the
soul;
And, weary seekers of the best,
We come back laden from the quest,
To find that all the sages said
Is in the Book our mothers read.

450. A New Light

Softly I closed the Book as in a dream
And let its echoes linger to redeem
Silence with its music, darkness with
its gleam.

That day I worked no more. I could
not bring
My hands to toil, my thoughts to
trafficking.
A new light shone on every common
thing.

Celestial glories flamed before my gaze.
That day I worked no more. But, to God's praise,
I shall work better all my other days.

EMMANUEL — GOD WITH US

451. The Spirit of the Christ Child

The Christmas candles are burned out;
the carols have died away; the star
is set; all the radiant song-thrilled
night is past.
Thou alone, the eternal, remainest,
and thou art enough.
Remain to me more beautiful, more
beloved, more real than any of the
romance that clusters around thy
Birthday.

452. Christmas Everywhere

Everywhere, everywhere, Christmas
to-night!
Christmas in lands of the fir tree and
pine,
Christmas in lands of the palm tree and
vine,
Christmas where snow peaks stand
solemn and white,
Christmas where corn fields lie sunny
and bright,
Christmas where children are hopeful
and gay,
Christmas where old men are patient
and gray,
Christmas where peace like a dove in
its flight
Broods o'er brave men in the thick of
the fight;
Everywhere, everywhere, Christmas
to-night!
For the Christ child who comes is the
Master of all;
No palace too great and no cottage
too small.

453. Far Trumpets Blowing

A King might miss the guiding star,
A wise man's foot might stumble;
For Bethlehem is very far
From all except the humble.

But he who gets to Bethlehem
Shall hear the oxen lowing;
And, if he humbly kneel with them,
May catch far trumpets blowing.

454. Room for the Christ Child

The blasts of winter are fierce and cold,
The snow lies deep over hill and wold,
But a star shines bright through the
deepening gloom,
Room for the Christ Child, room.

Where man's distrust and his greed for
gain
Have frozen the floods of tender rain,
Till never a flower of hope can bloom;
Room for the Christ Child, room.

In homes that deepest griefs have
borne,
'Mid silent forms of those that mourn,
In the shadows that gather round the
tomb;
Room for the Christ Child, room.

Where nations are warring, life for life,
And a cry rings out from the fearful
strife
As a dying people sinks to its doom;
Room for the Christ Child, room.

THE GROWING CHRIST

455. Christ, Straight and Wise*

The young child, Christ, is straight
and wise
And asks questions of the old men,
questions
Found under running water for all
children,
And found under shadows thrown on
still waters

* From *Chicago Poems* by Carl Sandburg, copyright by Henry Holt and Company

By tall trees looking downwards, old
and gnarled,
Found to the eyes of children alone,
untold,
Singing a low song in the loneliness.
And the young child, Christ, goes asking,
And the old men answer nothing, and
only know love
For the young child, Christ, straight
and wise.

456. Judean Hills are Holy

Judean hills are holy,
Judean hills are fair,
For one can find the footprints
Of Jesus everywhere.
One finds them in the twilight
Beneath the singing sky
Where shepherds watch, in wonder,
White planets wheeling by.

His trails are on the hillsides
And down the dales and deeps;
He walks the high horizons
Where vesper-silence sleeps.
He haunts the lowly highways
Where human hopes have trod
The Via Dolorosa
Up to the heart of God.

He looms a lonely figure
Along the fringe of night,
As lonely as a cedar
Against the lonely light.
Judean hills are holy,
Judean hills are fair,
For one can find the footprints
Of Jesus everywhere.

457. Joses, the Brother of Jesus

Joses, the brother of Jesus, plodded
from day to day
With never a vision within him to
glorify his clay;
Joses, the brother of Jesus, was one
with the heavy clod,

But Christ was the soul of rapture, and
soared, like a lark, with God.
Joses, the brother of Jesus, was only
a worker in wood,
And he never could see the glory that
Jesus, his brother, could.
"Why stays he not in the workshop?"
he often used to complain,
"Sawing the Lebanon cedar, imparting
to woods their stain?
Why must he go thus roaming, for-
saking my father's trade,
While hammers are busily sounding,
and there is gain to be made?"
Thus ran the mind of Joses, apt with
plummet and rule,
And deeming whoever surpassed him
either a knave or a fool, —
For he never walked with the prophets
in God's great garden of bliss —
And of all mistakes of the ages, the
saddest, methinks, was this:
To have such a brother as Jesus, to
speak with him day by day,
But never to catch the vision which
glorified his clay.

458. Jesus Saith

A little Child, a Joy-of Heart, with eyes
Unsearchable, he grew in Nazareth,
His daily speech so innocently wise
That all the town went telling: "Jesus
saith."

MASTER AND FRIEND

459. Who are You, Jesus?

Who are you, Jesus?
I am the Light of the World,
I am the Water of Life,
I am the Good Shepherd,
I will see you again and your heart
shall rejoice,
And your joy no one taketh away from
you.
These things have I spoken unto you

that my joy may be in you, and that your joy may be full.
The fruit of the Spirit is joy.
And God is like that.

460. The Song of a Heathen

(Sojourning in Galilee, A. D. 32)

If Jesus Christ is a man —
  And only a man — I say
That of all mankind I cleave to him,
  And to him will I cleave alway.

If Jesus Christ is a god —
  And the only God — I swear
I will follow him through heaven and hell,
  The earth, the sea and the air!

461. A Fisherman Speaks

Anno Domini 33

Oh, he who walked with fishermen
  Was man of men in Galilee;
He told us endless wonder-tales,
  His laugh was hale and free.

The water, changed he into wine,
  To please a poor man's company;
I saw him walk one wretched night
  Upon a troubled sea.

And when the rabble cried for blood,
  I saw him nailed upon a tree;
He showed how a brave man could die;
  The Prince of Men was he.

And rough men, we, who never wept,
  Wept when they nailed him to the tree;
Oh, he was *more than man*, who walked
  With us in Galilee.

462. Napoleon Speaks for Christ

Alexander, Caesar, Charlemagne and I have founded great empires, but upon what did these creations of our genius depend? Upon force! Jesus alone founded his empire on love, and to this very day millions would die for him. I think I understand something of human nature, and I tell you that all these were men, and I am a man. None else is like him. Jesus Christ was more than a man.

463. Fling Wide the Gates

Love Divine, love lowly-hearted,
Our city's gates stand widely open to thy welcome.
Without thee the people are uncrowned,
Tumult and rebellion break forth,
Truth is perished in the street,
And justice fallen at our gates.
Come and establish thy kingdom in our midst,
Sending peace on the earth,
Peace in the hearts of men.
Apart from thee all temples stand desolate,
Unblessed by sacrifice,
Unsanctioned by altar fires,
Unhallowed by thankful song.
Hear us as we cry:
Hosanna in the highest;
Blessed is he that cometh in the name of the Lord.

464. Palm Sunday

He is coming! He is coming!
We hear triumphal shoutings from the eager marching throng;
We catch the thrilling music of the children's lifted song;
The very stones are throbbing to break into acclaim,
And all the hills exultant to re-echo back his name.
Break all our fronded branches and strew them in his way,
Our strength and all our beauty belong to him to-day.

Devotional Poetry and Prose

THE LIVING CHRIST
465. He Still Lives!

The world cannot bury Christ.
The earth is not deep enough for his
tomb;
The clouds are not wide enough for
his winding sheet.
He ascends into the heavens,
But the heavens cannot contain him.
He still lives — in the church which
burns unconsumed with his love;
In the truth that reflects his image;
In the hearts which burn as he talks
with them by the way.

466. Nature's Victorious Life

O ice and snow, O frost and cold,
O bitter death, that bound the world!
O biting winds and frozen mold —
Farewell!
Ho, land! ho, living waters, sing!
For God has sent us back his spring!
Hark how the sylvan voices cry,
Our God is love! Love cannot die!
Sure as the peace that follows strife,
The resurrection's glorious life!

FOLLOWING THE CHRIST
467. I Know a Name

I know a soul that is steeped in sin,
That no man's art can cure;
But I know a Name, a Name, a Name,
That can make that soul all pure.

I know a life that is lost to God,
Bound down by things of earth;
But I know a Name, a Name, a Name,
That can bring that soul new birth.

I know of lands that are sunk in shame,
Of hearts that faint and die;
But I know a Name, a Name, a Name,
That can set those lands on fire.
Its sound is a brand, its letters flame,
I know a Name, a Name, a Name,
That will set those lands on fire.

468. The Everlasting Mercy*

The water's going out to sea
And there's a great moon calling me;
But there's a great sun calls the moon,
And all God's bells will carol soon
For joy and glory and delight
Of some one coming home to-night.

O glory of the lighted mind,
How dead I've been, how dumb, how
blind.
The station brook, to my new eyes,
Was babbling out of Paradise,
The waters rushing from the rain
Were singing Christ has risen again.
I thought all earthly creatures knelt
From rapture of the joy I felt.

THE TEMPLE OF THE BODY
469. My Body**

My body is a cathedral where I am
supreme;
I am the priest,
The congregation,
The altar, and the white
Burning candles and their yellow light
My solitude is multitude
For there I speak with God.

470. Life of My Life***

Life of my life, I shall ever try to
keep my body pure, knowing that thy
living touch is upon all my limbs.

I shall ever try to keep all untruths
out of my thoughts, knowing that
thou art that truth which has kindled
the light of reason in my mind.

I shall ever try to drive all evils away
from my heart and keep my love in
flower, knowing that thou hast thy
seat in the inmost shrine of my
heart.

And it shall be my endeavor to reveal thee in my action, knowing it is
thy power gives me strength to act.

* From *The Everlasting Mercy* by John Masefield, copyright by The Macmillan Company
** From *Singing Youth* by Mabel Mountsier, copyright by Harper and Brothers
*** From *Gitanjali* by Tagore, copyright by The Macmillan Company

Devotional Poetry and Prose

THE RULE OF THE SPIRIT

471. Self-Mastery

Let us fight the good fight of him who
strives for self-mastery.
I will seek to win the noble victory of
one who conquers himself.
Who liveth bravely?
He who fears nothing but to do wrong.
Who liveth greatly?
He who adorns each day with victories
over himself.
Who liveth in freedom?
He who learns to do easily what at
first was hard, — because it makes
for the welfare of others.

472. Gifts of the Spirit*

These are the gifts I ask
Of thee, Spirit serene;
Strength for the daily task,
Courage to face the road,
Good cheer to help me bear the travel-
ler's load,
And, for the hours of rest that come
between,
An inward joy in all things heard and
seen.

These are the sins I fain
Would have thee take away;
Malice and cold disdain,
Hot anger, sullen hate,
Scorn of the lowly, envy of the great,
And discontent that casts a shadow
gray
On all the brightness of the common
day.

473. Lord of the Mountain

Lord of the mountain,
Hear a young man's prayer.
Hear a prayer for cleanness.
Keeper of the strong rain
Drumming on the mountain;
Lord of the small rain
That restores the earth in newness,

Keeper of the clean rain,
Hear a prayer for wholeness.
Keeper of the paths of men,
Hear a prayer for straightness,
Hear a prayer for courage.
Lord of the thin peak,
Keeper of the headlands,
Keeper of the strong rocks,
Hear a prayer for staunchness,
O Lord and spirit of the mountain.

474. Temptation

Was the trial sore?
Temptation sharp? Thank God a
second time!
Why comes temptation but for man to
meet
And master, and make crouch beneath
his foot,
And so be pedestalled in triumph?
Pray
"Lead us into no such temptations,
Lord!"
Yea, but, O thou whose servants are
the bold,
Lead such temptations by the head
and hair,
Reluctant dragons, up to who dares
fight,
That so he may do battle and have
praise.

475. For Loyalty

The spirit of loyalty be ours that we
may make the most and the best of
life: loyalty to convictions, which
imparts strength of character and
creates the straight path of action;
loyalty to friends, which is the sign
and token of a noble heart; loyalty to
country, for enlightened patriotism is
the very soul of our republic. In-
spired by this spirit we shall walk, not
in the darkness of indecision and
weakness, but in the light, as loyal
followers of him who was the Light of
the world.

* From *Music and Other Poems* by Henry Van Dyke, copyright by Charles Scribner's Sons

Devotional Poetry and Prose

476. The Voice, the Power, and the Angel

For the Voice within us which bids
us do right, and yet leaves us free,
For our Power to obey the Voice,
For the Angel of Shame that besets
us, when we do not obey it, we are
thankful: the Voice and the Power
and the Angel, they all are from thee.
May we learn to say, — What we
ought, that we can; what we can, God
helping, we will!

COURAGE

477. For Strength

This is my prayer:
Give me the strength lightly to bear
my joys and sorrows.
Give me the strength to make my
love fruitful in service.
Give me the strength never to disown the poor or bend my knees before
insolent might.
Give me the strength to raise my
mind high above daily trifles.
And give me the strength to surrender my strength to thy will in love.

478. Fight On

When the fight begins within himself,
A man's worth something. God
stoops o'er his head,
Satan looks up between his feet, —
both tug —
He's left, himself, i' the middle: the
Soul awakes
And grows. Prolong that battle
through this life!
Never leave growing till the life to come.

479. Right and True

O, that I as right and true might be
As a flower or a tree.
That the sweetness of the wheat
Into my soul might pass,
And the clear courage of the grass.

GOOD WORKMANSHIP

480. Youth Builds

Youth of the world, unite!
Youth of the world, strive, fight
For what you deem the right.

Youth sees with surer eyes,
Because its eyes are clear
Of prejudice and fear.
Youth need not compromise.

No compromise with wrong —
Let this our slogan be.
The league of youth is strong,
Stretching from sea to sea.

This world is ours to take;
This world is ours to make.
Let us build true and sure
A world that will endure;
Build out of right and truth,
Reared with this tool — our youth.

481. Building Forever

When we build, let us think that we
build forever.   Let it not be for present
delight, nor for present use alone; let
it be such work as our descendants will
thank us for, and let us think, as we
lay stone on stone, that a time is to
come when those stones will be held
sacred because our hands have touched
them, and that men will say as they
look upon the labor and wrought
substance of them — "See!   This our
Fathers did for us."

482. The Gift of Labor

"O, I will give you glory," said God,
as he bent him over
Man, asleep in the Garden, breathing
his soul awake;
"I give you the Urge of Doing, and
it shall be like a lover,
To flower your life, and fruit it; you
shall grow by the things you make."

So there were men in Iran who wrought
black tents, and saddles;
And swarthy Egyptians, gladdened by
the Cheop's slow increase;
So there were boatmen, northward,
who hewed broadbladed paddles,
And set slim shallops for venture on the
rim of the Seven Seas.

So came frowning Homer, with the
poet's nice decisions,
Raphael at a canvas, bewitched by
a dream sublime;
Plato's thought, rebuilding the world
to its broader visions;
Prophets, stepping over the broken
walls of time;

Statesmen, piecing nations from the
scraps of a hundred quarrels;
Women, weaving baskets in a mist-
blue mountain cove;
And not one thinking of silver, not
one of the wreath of laurels,
But each of the lifting vision that
should end in a thing to love.

"O, I shall give you gladness," said
God, as he brooded over
Man, awake in the Garden, with the
ages before him laid;
"King, you may be, or peasant, builder,
weaver, or rover —
But your soul must come to beauty
through the things that your dreams
have made."

483. We Shall Build On

We shall build on!
Firm on the Rock of Ages,
City of saints and sages,
Laugh while the tempest rages,
We shall build on!
Christ, though my hands be bleeding,
Fierce though my flesh be pleading,
Still let me see thee leading,
Let me build on!
Till through death's cruel dealing,

Brain-wrecked and reason-reeling,
I hear Love's trumpets pealing,
And I pass on!

TRUSTWORTHINESS
484. The Spirit of Reality

Christ, whom the common people
heard gladly,
Lord of sincerity and truth,
Before whom all that is hollow
And unreal shrivels up and is con-
sumed away;
Give us the spirit of reality;
Help us fearlessly and honestly
To seek for truth and to listen to thy
challenge;
Cleanse us from prejudice and parti-
sanship,
And purge out from our inmost souls,
O Lord, whatsoever loveth and maketh
a lie.

485. Four Things

Four things a man must learn to do
If he would make his record true:
To think without confusion clearly;
To love his fellowmen sincerely;
To act from honest motives purely;
To trust in God and heaven securely.

THE QUEST OF TRUTH
486. There is no Unbelief

There is no unbelief;
Whoever plants a seed beneath the sod
And waits to see it push away the
clod —
He trusts in God.
There is no unbelief;
Whoever says beneath the sky,
"Be patient, heart; light breaketh
by and by,"
Trusts the Most High.

There is no unbelief;
Whoever sees 'neath winter's field of
snow,

The silent harvest of the future grow —
God's power must know.

There is no unbelief;
Whoever lies down on his couch to
sleep,
Content to lock each sense in slumber
deep,
Knows God will keep.

There is no unbelief;
For thus by day and night uncon-
sciously
The heart lives by the faith the lips
deny.
God knoweth why.

487. Great is Truth

Great is the earth, high is the heaven,
swift is the sun in his course, for he
compasseth the heavens round about
and fetcheth his course again to his
own place. Is not the Maker of these
things great? All the earth calleth
upon Truth, and the heaven blesseth
her: for with her is no unrighteous
thing. . . . As for Truth, she abideth
and is strong forever; she liveth, and
conquereth for evermore. . . . She is
the strength, and the kingdom, and
the power, and the majesty, of all
ages. Blessed be the God of Truth.
. . . Great is Truth, and strong above
all things.

THE QUEST OF BEAUTY
488. The Things of the Spirit

Thank God for the things of the spirit!
There! A meadow lark sings! Do
    you hear it?
For the sigh of the heart,
The contagion of laughter,
For the longing apart,
For the joy that comes after
For the things that we feel
When we clasp, when we kneel —

Thank God for the sharing,
The caring, the giving,
For the things of Life's living.

Thank God for the riches
Of flowers in the ditches,
For the roof from the weather,
The fireside together,
For the step at the portal,
For the love we have treasured,
For something unmeasured,
For something immortal,
For our grief, for our mirth,
For our heavens on earth.
For the things of the spirit!
There! A meadow lark sings! Do
    you hear it?

489. The Sky-Born Music

Let me go where'er I will
I hear sky-born music still;
It sounds from all things old,
It sounds from all things young,
From all that's fair, from all that's foul
Peals out a cheerful song.

It is not only in the rose,
It is not only in the bird,
Not only when the rainbow glows,
Nor in the song of women heard,
But in the darkest, meanest things
There alway, alway, something sings.

'Tis not in the high stars alone,
Nor in the cups of budding flowers,
Nor in the redbreast's mellow tones,
Nor in the bow that smiles in showers,
But in the mud and scum of things
There alway, alway, something sings.

490. Vision

Not for more beauty would our eyes
    entreat thee,
Flooded with beauty, beauty every-
    where.
Only for keener vision that may greet
    thee
In all thy vestures of the earth and air.

Devotional Poetry and Prose

491. The Inspirations of Beauty

A thing of beauty is a joy forever.
Its loveliness increases; it will never
Pass into nothingness; but still will
  keep
A bower quiet for us, and a sleep
Full of sweet dreams, and health and
  quiet breathing.

If you get simple beauty and naught
  else,
You get about the best thing God
  invents.

Broad is the carpet God has spread,
  and beautiful are the colors he has
  given.
O God, whatever road I take joins the
  highway that leads to thee.

Earth's crammed with heaven,
And every common bush afire with God.

In mystery of arch and aisle, in
splendor of massive towers and tall
spires — in the towers of York and
the spire of Salisbury, in Bach's Mass
in B Minor — there is the Kingdom
and the Power and the Glory.

492. O Beautiful Human Life

O beautiful human life!
Tears come to my eyes as I think of it.
So beautiful, so inexpressibly beautiful.
How willingly I would strew the paths
  of all with flowers; how beautiful
  a delight to make the world joyous!
The song should never be silent, the
  dance never still, the laugh should
  sound like water which runs forever.

493. The Inspiration of Nature

I pray that the life of this spring and
  summer may ever lie fair in my
  memory.
May I dare as I have never done.
May I persevere as I have never done.

May I purify myself anew as with
  fire and water, soul and body.
May my melody not be wanting to the
  season.
May I gird myself to be a hunter of
  the beautiful, that naught escape me.

494. Thanks

When I read a beautiful book or a
great poem, or see lovely pictures —
then it comes to me that I want to
raise my hand to my forehead and
salute, as the soldiers do when their
officers go past. I want to say, "To
all the great dead, to all the men and
women who have been before me whose
names will never be known, without
whom I could never know what I
know, or understand as I understand,
or think as I think — Be Thanks!"
I want to say, "To all the gardeners
that have been before me — to the
little old first mother, who scratched
earth and put in roots and grasses —
to men and women of races whose
names I shall never know, without
whom I should never have this beauty
— Thanks!"

THE QUEST OF GOODNESS

495. To Strive, to Seek, to Find

The lights begin to twinkle from the
  rocks:
The long day wanes: the slow moon
  climbs: the deep
Moans round with many voices.
Come, my friends,
'Tis not too late to seek a newer world.

Push off, and sitting well in order
  smite
The sounding furrows; for my purpose
  holds
To sail beyond the sunset, and the
  paths
Of all the western stars, until I die.

It may be that the gulfs will wash us
down:
It may be we shall touch the Happy
Isles,
And see the great Achilles, whom we
knew.
Though much is taken, much abides;
and though
We are not now that strength which in
old days
Moved earth and heaven; that which
we are, we are;
One equal temper of heroic hearts,
Made weak by time and fate, but
strong in will
To strive, to seek, to find and not to
yield.

496. Life's Victors

Speak, History! Who are life's victors?
Unroll thy long annals, and say,
Are they whom the world called the
victors — who won the success of a
day?
The martyrs, or Nero? The Spartans
who fell at Thermopylae's tryst,
Or the Persians and Xerxes? His
judges or Socrates?
Pilate or Christ?

497. Faithful Souls

And I?
Is there some desert or some pathless
sea
Where thou, good God of angels, wilt
send me?
Some oak too for me to rend; some sod,
Some rock for me to break;
Some handful of his corn to take
And scatter far afield,
Till it, in turn, shall yield
Its hundredfold
Of grains of gold
To feed the waiting children of my
God?

Show me the desert, Father, or the
sea.
Is it thine enterprise? Great God,
send me.
And though this body lie where ocean
rolls,
Count me among all Faithful Souls.

498. Build Thee More Stately Mansions

Build thee more stately mansions, O
my soul,
As the swift seasons roll!
Leave thy low-vaulted past!
Let each new temple, nobler than the
last,
Shut thee from heaven with a dome
more vast,
Till thou at length art free,
Leaving thine outgrown shell by life's
unresting sea!

499. Greatheart

Where are you going, Greatheart?
To lift to-day above the past;
To make tomorrow sure and fast;
To nail God's colors to the mast?
Then God go with you, Greatheart.

FRIENDSHIP

500. Unselfish Giving

The Holy Supper is kept indeed,
In what we share with another's need.
Not what we give but what we share,
For the gift without the giver is bare;
Who gives himself with his alms feeds
three,
Himself, his hungering neighbor, and
me.

501. Friendship Fire

One of the most winsome stories of
Jesus is of the building of the friendship fire, the preparing of the picnic
breakfast for those friends of his who

were to find him there on the beach, after his resurrection, just where they may often have tramped and talked and broken bread with him before.

502. The Upward Road

I will follow the upward road to-day
I will keep my face to the light,
I will think high thoughts as I go my way,
I will do what I know is right.
I will look for the flowers by the side of the road,
I will laugh and love and be strong,
I will try to lighten another's load,
This day as I fare along.

503. The Arrow and the Song

I shot an arrow into the air,
It fell to earth, I knew not where;
For, so swiftly it flew, the sight
Could not follow it in its flight.

I breathed a song into the air,
It fell to earth, I knew not where;
For who has sight so keen and strong,
That it can follow the flight of song?

Long, long afterward, in an oak
I found the arrow still unbroke;
And the song, from beginning to end,
I found again in the heart of a friend.

504. Cooperation

Begin the morning by saying to thyself, I shall meet with the busybody, the ungrateful, arrogant, deceitful, envious, unsocial.

All these things happen to them by reason of their ignorance of what is good and evil.

But I who have seen the nature of the good, that it is beautiful, and of the bad and that it is ugly, and the nature of him who does wrong, that it is akin to me, not only of the same blood but that it participates in the same intelligence and the same portion of the divinity, I can neither be injured by any of them, nor hate them.

For we are made for cooperation, like feet, like hands.

To act against one another, then, is contrary to nature;
And it is acting against one another to be vexed and to turn away.

The best way of avenging thyself is not to become like the wrong-doer.

Men exist for the sake of one another. Teach them, then, or bear with them.

THE CHALLENGE OF SERVICE

505. Pass on the Torch

I am of the opinion that my life belongs to the whole community, and as long as I live, it is my privilege to do for it whatsoever I can.

I want to be thoroughly used up when I die, for the harder I work, the more I live.

I rejoice in life for its own sake.

Life is no "brief candle" for me,

It is a sort of splendid torch which I have got hold of for a moment, and I want to make it burn as brightly as possible before handing it on to future generations.

506. The Surgeon's Hands

His face? I know not whether it be fair,
Or lined and grayed to mark the slipping years.
His eyes? I do not glimpse the pity there,
Or try to probe their depths for hopes or fears.
Only upon his wondrous hands I gaze,
And search my memory through so fittingly

To voice their loveliness. In still
amaze
I bow before their quiet dignity.
They make the crooked straight and
heal old sores;
The blind to see, the war-torn clean
and whole.
Throughout the suffering world they
touch the doors
That open wide to life. The bitter
bowl
Of pain they sweeten till the weary
rest,
As though the hands of Christ had
served and blest.

TORCHBEARERS

**507. Evidence of Faith in Modern
Achievement**

By faith Marconi reached out into
the air, and sent the messages of man-
kind around the world, thus drawing all
mankind into a unity of thought which
makes for world friendship.

By faith Alexander Bell, in long,
weary hours of study and work,
achieved the telephone, linking towns,
states, and continents into a fellowship of work and pleasure through
the extended sound of the human voice.

By faith Edison, taking the spark of
power generated in the worship of God,
gave to our homes light and power for
the comfort and efficiency of our daily
lives.

By faith Lindbergh, solitary, and
unknown, traced a pathway through
the uncharted reaches of the heavens,
daring the cold of the upper reaches,
the depths of the waters below, and
the hunger and weariness of long hours
of heroic endurance, giving a new and
swift way for the journeys of man-
kind.

What more shall we say of our great
men of science, who seek out the uncharted paths of discovery; delving
deep into the mysteries of the laws of
the Creator, thinking God's thoughts
after him, enduring many hardships
and great dangers that they may make
known his wonders through faith?

By faith they conquer the elements,
discover the treasures of the earth, and
increase the power of man until he is
indeed but a little lower than God.

By faith these men have entrusted
us with vast power and limitless
strength in the use of their great
inventions.

Wherefore, seeing that we are surrounded by so great a cloud of witnesses, let us lay aside evil habits, and
the little sins that so easily beset us,
and let us worthily maintain and increase our heritage, looking unto
Jesus the Author and Finisher of our
Faith.

508. Livingstone

"Recall the twenty-one years, give
me back all its experiences, give me its
shipwrecks, give me its standings in
the face of death, give it me surrounded
with savages with spears and clubs,
give it me back again with spears
flying about me, with the club knocking
me to the ground, give it me back, and
I will still be your missionary."

Forth to the fight he fared,
High things and great he dared,
He thought of all men but himself,
Himself he never spared.
He greatly loved,
He greatly lived,
And died right mightily.
He passed like light across the dark-
ened land,

And, dying, left behind him this command:
"The door is open. So let it ever stand."
For mightily wrought he.

509. The Spirit of Amundsen

Your goal was not some island of the blessed,
A zone of gardens, sweet with pink and chrome;
You had no thought to find at last a home
Where you might pause, by labors un-oppressed.

Fearless and strong, you set upon your quest;
Ice-fanged the ways that lured your dauntless ship,
Endless the night that held you in its grip,
But stout the heart that beat within your breast.

You are of Norman breed, brave Viking soul;
You rode the ice-bergs as a summer sea;
Their crystal peaks, their cold, strange mystery
Lured on and on, till Fate revealed your goal.

510. On! Sail On!

They sailed! They sailed! Then spake the mate:
"This mad sea shows his teeth to-night.
He lifts his lip, he lies in wait,
With lifted teeth, as if to bite.
Brave Admiral, say but one good word:
What shall we do when hope is gone?"
The words leaped like a leaping sword:
"Sail on! sail on! sail on! and on!"
*   *   *   *
And then a speck!
A light! a light! a light! a light!
It grew, a starlit flag unfurled!

It grew to be Time's burst of dawn!
He gained a world; he gave that world
Its grandest lesson: "On! sail on!"

511. Latimer's Light

In Oxford town the faggots they piled,
With furious haste and curses wild,
Round two brave men of our British breed,
Who dared to stand true to their speech and deed;
Round two brave men of that sturdy race,
Who with tremorless souls the worst can face;
Round two brave souls who could keep their tryst
Through a pathway of fire to follow Christ.
And the flames leaped up, but the blinding smoke
Could not the soul of Hugh Latimer choke;
For, said he, "Brother Ridley, be of good cheer,
A candle in England is lighted here,
Which by grace of God shall never go out, — "
And that speech in whispers was echoed about, —
Latimer's Light shall never go out,
However the winds may blow it about;
Latimer's Light is here to stay
Till the trump of a coming judgment day.

COMMUNITY LOVE

512. What Makes a City Great?

What makes a city great?
Huge piles of stone heaped heavenward?
Vast multitudes who dwell within wide circling walls?
Palace and throne and riches past the

count of man to tell, and wide
domain?
Nay, these the empty husk!
True glory dwells where glorious deeds
are done,
Where great men rise whose names,
athwart the dusk of misty centuries,
gleam like the sun!
In Athens, Sparta, Florence 'twas the
soul
That was the city's bright immortal
part.
The splendor of the spirit was their
goal, their jewel, the unconquerable
heart!
So may the city that I love be great,
Till every stone shall be articulate.

513. The Higher Citizenship

Athenians, I hold you in the highest
regard and love,
But I will obey God rather than you;
And as long as I have breath and
strength
I will not cease from philosophy, and
from exorting you,
And declaring the truth to every one
of you whom I meet,
Saying, as I am wont, You are a citizen
of Athens,
A city which is very great and famous
for wisdom and power of mind.
Are you not ashamed of caring so much
for the making of money,
And for reputation?
Will you not think or care about
wisdom,
And truth, and the perfection of your
soul?

FATHERLAND

514. Lincoln's Speech at Gettysburg

Fourscore and seven years ago
Our fathers brought forth upon this
continent a new nation,
Conceived in liberty, and dedicated to
the proposition that all men are created equal.
Now we are engaged in a great civil
war,
Testing whether that nation or any
nation,
So conceived and so dedicated, can
long endure.

We are met on a great battlefield of
that war.
We have come to dedicate a portion
of that field as a final resting place
for those who here gave their lives
that that nation might live.
It is altogether fitting and proper that
we should do this.
But in a larger sense we cannot dedicate,
We cannot consecrate,
We cannot hallow this ground.

The brave men, living and dead, who
struggled here,
Have consecrated it far above our poor
power to add or detract.
The world will little note or long
remember what we say here, but it
can never forget what they did here.
It is for us, the living, rather to be
dedicated here to the unfinished
work which they who fought here
have thus far so nobly advanced.

It is rather for us to be here dedicated
To the great task remaining before us:
That from these honored dead we take
increased devotion
To that cause for which they gave the
last full measure of devotion:

That we here highly resolve
That these dead shall not have died in
vain;
That this nation, under God,
Shall have a new birth of freedom;
And that government of the people,
By the people, for the people,
Shall not perish from the earth.

Devotional Poetry and Prose

515. America's Making

God built him a continent of glory
and filled it with treasures untold;
He studded it with sweet flowing
fountains and traced it with long
winding streams;
He carpeted it with soft rolling prairies
and columned it with thundering
mountains;
He graced it with deep-shadowed
forests and filled them with song;
Then he called unto a thousand peoples
and summoned the bravest among
them.
They came from the ends of the
earth, each bearing a gift and a
hope.
The glow of adventure was in their
eyes, and in their hearts the glory
of hope.
And out of the bounty of earth and the
labor of men;
Out of the longing of hearts and the
prayer of souls;
Out of the memory of ages and the
hopes of the world,
God fashioned a people in love, blessed
it with purpose sublime, and called
it America.

516. The American Flag

I am whatever you make me, nothing
more.
I swing before your eyes as a bright
gleam of color,
A symbol of yourself,
A pictured suggestion of that big thing
Which makes this nation.
My stars and my stripes are your dream
and your labors.
They are bright with cheer,
Brilliant with courage, firm with faith,
Because you have made them so out
of your hearts.
We are all making the flag.

517. Dost Thou Prosper, Dearest Land?

They tell me thou art rich, my country;
Gold in glittering flood has poured into
thy chest;
Thy flocks and herds increase, thy
barns are pressed
With harvest, and thy stores can hardly
hold
Their merchandise; unending trains
are rolled
Along thy network rails of East and
West;
Thy factories and forges never rest;
Thou art enriched in all things bought
and sold.
But dost thou prosper? Better news
I crave.
O dearest country, is it well with thee
Indeed, and is thy soul in health?
A nobler people, hearts more wisely
brave,
And thoughts that lift men Godward,
make them free —
These are prosperity and vital wealth.

WORLD FRIENDSHIP

518. O Thrilling Age

To be alive in such an age!
With every year a lightning page
Turbed in the world's great wonder-
book
Whereon the leaning nations look
Where men speak strong for brother-
hood,
For peace and universal good;
When miracles are everywhere
And in every inch of common air
Throbs a tremendous prophecy
Of greater marvels yet to be.
O Thrilling Age!
O Willing Age!
When steel and stone and rail and rod
Welcome the utterance of God;
A trump to shout his wonder through
Proclaiming all that man can do.

519. Let the People Love

There is an enticing dream: the dream
of wise freedom made contagious;
The dream of nations in love with each
other, without a thought of hatred,
of danger.
Clear the field for the grand tournament of the nations!
Clear the field for the tournament of
man.
And who will lead the way? The
good and wise must lead.
Let the people love, and they will lead.
Let the people love, and theirs is the
power.

520. In the Dawn

We are standing in the great dawn of a
day they did not know,
On a height they only dreamed of, toil-
ing darkly far below;
But our gaze is toward a summit loft-
ier, airier, mist-encurled,
Soaring skyward through the twilight
from the bases of the world.
Up and up, achieving, failing, weak in
flesh but strong of soul.
We may never live to reach it.—
Ah, but we have seen the goal!

521. Make Way for Brotherhood

Of all things beautiful and good,
The kingliest is brotherhood;
For it will bring again to earth
Her long lost poesy and mirth;
And till it comes these men are slaves,
And travel downward to the dust of
graves.
Clear the way, then, clear the way;
Blind creeds and kings have had their
day.
Break the dead branches from the path;
Our hope is in the aftermath.
To this event the ages ran:
Make way for brotherhood — make
way for man.

522. Vision

Men, my brothers, men the workers,
ever reaping something new;
That which they have done but earnest
of the things that they shall do.
For I dipped into the future, as far as
human eye could see,
Saw the Vision of the world, and all
the wonder that would be;
Saw the heavens fill with commerce,
argosies of magic sails,
Pilots of the purple twilight, dropping
down with costly bales;
Heard the heavens filled with shouting,
and there rained a ghastly dew
From the nation's airy navies grappling
in the central blue;
Far along the world-wide whisper of
the south-wind rushing warm,
With the standards of the peoples
plunging thro' the thunder-storm;
Till the war-drum throbbed no longer,
and the battle-flags were furled
In the Parliament of man, the Federa-
tion of the world.

(Written 1842, fifty years before a practical
airplane was flown.)

523. World Fellowship in Christ

In Christ there is no East or West,
In him no North or South,
But one great fellowship of love,
Throughout the whole wide earth.

THE LIVING CHURCH

524. The Christian Church

Let us have a church that dares
Imitate the heroism of Jesus;
Seek inspiration as he sought it;
Judge the past as he;
Act on the present like him;
Pray as he prayed;
Work as he wrought;
Live as he lived.

Devotional Poetry and Prose

Let us have a church for the whole
man:
Truth for the mind,
Good works for the hands,
Love for the heart;
And for the soul, that aspiration after
perfection,
That unfaltering faith in God,
Which, like lightning in the clouds,
Shines brightest when elsewhere it is
most dark.

525. The Church of God

Thou, whose unmeasured temple stands,
Built over earth and sea,
Accept the walls that human hands
Have raised, O God, to thee.

May erring minds that worship here
Be taught the better way;
And they who mourn and they who
fear,
Be strengthened as they pray.

May faith grow firm, and love grow
warm,
And pure devotion rise,
While round these hallowed walls, the
storm
Of earthborn passion dies.

526. Church of the Living God

This is the church of my dreams:
The church of the warm heart,
Of the open mind,
Of the adventurous spirit;
The church that cares,
That heals hurt lives,
That comforts old people,
That challenges youth;
That knows no divisions of culture or
class,
No frontiers, geographical or social;
The church that inquires as well as
avers,
That looks foward as well as backward,
The church of the Master,

The church of the people,
High as the ideals of Jesus,
Low as the humblest human;
A working church,
A worshipping church,
A winsome church;
A church that interprets the truth in
terms of truth;
That inspires courage for this life and
hope for the life to come;
A church of courage,
A church of all good men,
The church of the living God.

HOME SHRINES

527. House Blessing*

Bless the four corners of this house,
And be the lintel blest;
And bless the hearth and bless the
board
And bless each place of rest;
And bless the door that opens wide
To stranger as to kin;
And bless each crystal window-pane
That lets the starlight in;
And bless the roof-tree overhead
And every sturdy wall.
The peace of man, the peace of God,
The peace of love on all.

528. Beatitudes for the Home**

Blessed are they who rejoice in their
children;
To them is revealed the Fatherhood of
God.
Blessed are they who know the power of
love;
They dwell in God, for God is love.
Blessed are the songful of soul;
They carry light and joy to shadowed
lives.
Blessed are they that see visions;
They shall rejoice in the hidden ways
of God.
Blessed are they that have under-
standing hearts;

* From *House Blessing* by Arthur Guiterman, copyright by Harper and Brothers
** From *The Vision Splendid* by John Oxenham. copyright, 1917, by Doubleday, Doran & Co.

To them shall be multiplied kingdoms of delight.

Blessed are the childless, loving children still;

Theirs shall be a mightier family — even as the stars of heaven.

Blessed are they whose memories we cherish;

Our thoughts add jewels to their crowns.

529. The Family Altar

We build an altar here, and pray
That thou wilt show thy face.
Dear Lord, if thou wilt come to stay,
This home we consecrate to-day
Will be a Holy Place.

Lord, look upon our family kneeling before thee;
And grant us a holy, happy hour.
Help us to make this home a place of love,
A place of prayer,
A place of all beautiful living,
A place sweet with heaven's fragrance.
Help us to live each for the other,
And to find our happiness in doing good and denying ourselves.
O dear God, love this home of mine,
And all who dwell therein;
Care for our bodies, bless our hearts,
And keep our lives from sin.
God make my home a house of joy,
Where love and faith are given,
Make it the dearest place to you,
The nearest place to heaven.

530. The House Beautiful
Prayer for This House*

May nothing evil cross this door,
And may ill-fortune never pry
About these windows; may the roar
And rains go by.
Strengthened by faith, the rafters will
Withstand the battering of the storm.

This hearth, though all the world grow chill,
Will keep you warm.
Peace shall walk softly through these rooms,
Touching your lips with holy wine,
Till every casual corner blooms
Into a shrine.
Laughter shall drown the raucous shout
And, though the sheltering walls are , thin,
May they be strong to keep hate out
And hold love in.

SEASONS AND HOLY DAYS

531. Outward Bound

The tugging ship is unmoored; her sails are filling with the breeze; she sniffs the spray in her nostrils; her rigging grows taut like giant muscles; the course is set; the pilot is at the helm — the New Year is outward bound!

We, too, are a ship.

Each New Year we sail forth upon a sea heretofore untraveled by our humankind.

The winds of ambition fill our sails, and the waves of adversity dash upon our decks.

We touch at ports of call — the old familiar duties; but, O, the new ports with wealth of experience and color and adventure!

Sail out, O soul of mine!

That which alone matters is that the pilot has enough faith to trust the unknown!

532. A Blessing for the Loaf

Back of the loaf is the snowy flour,
And back of the flour, the mill;
And back of the mill is the wheat and the shower,
And the sun and the Father's will.

533. Autumn

A haze on the far horizon,
The infinite tender sky,
The ripe, rich tints of the cornfields,
And the wild geese sailing high, —
And all over upland and lowland
The charm of the golden-rod,
Some of us call it Autumn
And others call it God.

534. All Hail to the New

All hail, all hail to the New!
The future lies like a world new born,
All steeped in sunshine and mists of
morn,
And arched with a cloudless blue:
All hail, all hail to the New!

LIFE EVERLASTING

535. Building Eternity

We men of earth have here the stuff of
paradise.
We have enough.
We need no other stones to build the
stairs into the Unfulfilled.
No other ivory for the doors, no other
marble for the floors,
No other cedar for the beam and dome
of man's immortal dream.
Here on the common, human way is all
the stuff to build a heaven.
Ours the task sublime to build eternity
in time!

536. Crossing the Bar

Sunset and evening star,
And one clear call for me!
And may there be no moaning of the
bar,
When I put out to sea,

But such a tide as moving seems
asleep,
Too full for sound and foam,

When that which drew from out the
boundless deep
Turns again home.

Twilight and evening bell,
And after that the dark!
And may there be no sadness of fare-
well,
When I embark;

For though from out our bourne of
Time and Place
The flood may bear me far,
I hope to see my Pilot face to face
When I have crossed the bar.

537. Some Late Lark Singing

A late lark twitters from the quiet
skies:
And from the west,
Where the sun, his day's work ended,
Lingers as in content,
There falls on the old, gray city
An influence luminous and serene,
A shining peace.

The smoke ascends
In a rosy-and-golden haze.   The spires
Shine and are changed.   In the valley
Shadows rise.   The lark sings on.
The sun,
Closing his benediction,
Sinks, and the darkening air
Thrills with a sense of the triumphing
night —
Night with her train of stars
And her great gift of sleep.

So be my passing!
My task accomplished and the long
day done,
My wages taken, and in my heart
Some late lark singing,
Let me be gathered to the quiet west,
The sundown splendid and serene,
Death.

WHAT YOUTH LIVES BY

538. My Life Dynamic

I believe in the wonder of the out-of-doors, in the inspiration of the stars; I believe in the strength of the hills, in the silence of the night, and in the music of the birds and trees; I believe that my body was made for action, that my mind was made for thinking, and that my heart was made for loving.

539. My Future

I believe that he whose mercies are new every morning and fresh every evening, who brings into every epoch of my life a new surprise, and makes in every experience a new disclosure of his love, who sweetens gladness with gratitude and sorrow with comfort, who makes every year better than the year preceding and every new experience an evidence of his skill in gift-giving, has for me a future of glad surprise, which I would not forecast if I could.

540. Immortality

I believe that the life everlasting flows from the Fatherhood of God as the stream from the spring.

I believe that the Risen Christ is the visible witness to the sublime truth that the grave has no victory, and death no sting.

I believe that immortality is something to be lived rather than something to be proved.

I believe that the universe is God's house, that this world is not the only habitat of the living, but that in his house are many rooms.

I believe in holding daily life under the quiet light of eternity, and in pasturing our thoughts in the amazing love of God.

I. Mountains of Vision

A Service, using Unison and Responsive Readings from the King James, American Revised, and Goodspeed Translations of the Bible.

(For the New Year, Anniversary Occasions, and Rally Day)

Prelude—There's a Light upon the Mountains, No. 285

Preparation for Worship—(Responsive)

Exalt the Lord, our God, and worship at his holy hill.   For the Lord, our God, is holy.

I will give thanks unto thee.
I will pay my vows unto the Lord.   I will meditate on thy precepts, I will observe thy statutes.

Hymn Stanza—(To "Canonbury," No. 251)

Good Father, we thy children pray
For light and guidance on the way,
Reveal thy truth and give to each
Thy blessing of the upward reach. Amen.[1]

Visions of God in the Past—(Responsive)

The Lord spake unto Joshua: have I not commanded thee: be strong and of good courage; be not affrighted, neither be thou dismayed; for the Lord, thy God, is with thee whithersoever thou goest.   Joshua 1: 9

By faith Abraham, when he was called, obeyed to go out unto a place which he was to receive for an inheritance; and he went out, not knowing whither he went.   Hebrews 11: 8

(Elijah on Mount Horeb)

Behold, God the Lord passed by.
A great strong wind rent the mountains, and break in pieces the rocks before the Lord; but the Lord was not in the wind: after the wind an earthquake; but the Lord was not in the earthquake; after the earthquake a fire; but the Lord was not in the fire; after the fire a still small voice, and in that still voice onward came the Lord.   I Kings 19: 11, 12

1. Harry W. Kimball

341

Mountains of Vision

(The Vision of Isaiah)

I saw the Lord, sitting upon a throne, high and lifted up, and his train filled the temple.
Above him stood the seraphim; and one cried unto another and said:
Holy, holy, holy, is the Lord of hosts: the whole earth is full of his glory.
Then flew one of the seraphim unto me, having a live coal in his hand; and he touched my mouth with it.
And I heard the voice of the Lord, saying:
Whom shall I send, and who will go for us?
Then said I: Here am I; send me.   Isaiah 6: 1-9

(Christ in the Synagogue at Nazareth)

The spirit of the Lord is upon me, because he anointed me to preach good tidings to the poor.

He hath sent me to proclaim release to the captives, and recovering of sight to the blind, to set at liberty them that are bruised, to proclaim the acceptable year of the Lord.   Luke 4: 18, 19

(St. Stephen's Vision and Martyrdom)

When they heard Stephen, they were enraged and ground their teeth at him.
But he, full of the holy Spirit, looked up to heaven and saw God's glory and Jesus sitting at God's right hand.   And he said,

"Look! I can see heaven open, and the Son of Man sitting at God's right hand!"

But they uttered a great shout and stopped their ears, and they rushed upon him all together, and dragged him out of the city and stoned him, the witnesses throwing down their clothes at the feet of a young man named Saul.
As they stoned Stephen, he prayed,

"Lord Jesus, receive my spirit!"   Then falling on his knees, he cried out, "Lord, do not lay this sin up against them!"
With these words he fell asleep.[1]

Hymn Response—(To "All Saints New," No. 262)

The martyr first whose eagle eye
Could pierce beyond the grave;
Who saw his master in the sky
And called on him to save:
Like him with pardon on his tongue,
In midst of mortal pain,
He prayed for them that did the wrong:
Who follows in his train?   Amen.

(St. Patrick's Breastplate)

I bind myself to-day
The virtues of the starlit heaven,

Mountains of Vision

The glorious sun's life-giving ray,
The whiteness of the moon at even,
The flashing of the lightning free,
The whirling wind's tempestuous shocks,
The stable earth, the deep salt sea,
Around the old eternal rocks.

Christ be with me, Christ within me,
Christ behind me, Christ before me,
Christ beside me, Christ to win me,
Christ to comfort and restore me,
Christ beneath me, Christ above me,
Christ in quiet, Christ in danger,
Christ in hearts of all that love me,
Christ in mouth of friend and stranger.

Declaration of Purpose—(The Vow of St. Christopher)

(All uniting)

I stand up to do thy will, O God;
Thou hast kindled the desire in me to give myself to no master but the Highest;
In the way of this, my destiny, thou from my mother's arms hast blessed me even until now.
Unto thee be the glory in my life, world without end.   Amen.

Hymn—We Bless Thee, Lord, for All This Common Life, No. 221

Prayers—(All uniting)

Help us, our Father, to enjoy the blessed surprise of a beautiful Vision: the Master who preached among the glorious lilies of the field, above the Sea of Galilee, in full sight of the high city on the hill, and the snowy peaks of Hermon: the convincing, intimate good news of a heavenly Father, who careth even for the sparrows on the housetop, and how much more then for us, his foolish, human children?
Lift us up, day by day, to the heart of heaven, with a cry from our inmost being:
"Up with me, into the sky, singing, singing, and all the heavens about me ringing,
O thou God of our never dying aspiration and eternal peace."   Amen.[1]

(Alternative prayer for Younger Group)

We praise thee, O God, for thy great, wonderful world, larger than we can measure, more beautiful than we can see, and continually becoming more marvelous as we learn more about it.

1. "Mystical Religion" by Guthrie. Copyright by The Century Co.

343

Mountains of Vision

Help us, our Father, to learn more about thee, as we live in thy world, and try to learn how to use all thy good gifts.

Teach us to grow taller than we are, so that we may reach up unto some measure of thy great goodness.   Amen.[1]

Offertory

Unison Prayer

Father of lights, from whom cometh every good and perfect gift, accept these gifts of ours.   Amen.

Hymn Stanza—(To " Pentecost," No. 207)

All things are thine; no gift have we,
Lord of all gifts, to offer thee;
And hence with grateful hearts to-day,
Thine own before thy feet we lay.   Amen.[2]

1. Laura M. Armstrong
2. John Greenleaf Whittier

II. Broad Stripes and Bright Stars

A Service with Pledges of Loyalty and Salutes to the Flag

(For Patriots' Birthdays, Flag Day, Fourth of July, and Home Missions)

Prelude—The Land We Love is Calling, No. 276

Scripture Words of Counsel—(Responsive)

Except the Lord build the house, they labor in vain that build it.
Except the Lord keep the city, the watchman waketh but in vain.
Blessed is the nation whose God is the Lord, the people whom he hath chosen for his own inheritance.
Righteousness exalteth a nation; but sin is a reproach to any people.

Hymn—God of the Nations, Who from Dawn of Day, No. 274

or

O Beautiful, My Country, No. 275

Words of Instruction and Petition—(Unison)

Let every man remember that to violate the law is to trample on the blood of his father and to tear down the character of his own and his children's liberty.[1]

No nation can live without vision, and no vision will exalt a nation except the vision of real liberty and real justice and purity of conduct.[2]

We will never bring disgrace to this nation by any act of dishonesty or cowardice.
We will respect our nation's laws and obey them, that we may be an example to others.
We will seek to make justice, peace and brotherhood prevail.
We will pass on this nation not less, but greater, better and more beautiful than it came to us.[3]

Almighty God: we make our earnest prayer that thou wilt keep the United States in thy holy protection; that thou wilt incline the hearts of the citizens to cultivate a spirit of subordination and obedience to government; and entertain affection and love for one another.   Amen.[4]

1. Abraham Lincoln
2. Woodrow Wilson
3. Athenian Oath
4. George Washington

Broad Stripes and Bright Stars

Offertory Sentences—(Optional for leader or congregation)

To the preaching of good tidings of salvation
we consecrate our powers;
To the healing of broken bodies and the relief of distress
we consecrate our gifts;
To the leading of every soul to the knowledge and love of Christ
we consecrate our influence;
To the Christianization of our city,
To the building of the kingdom of God;
we consecrate our money, our efforts and our lives.   Amen.[1]

America First—(Responsive)

Not merely in matters material,
  but in things of the spirit;
Not merely in science, inventions, motors and skyscrapers,
  but also in ideals, principles, character;
Not merely in the calm assertion of rights,
  but in the glad assumption of duties;
Not flaunting her strength as a giant,
  but bending in helpfulness over a sick and wounded world like a good Samaritan;
Not in splendid isolation,
  but in courageous cooperation;
Not in pride, arrogance and disdain of other races and peoples,
  but in sympathy, love and understanding;
Not in treading again the old, worn, bloody pathway which ends inevitably in chaos and disaster,
  but in blazing a new trail along which, please God, other nations will follow into the New Jerusalem where war shall be no more.
Some day some nation must take that path unless we are to lapse once again into utter barbarism, and that honor we covet for our beloved America;
  So in that spirit and with these hopes we say with all our heart and soul: AMERICA FIRST.[2]

Hymn—O Beautiful for Spacious Skies, No. 271

("America the Beautiful" is being used the world around. It is sung in Canada with the refrain, "O Canada", and in Mexico with "Mi Mejico." When asked about the popularity of this hymn, Miss Bates remarked: "That the hymn has gained, in these years, such a hold as it has upon our people, is clearly due to the fact that Americans are at heart, idealists, with a fundamental faith in human brotherhood.")

1. Charles W. Merriam
2. Bishop Oldham

346

Broad Stripes and Bright Stars

Responsive Service with Pledges of Loyalty

Our flag symbolizes for us all the beauty and charm and high ideals of our homeland.

Its red stands for courage, moral as well as physical.

Its white is symbolic of purity, which cannot flourish amidst hate and fear and prejudice.

Its blue stands for truth and loyalty.

Let us then pledge allegiance to our flag, with a renewed sense of being loyal every day of our lives.

Let us see that everyone in this country gets an equal opportunity to enjoy its privileges.[1]

Salute to the American Flag:

I pledge allegiance to the flag of the United States and to the Republic for which it stands: one Nation, indivisible, with liberty and justice for all.

Hymn Stanza—(To "America," No. 279)

Our father's God, to thee,
Author of liberty,
To thee we sing.
Long may our land be bright
With freedom's holy light,
Protect us by thy might,
Great God, our King.   Amen.

One holy Church, one army strong,
One steadfast, high intent,
One working band, one harvest song,
One King omnipotent.

Salute to the Christian Flag

I pledge allegiance to the Christian Flag, and to the Saviour for whose kingdom it stands,—one brotherhood, uniting all mankind in service and love.

Hymn Stanza—(to "Waltham," No. 304)

Fling out the banner, let it float,
Skyward and seaward, high and wide;
The sun that lights its shining folds,
The cross on which the Saviour died.   Amen.

1. Jesse H. Holmes

III.   Following the Master[1]

A Picture Service using Zimmermann's "Christ and the Fishermen"

(For the Lenton Season, Decision Days and Youth Conferences and Camps)

(Purpose: The purpose of this service is to use objects of art as avenues by which one may enter into the realm of true worship. We are about to relive the experiences of the artist as well as to experience the real message of the picture. Such a picture service opens the doors to treasure houses which we have, thus far, passed by unnoticed.)

Hymn Prelude—Great Master, Touch Us with Thy Skilful Hand, No. 222

(The words should be read silently while the music is being played.)

Call to Worship—(Responsive)

The Lord, our God, is a creative Spirit, the leaping flame which lights men's hearts, which makes clear the pathways of men.

Let us seek to hold high this spirit of creation in beauty and in truth.

Hymn—Thou Who Taught the Thronging People, No. 113

Unison Scripture Reading

And Jesus, walking by the Sea of Galilee, saw two brethren, Simon called Peter, and Andrew his brother, casting a net into the sea: for they were fishers.

And he saith unto them: Follow me, and I will make you fishers of men.

And they straightway left their nets, and followed him.

And going on from thence, he saw two other brethren, James, the son of Zebedee, and John his brother, in a ship with Zebedee their father, mending their nets; and he called them.

And they left the ship and their father, and followed him.

Litany of the Creators—(Responsive)

Since the first sunrise of primeval man, there has always been some one with the urge to capture nature. The man who made vivid the walls of his cave with red and yellow clays, was the beginning of a long line of artists.

For this man, whoever he may have been, we thank thee, Lord.

The tribesman who stretched dried skins and painted upon them records of the rising and the setting of the sun, and of the happiness and the sorrows of his tribes, was also a creator.

For this man we thank thee, Lord.

1. Service prepared by Frank Grebe

Following the Master

Giotto, who dared to be different, who painted what he thought, raised the flag of true art higher than it had ever been before.

For this pioneer we thank thee, Lord.

Fra Angelico, devout, gentle soul who sang quiet songs in gold and red, was never known to have painted the Child Jesus without kneeling before his canvas all the while he painted.

For this gentle soul we thank thee, Lord.

Michael Angelo, giant wielder of color and colossal hewer of marble was an indomitable spirit in the hand of God. The work of his hands has struck men dumb.

The subtlety of his vision has lifted men to unparalleled heights.

The power of God within him has renewed the faith of men.

For this mighty spirit we thank thee, Lord.

Men to-day see the work of God's hands about them.

They who follow in their steps will perfect their work with even greater skill and keener insight into the beauties of God.

For these artists who are, and who are still to come, we thank thee, Lord.

An Interpretation of Zimmermann's " Christ and the Fishermen " :

(To be read by the Leader or three Pupils)

FIRST VOICE

It is a late spring afternoon in Galilee. The sun has clothed the distant hills of Moab with golden brown and dusky amber. The sea has quieted to a silent blue. No longer do its quick, short ripples catch the gleam of the sun, for a brooding silence rests over all the water. Rough fishermen of the nearby village of Tiberias are warming themselves in the afternoon sun, as they mend their drying nets which they had used during the morning. Zebedee, with his two sons, James and John, have been talking about the prospects of the fishing season.

SECOND VOICE

Jesus, who has been in Tiberias, comes walking by the sea. When he sees James and John again, he remembers his conversations with them on previous evenings. He meets Zebedee for the first time. The old fisherman asks Jesus to repeat the words he had told James and John. Zebedee hears for the first time: "Love the Lord, thy God, with all thy strength, with all thy heart, with all thy soul, with all thy might, and love thy neighbor as thyself." Zebedee questions: "But, is this all?" For the first time does this old toil-wearied man of Galilee hear so simple a formula for life. James and John, young in body and elastic in mind, have no difficulty in comprehending Jesus' message. Zebedee, however, seems unable to understand. It is bewildering and perplexing. Jesus shows his skill in understanding men by his gentle, patient and persistent efforts to lead Zebedee into the light.

Following the Master

THIRD VOICE

It is just here that Zimmermann shows his greatest skill as a painter. He has not only portrayed the figure of Jesus with both hands resting on the arm of him who cannot understand, but he has placed us in the picture also. If we abide by the commandments of Jesus, we assume the position of him who sits in the right hand side of the picture. Our mission in life will be not only that of helping those who are easily helped, but more. We will seek to lift unusual burdens and help sorely tried men and women. Then we become not merely fishermen on the Sea of Galilee, but fearless fishermen on the Sea of Life.

Prayer—(All uniting)

> Almighty God, we thank thee for all beauty everywhere, for the rapture of a Madonna's face, for the invigorating challenge which hurls itself from the brush of one inspired by thee.
>
> Help us that we may, in turn, create new beauty by living in thy presence. Cause us to live in the spirit of that inspiration so that we may become holy artists of life. This we ask in Jesus' name. **Amen.**

Offertory

Hymn Stanza—(To "Hesperus," No. 63)

> All things are thine, no gift have we,
> Lord of all gifts, to offer thee;
> And hence with grateful hearts to-day,
> Thine own before thy feet we lay. **Amen.**

Closing Hymn—Draw Thou My Soul, O Christ, No. 149

Suggested Pictures for Similar Services of Worship

Botticelli	—Moses and the Burning Bush
Brown	—Christ Washing Peter's Feet
Da Vinci	—The Last Supper
Hofmann	—Christ in the Temple with the Doctors
Hunt	—The Light of the World
Lerolle	—The Arrival of the Shepherds
Michelangelo	—Moses and David
Plockhorst	—Easter Morning
Raphael	—The Transfiguration
Sargent	—Hosea and Isaiah
Titian	—The Tribute Money

IV.   The Singing World

A Hymn Service, featuring Chant and Doxology, the Reading and Singing of Hymns, and Antiphonal and Dramatic Hymns.

(For Easter, Springtime, Children's Day and General Praise)

Hymn Prelude—Rejoice, Ye Pure in Heart, No. 27

or

Bring, O Morn, Thy Music, No. 5

Music Everywhere—(Responsive)

Sing, let us sing!
For the life of the world, the love which begetteth our life, our Lord, is song.
Sing unto him, let us sing; for our Lord is song.[1]

Hymn Stanza—(To "Old Hundredth," No. 334)

We'll crowd thy gates with thankful song,
High as the heavens our voices raise;
And earth, with her ten thousand tongues,
Shall fill thy courts with sounding praise.   Amen.

Our Lord is he who maketh the desolate places musical, with the rushing of waters, mingling together.

God is at the organ:
I can hear a mighty music echoing
Far and near.
God is at the organ,
And the keys are storm-strewn billows,
Moorlands, trees.[2]

Prayer—(All uniting)

Give us thy harmony, O Lord, that we may understand the beauty of the sky, the rhythm of the soft wind's lullaby, the sun and shadow of the woods in spring, and thy great love that dwells in everything.   Amen.[3]

Songs from the Torchbearers of History

LEADER:

Praise we the great of heart and mind,
The singers nobly gifted,
Whose music like a mighty wind
The souls of men uplifted.

1. Percy Mackaye
2. Joyce Kilmer
3. Alexander Pringle

351

The Singing World

1. Gloria Patri—The Hymn of the early Christian Martyrs

LEADER:

What a record for this doxology! Seventeen hundred years of uninterrupted singing in many languages.

How many millions of Christians have chanted it in cathedrals, at festive rites, on pilgrimages, in caves and dungeons, amid perils of the sea?

In the gardens of Nero, in the runways at Ephesus, chained to burning galleys and sinking hulls, with death lurking everywhere in its most hideous form, the early Christians sang:

Gloria patri et Filio et Spiritui Sancto; Sicut erat in principio, et nunc, et semper, et in saecula saeculorum, Amen.

Let us sing it in English: No. 335

Chant—

Glory be to the Father, and to the Son, and to the Holy Ghost; as it was in the beginning, is now, and ever shall be, world without end. Amen.

2. Shepherd of Tender Youth

LEADER:

A Strong and Beautiful Apostrophe to Christ coming from Alexandria, Egypt, Third Century. Let us read in unison some of these vivid words of Saint Clement translated from the Greek:

Shepherd of tender youth,	Ever be thou our Guide,
Guiding in love and truth	Our Shepherd and our Pride,
Through devious ways;	Our Staff and Song;
Christ our triumphant King,	Jesus, thou Christ of God,
We come thy name to sing,	By thy perennial Word,
And here our children bring	Lead us where thou hast trod,
To shout thy praise.	Make our faith strong.

3. The Canticle to the Sun (The Hymn and Its Story)

LEADER:

No one loved the birds and flowers and the eternal hills, the Apennines, more than Francesco.

Troubadour he was, living like a prince, dressed in silk and in the latest fashion, singing under the dark blue of an Italian night with his gay young companions.

At the age of twenty-five the reveler became Little Brother of the Sun.

He called all creatures his brothers, loving them and caring for them, and even preaching to them.

One year before his death, he lay prostrate and depressed by blindness, unable to endure any light on his weak eyes, and plagued by swarms of field mice that ran over his face, so that he had no peace day or night. Precisely in this wretched illness, he composed his Canticle to the Sun.

The Singing World

This summer of 1225 was everywhere remembered throughout Italy because of the fierce heat and drought.

(Read John Ruskin's translation of the Canticle, No. 440)

or

(Sing the Canticle—All Creatures of our God and King, No. 45)

(Antiphonal between soloist or choir and congregation.)

4. The Day of Resurrection

An Easter Festival of Song and Light in Greek and Russian churches throughout a thousand years.

LEADER:

The scene is this:

On the evening before Easter (Athens) as midnight approaches, the archbishop and his priests, with the king and queen, leave the cathedral and take their places on a high platform outside.

Thousands of people with unlighted tapers gather expectantly, while the priests begin chanting softly. At precisely midnight, the archbishop elevates the cross and sings, "Christos anesti!" (Christ is risen), which echoes and re-echoes as caught up by thousands of voices. Simultaneously a burst of light spreads everywhere through hundreds of lighted tapers. Bands play, rockets burst in mid-air, while voices everywhere join in the grand old Easter Hymn:

(Let us all unite to sing)

The Day of Resurrection, No. 127

Dramatization: Darkness everywhere, then one light, multiplying to twelve in the hands of selected singers, and amid a crescendo through the three stanzas, a lighting of all lights and tapers everywhere until church is aglow with light and vibrant with tone.

The Easter Story—(No. 381.)

An Act of Adoration—(Responsive)

For laughter, for cheery companionship, for old recollections revived, of labors and joys and dangers gone by.

God's name be praised.

For the humor, the genial good-will of everyday friendship,

God's name be praised.

For music,
Music that lifts a man's heart from earth
And flings wide the portals of heaven,

God's name be praised.

And for song,
The gracious flower of perfect song,

God's name be mightily praised.[1]

1. J. S. Hoyland. Copyright by W. Heffer and Sons Ltd.

V. Friendship

A Brief Service for General Use

Prelude—O Son of Man, Our Hero (The Londonderry Air), No. 109

Salutation—(Leader) The Upward Road, No. 502

Scripture—Exploring the Pathways to Friendship
Ruth and Naomi, No. 368

Hymn—Along the Road of Friendly Hearts
O Son of Man, Our Hero, No. 109
or
Heaven Is Here, Where Hymns of Gladness, No. 240

Responses—The Fellowship of Love

This is the message that we have heard from the beginning, that we should love one another.

> He that loveth not his brother whom he hath seen, how can he love God whom he hath not seen?

We know that we have passed from death unto life, because we love the brethren,

> Let us not love in word, neither in tongue but in deed and truth.

Greater love hath no man than this, that he lay down his life for his friend.

> There is no fear in love, but perfect love casteth out fear.
> Now abideth faith, hope, love, these three; and the greatest of these is love.

Unison Prayer—Ambassadors of God Among Men

Master and Lord, teach us to love our fellow men
With a love that shall be thy love breaking into the world through us.
Illumine our souls with a knowledge of thy divine beauty and truth
That shall fill us with joy and peace.
Make us messengers of thy grace, ambassadors of God among men.
Make us doorways through which thou thyself mayest enter freely into thy world. Amen.

Offertory

Closing Stanza—(To "Sardis," No. 90)

> Father, give thy benediction;
> Give thy peace before we part.
> Still our minds with truth's conviction,
> Calm with trust each questioning heart. Amen.

354

VI. The Temple of the Out-of-Doors

A Service of Prayers and High Resolves, with Special Music

(For All Seasons of the Year)

Prelude—The Spacious Firmament on High, No. 47

Opening Hymn—This Is My Father's World, No. 39

Exaltation—(Leader)

> Lord, I do fear
> Thou hast made the world too beautiful this year.
> My soul is all but out of me—let fall
> No burning leaf; prithee, let no bird call.[1]

Stanza of Joy—(To "Chautauqua," No. 17)

> Holy, holy, holy, Lord God of Hosts,
> Heaven and earth are full of thee,
> Heaven and earth are praising thee,
> O Lord, most high.   Amen.

High Resolves—(Reading alternately)

The Mountains (First Group)

We think of thee as we look out over the green valleys to the mountain peaks.
The whole earth seems silent and peaceful.
The clouds move off unto the unending sky, and our thoughts go with them
    out into the vastness of the world.
We thank thee for the thrilling, uplifting beauty of the sky and hills!
As we watch them, all the low desires go out of our hearts, and we pray that
    we may be stronger and nobler than we have ever been before.
Help us to live a mountain-top life.[2]

Instrumental—Hymn to the Mountains—Torjussen[3]

In the Woods (Second Group)

Maker of trees, flowers and birds, we love to steal away to the Temple of the
    Out-of-doors, and think of thee.
As we lie on the warm earth and look out toward the sunlight, we pray that
    we may live closer to nature, that we may have the calm spirit of the out-of-
    doors, be brave like the creatures of the woods, clean and upright like the
    trees.
Help us to keep our lives in tune with the law of the forest.[4]

1. Edna St. Vincent Millay
2, 4. Robert M. Bartlett from a " Boy's Book of Prayers "   Copyright by the Pilgrim Press
3. Sheet music published by Arthur P. Schmidt Co.

The Temple of the Out-of-Doors

Vocal—("Trees" Rasbach.[1] Poem by Joyce Kilmer, No. 437)

At the Seashore (First Group)

We feel that thou art very near as we look out on the wonder of the ocean.

When the ships are sailing off toward the sunset sky and to distant lands, when the beach echoes with the thunder of the deep, our hearts turn to thee as the Maker of the majestic scene.

The endless water, the rising tide and the roar of the breakers tell us something of thy power.

We thank thee, God of nature, for the ocean, for the treasures that it holds, for the courage that it teaches, for its ships and islands and inspiring beauty.

May we have more faith in thy power to help us do wonderful things.[2]

Instrumental—The Majesty of the Deep—Hamer[3]

Autumn Splendor (Second Group)

Thy beauty, O God, is upon us; autumn splendor everywhere! days lucid with vision, or dim with mist, haze and smothered sunshine; nights wistful with summer memories.

Thou hast made our life a summer sowing, an autumn harvest and a great white winter; too short for hate, and only long enough for the love that lifts the load we all must bear.

Who does not hear an autumn anthem singing low in his heart.

Help us to make the life of youth as lovely as the world in which he lives; the brotherliness of humanity equal to the beauty of nature.[4]

Hymn—God of the Earth, the Sky, the Sea, No. 49

Offertory

LEADER:

Remember the words of the Lord Jesus, that he himself said: It is more blessed to give than to receive.

Hymn Stanza (To "Wellesley," No. 55)

> Grant us, Lord, the grace of giving
> With a spirit, large and free,
> That ourselves and all our living
> We may offer unto thee.   Amen.

Tributes to Nature from Poets of Japan, America and Egypt

> Climbing the mountain pathway,
> No lovelier flower I see
> Than the shy little violet, hiding modestly.   (Japanese)

> **Hast thou named all the birds without a gun?**
> **Loved the wood-rose, and left it on its stalk?**
> **O, be my friend, and teach me to be thine!**   (American)

---

1. Song published by G. Schirmer Co.
2. Robert M. Bartlett from a "Boy's Book of Prayers."   Copyright by the Pilgrim Press
3. Sheet music published by Arthur P. Schmidt Co.
4. Joseph Fort Newton

The Temple of the Out-of-Doors

All cattle rest upon their herbage,
All trees and plants flourish,
The birds flutter in their marshes,
Their wings uplifted in adoration to thee.
All the sheep dance upon their feet,
The fish in the river leap up before thee,
And thy rays are in the midst of the great sea. (Egyptian)

Unison Prayer

O Lord, our God, thou art greater than the ocean, more beautiful than the sunset, more powerful than the earthquake, more tender than a mother's heart. Thy mercies unto us are countless, as the sands of the seashore, or the stars of a summer sky. Help us to feel our incompleteness and dependence upon thee. May we worship thee in the sanctuary, acknowledge thee in the place of business, enshrine thee in the home and praise thee all the day long. Amen.

Closing Hymn—For the Beauty of the Earth, No. 46

VII. Be Still, and Know That I Am God

A Service of Silences

(For Vespers, Summer Camp, and General Worship)

Prelude—Hark! the Vesper Hymn Is Stealing, No. 16

Period of Meditation—(During which the Leader will quietly direct the thinking as follows)

Let us think of the woods and flowers and streams and hills—gifts of the Father God.

Let us think of the sun and moon and stars—lights in God's heaven.

Let us think of man, to whom the Father God has given all these things, for his use and personal development.

Father God, for all thy material gifts we give thee thanks, in Jesus' name. Amen.

Silence

Hymn—Slowly, by Thy Hand Unfurled, No. 217

Prayer

Lord, we thank thee for thy inward voice, which ever and again calleth us away from the clamor and dusty strife of this life, into the cool, quiet groves of eternity. We thank thee that close around us, ever pressing in on us, is thine eternal world, full of peace and joy. We thank thee that a hundred times a day we may take refuge therein, feel thy cool fingers soothing our fevered foreheads, look steadily into thy quiet eyes, drink in unto our souls from that gaze the strength and peace of eternity. Amen.[1]

Silence

My soul, wait thou in silence for God only, for my expectation is from him.
He leadeth me beside the still waters,
He restoreth my soul.

Thanksgiving—(Responsive)

We thank thee, Lord,
For all thy Golden Silences—
For every Sabbath from the world's turmoil;
For every respite from the stress of life;
Silence of moorlands rolling to the skies,

1. J. S. Hoyland, from a "Book of Prayers for an Indian College." Copyright by W. Heffer and Sons Ltd.

358

Be Still, and Know That I Am God

Silence of deep woods' mystic, cloistered calm;
Silence of wide seas basking in the sun;
Silence of white peaks soaring to the blue;
Silence of dawnings, when, their matins sung,—
The little birds do fall asleep again;
    For the deep silence of high golden noons;
    Silence of gloamings and the setting sun;
    Silence of moonlit nights and patterned glades;
    Silence of stars, magnificently still,
    Yet ever chanting their Creator's skill;
For that high silence of thine Open House,
Dim-branching roof and lofty-pillared aisle,
Where burdened hearts find rest in thee awhile;
    Silence of friendship, telling more than words;
    Silence of hearts, close-knitting heart to heart;
    Silence of joys too wonderful for words;
    Silence of sorrows, when thou drawest near;
    Silence of soul, wherein we come to thee,
    And find ourselves in thine Immensity;
For that great silence where thou dwell'st alone—
—Father, Spirit, Son, in One,
Keeping watch above thine Own,
Deep unto deep, within us sound sweet chords
Of praise beyond the reach of human words;
In our souls' silence, feeling only thee—
    We thank thee, thank thee, thank thee, Lord.[1]

Silence

Hymn—Dear Lord and Father of Mankind, No. 152

1. John Oxenham, from a "Silent Te Deum"
   Copyright by Methuen and Co.

VIII. The Light

An Outline Service of Symbols

(For Christmas, Bible Sunday, and the Quest of Youth)

Prelude—Father of Lights, No. 1

Call to Worship

God is light, and in him is no darkness at all.
O send out thy light and thy truth,
Let them lead me.

A. The Star

Responsive Reading

Now when Jesus was born, behold there came wise men from the east, saying:
Where is he that is born king of the Jews?
For we have seen his star in the east, and are come to worship him.
And when they were come into the house, they saw the young child with Mary, his mother, and fell down and worshipped him.
And when they had opened their treasures they presented unto him gifts: gold and frankincense and myrrh.
And they, having heard the king, went their way; and, lo, the star, which they saw in the east, went before them, till it came and stood over where the young child was.
And when they saw the star, they rejoiced with exceeding great joy.

Hymn—Christians, Lo, the Star Appeareth, No. 90

Offertory—(All uniting)

We open here our treasures and our gifts; and some of it is gold, and some is frankincense, and some is myrrh; for some has come from plenty, and some from joy, and some from deepest sorrow of the soul. But thou, O God, dost know the gift is love, our pledge of peace, our promise of good will. Accept the gift and all the life we bring. Amen.[1]

1. Herbert H. Hines

The Light

B. The Lamp

Meditation

Quiet Music—(Break Thou the Bread of Life, No. 71)
(Played softly during the following Unison Reading and Meditation)

Open thou my eyes,
That I may behold wondrous things out of thy law.   (Music continuing
Thy word have I hid in my heart,
That I might not sin against thee.   (Music continuing)
Thy word is a lamp unto my feet,
And a light upon my path.

Hymn—Break Thou the Bread of Life, No. 71

Thanksgiving for Biblical Scholarship

Read the hymn—Book of Books, Our People's Strength, No. 69

C. The Welding Flame

LEADER:

Have we not all one Father?
Hath not one God created us?

Hymn Stanza—(To "St. Peter," No. 299)

In Christ there is no East or West,
In him no North or South,
But one great fellowship of love
Throughout the whole wide earth.   **Amen.**

Prayer—(All uniting)

May naught mar our fellowship and joy, O Father.   May none remain lonely and hungry of heart here among us.   Let none go hence without the joy of new friendships.   Give us more capacity for love and richer consciousness of being loved.   Overcome our coldness and reserve that we may throw ajar the gates of our hearts, and keep open house this day and every day. Amen.[1]

Hymn—O Brother Man, No. 244

Dedication—(All uniting)

Lord of Life and Love: I would make my actions show love to all persons whom I meet.   I will accept them as they are, with all their mistakes and failures, and declare my common interests and responsibilities with them. If any have wronged or hurt me, I will place my mind within the all-understanding and all-loving mind of God, and here and now forgive.   I desire to give forth God's love to men and to make no hinderance to his love coming through me.   Amen.[2]

[1, 2.] Walter Rauschenbusch

361

The Light

D. The Torch

Salutation—See the race of hero spirits pass the torch from hand to hand!

Torchbearers of Israel.   Read Hebrews 12

or

The Torchbearers of the Early Church.   Read ⎰Life's Victors, No. 496
⎱Latimer's Light, No. 511

or

The Modern Torchbearers.   Read ⎰Evidences of Faith, No. 507
⎱Livingstone, No. 508

Hymn—Pass on the Torch, No. 229

Litany

We bless thee, our Father, for the stirring ministry of the past, for the story of noble deeds, the memory of holy men.

God be praised for holy men.

We bless thee for the dawning of the light in far-off ages, as soon as human eyes could bear its rays.

God be praised for the light.

We remember those who bore aloft the torch of truth when all was false and full of shame; the far-sighted souls who from the mountain-tops of vision heralded the coming day; those who labored in the darkened valleys to lift men's eyes to the hills.

God be praised for torchbearers.

Most of all we thank thee for Jesus,
The light of the world.

Light of the world, we hail thee!

IX. Commemoration

Using Litanies and the Offertory as a Climax

(For Columbus Day, Washington's and Lincoln's Birthdays, Decoration and Armistice Days)

Prelude and Opening Hymn—
God of Our Fathers, Whose Almighty Hand, No. 273

Salutation (Leader)
Let us now praise famous men,
in whom the Lord showed forth his glory;
his mighty power in the days of old.

Response (All uniting)
Praise be to these who by faith removed mountains
and bridged rivers;
who brought waters to a thirsty land
and made the desert rejoice and blossom as the rose;
who gave sight to the blind, cleansed the lepers,
and caused the lame to walk;
who went over the sea to share the perils of oppressed peoples;
who suffered torment and death from fire and smoke;
who took food to the starving in strange lands;
who went down to the sea in ships and into
the air like eagles.

Optional Message or Reading—America's Making, No. 515

Prayer (All uniting)
O thou who art Heroic Love,
keep alive in our hearts that adventurous spirit,
which makes men scorn the way of safety,
if only thy will be done.
For so only, O Lord, shall we be worthy of those
courageous souls who in every age have ventured all
in obedience to thy call,
and for whom the trumpets have sounded on the other side; through
Jesus Christ our Lord. Amen.[1]

1. The New Prayer Book. Copyright by Oxford University Press

363

Commemoration

Hymn Response (Solo or choir or sung softly), No. 330

Thou wast their rock, their fortress and their might,
Thou, Lord, their captain in the well-fought fight;
Thou in the darkness drear, their one true light,
Alleluia.

O may thy soldiers, faithful, true and bold,
Fight as the saints who nobly fought of old,
And win with them the victor's crown of gold,
Alleluia. Amen.

Litany of Heroes (Responsive)

Sound the name of Columbus, brave Admiral;
He gained a world; he gave that world
Its grandest lesson: On, sail on.

O thou Preserver of men, we thank thee for
mariners who smote the sounding furrows,
who sailed beyond the sunset and the western stars.

By faith the Pilgrim Fathers left their homes,
seeking liberty to worship God in the savage
wilderness of the western world.

We bless thee, our Father, for the stirring ministry
of the past, for the story of noble deeds,
the memory of holy men.

Who was the man who made us.
Who smote for the world to be,
Breaking the bonds of an old world,
Welding with mighty strokes
The thirteen links of the new;
Who, midst the blackening war-storm,
Baffled but unconquered, firm,
Stood like a rock at Valley Forge,
Triumphed for freedom at Yorktown's field,
And gave the nation a soul?
Honor the memory of Washington![1]

We thank thee, our Father, for each mighty one through whom thy living
light hath shone.

With courage undaunted our fathers crossed the prairies, as, of old, their
fathers crossed the sea, to make the West as the East, the homestead
of the free.

Our grateful thanks for Western Youths,
So impatient, full of action,
Full of manly pride and friendship,
Tramping with the foremost; Pioneers, O Pioneers.

Hymn.—All the Past We Leave Behind, No. 211

1. Arthur Farwell. Copyright by John Church Co.

Commemoration

Litany (Continued)

Who was the man who saved us.
Our Captain through the storm;
Who dreamed of the Union's faith,
Firm, 'midst the clash of passions,
Deserted, threatened, denounced,'
Bowing his head in prayer;
Who held great love in his soul,
Love and anguish of love,
Love for North and South.
Honor the memory of Lincoln![1]
And so they buried Lincoln?
    Strange and vain!
Has any creature thought of Lincoln hid
In any vault, 'neath any coffin lid,
In all the years since that wild spring of pain?
They slew themselves, they but set Lincoln free.
In all the earth his great heart beats as strong,
Shall beat, while pulses throb to chivalry
And burn with hate of tyranny and wrong.[2]

(Reading or Solo and Congregation, No. 261)

Who goes there, in the night,
Across the storm-swept plain?
We are the ghosts of a valiant war —
A million murdered men.

**Who goes there, at the dawn,
Across the sun-swept plain?
We are the hosts of those who swear:
It shall not be again.[3]**

**Remembered be all those who gave their lives
for liberty, for righteousness, for truth and peace;
whose love, and service and devotion glorify
our earth and make it holy ground.**

Offertory (Leader)

The great and brave who have gone before us and blazed the trail, gave freely of their talents, their strength, their lives. We who would remember them today, unite our offerings in memory of their noble giving.

Response after Offering (All uniting)

We dedicate our gifts to the memory of those
whom we honor this day;
O Lord, bless what we have given to the building
of thy kingdom on earth as it is in heaven.   Amen.

Hymn—Forward Through the Ages, No. 263

1. Arthur Farwell. Copyright by John Church Co.
2. James T. Mackay
3. Thomas Curtis Clark

X.   The Human Race[1]

A Ceremonial of Maps

(For Armistice Day, Christmas, Missionary and Peace Sundays)

Introduction to the Service—(To be read by the Leader)

A Ceremonial of Maps

I stand before the maps of the world: before the rain map and the map of winds, and I know where rain is falling and where wind is blowing; before a road map of the world, and I see the roads of all lands, and people traveling on them; before a train map, and watch the trains going up and down the earth with pilgrims, guided, all, by a pillar of cloud by day and a pillar of fire by night; before a map of the lights of the world, and the fires; before a map of the homes of the world, and of the uncharted regions of the human hearts, which in all lands are fashioned alike.   What possessions we have in common!   Rain and wind and roads and trains and lights and fires and trees and birds and homes and hearts.

On this day I go into all the world, I make room in my heart for my brothers and sisters EVERYWHERE.[2]

Hymn—God the Omnipotent, No. 284
or
Down the Dark Future, No. 292
or
In Christ there is no East or West, No. 299

Responsive Service

A Little Child Shall Lead Them—(Responsive)

The wolf shall dwell with the lamb, and the leopard shall lie down with the kid: and the calf and the young lion and the fatling together, and a little child shall lead them.

In hearts too young for enmity
There lies the way to make men free.
When children's friendships are world-wide
New ages will be glorified.
Let child love child, and strife will cease;
Disarm the hearts, for that is peace.

---

1. Service arranged in part by Rev. and Mrs. Edward H. Bonsall
2. Girl's Everyday Book. Copyright by The Woman's Press. Used by permission

366

The Human Race

Prayer—(All uniting)

Dear God, help children everywhere to be friends of one another and help us to be friendly to the children of all lands.   May we remember that they are thy children, as we are, and so with us a part of God's family on earth. Teach us ways in which we may share our best with them, and in knowing them better, learn to love them more.

This we ask in the spirit of Jesus, who came a little child to earth to reveal thy love to all peoples.   Amen.[1]

Youth's Hymn of World Friendship

Far Round the World Thy Children Sing Their Song, No. 8

(This Service may be visualized by using a large flat map of the world and, during the progress of the service, placing lighted candles in sockets or clamps prepared to receive them at the countries indicated: England, China, Russia and America.)

Prophets in all Lands Speak Friendship—(Responsive)

Whatsoever ye would that men should do unto you, do ye even so to them.

Through winter's first cold snow
See the poor shivering rag-man go,
Yet he, too, is a son of man.   (Japan)

If you would be well spoken of, learn to speak well of others.   (Greece)

The night is beautiful,
So the faces of my people:
The stars are beautiful,
So the eyes of my people:
Beautiful also the sun,
Beautiful also are the souls of my people.

I will not be grieved that other men do not know me,
I will be grieved that I do not know other men.   (China)

He who hurts another, harms himself,
He who would help another, helps himself:
Where love is, there God is also.   (Russia)

Many nations shall come and say:
Come, let us go up to the mountain of the Lord,
And to the house of the God of Jacob.
He will teach us his ways and we will walk in his paths.
They shall beat their swords into ploughshares and their spears into pruninghooks.

Nation shall not lift up sword against nation, neither shall they learn war any more.

But they shall sit every man under his vine and under his fig tree, and none shall make them afraid, for the mouth of the Lord hath spoken it.
Micah 4: 2-4

1. Florence Buck

The Human Race

Pledge of Good Will and Love toward All   (Unison)

I pledge my loyalty to the goal of human brotherhood.
I will try to think of all peoples in a kindly spirit.
I will remember that they have rights and duties, as have I; that they are
   like myself, human beings.
I will work for some form of international organization that will outlaw war
   and bring the nations together, under common laws, and for the common
   good.   (America)

The Peace Pact, Outlawing War

(Signed by representatives of fifteen nations, August 27, 1928. Over thirty other nations
have since indicated their intention of ratifying the pact.)

Article 1

The high contracting parties solemnly declare in the name of their respective
   peoples that they condemn recourse to war for the solution of international
   controversies, and renounce it as an instrument of national policy in their
   relations with one another.

Article 2

The high contracting parties agree that the settlement or solution of all
   disputes or conflicts of whatever nature or of whatever origin they may
   be, which may arise among them, shall never be sought except by pacific
   means.

The Pledge of this School or Congregation   (Unison)

The teachers and pupils of this school, assembled together, gratefully
   praise Almighty God, our Father, for this great step toward the final end
   of the curse of war; and we dedicate ourselves anew to the cause of
   world peace and brotherhood.

Closing Meditation—(To be read silently)

Peace in our hearts, our evil thoughts assuaging,
Peace in thy church, where brothers are engaging,
Peace, when the world its busy war is waging;
Grant us thy peace, Lord.

Dismissal—(Unison)

Peace be within these walls.
Peace to young and old who enter here.
Hasten the time, O Lord God, when not alone the holy places where thine
   honor dwelleth, but the whole earth shall be full of thy glory.   Amen.